ELECTRONICS FOR EXPERIMENTATION AND RESEARCH

ELECTRONICS FOR EXPERIMENTATION AND RESEARCH

Brian K. Jones

Department of Physics,
University of Lancaster

Prentice/Hall International

Englewood Cliffs, New Jersey
London   Mexico   New Delhi
Rio de Janeiro   Singapore   Sydney
Tokyo   Toronto   Wellington

PHYSICS
7272-3580

Library of Congress Cataloging in Publication Data

Jones, Brian K., 1938–
  Electronics for experimentation and research.

  Bibliography: p
  Includes index.
  1. Electronics.   2. Research.   I. Title.
  TK7835.J6   1986   621.381   85-23104
  ISBN 0-13-250754-4

British Library Cataloguing in Publication Data

Jones, Brian K.
  Electronics for experimentation and research.
  1. Electronics
  I. Title
  537.5   TK7815

  ISBN 0-13-250754-4
  ISBN 0-13-250747-1 Pbk

Prentice-Hall, Inc., *Englewood Cliffs, New Jersey*
Prentice-Hall International (UK) Ltd, *London*
Prentice-Hall of Australia Pty Ltd, *Sydney*
Prentice-Hall Canada, Inc., *Toronto*
Prentice-Hall Hispanoamericana, S.A., *Mexico*
Prentice-Hall of India Private Ltd, *New Delhi*
Prentice-Hall of Japan, Inc., *Tokyo*
Prentice-Hall of Southeast Asia Pte Ltd, *Singapore*
Editora Prentice-Hall do Brasil Ltda, *Rio de Janeiro*
Whitehall Books Ltd, *Wellington, New Zealand*

Printed and bound in Great Britain for
Prentice-Hall International (UK) Ltd,
66 Wood Lane End, Hemel Hempstead, Hertfordshire, HP2 4RG
by A. Wheaton & Co. Ltd, Exeter

1 2 3 4 5   90 89 88 87 86

ISBN 0-13-250754-4
ISBN 0-13-250747-1 PBK

CONTENTS

PREFACE

Electronic equipment, devices, and techniques are now an accepted part of experiments in all science subjects. The research worker is thus required to have a sufficient knowledge of the complexities of electronics as well as his own specialism. Since electronics is developing very fast, there is a need for continual help for the researcher with current methods and approaches to the subject. This book is written for physical and biological scientists who use electronics as a tool for research and advanced experimental measurement. It is hoped that the book will enable the necessary electronic skills to be picked up easily without becoming a chore or a major part of the research activity. The aim is to give sufficient information so that an experiment may be designed to obtain the measurements in the best way, using the most suitable equipment and techniques. Sufficient information is given to enable simple circuits to be designed and made and existing equipment adapted for a specific use. The text is suitable for beginning research workers and to form the basis of a course for final-year undergraduates or first-year postgraduates to enable them to make the transition from the teaching laboratory to the research laboratory.

The assumption made is that projects should be finished as rapidly as possible and that the time taken is an important consideration. Although most circuits and systems can be constructed with the individual basic components such as transitors, it is better, faster, and often cheaper to use the most advanced circuit elements possible. Thus, the use of integrated circuits is described here as much as possible rather than discrete transistors. Similarly, for many purposes standard commercial 'black-box' equipment is available and is likely to perform better than many self-made circuits, especially in the critical parts of the circuit. However, the user must have sufficient knowledge to understand what equipment is needed and its purpose, the principles behind its operation, and the performance criteria that need to be specified for its selection. For many purposes, simple circuits may easily be designed and made that will perform the required functions perfectly adequately. Even if advanced commercial equipment is used, it often has to be modified or connected to the specific experiment involved with simple interface circuits. A good understanding of the circuits enables appropriate decisions to be made on the cost and suitability of self-made circuits compared with specialist designs.

This is not a complete text on electronics for the specialist or regular practitioner. It does not deal in great length with digital circuits or the operation and manipulation of microprocessors, since these are also specialist topics with which the ordinary experimenter should not be involved. Microcomputers and microcomputer software are also outside the scope of the book. However, the reader should be able to gain sufficient understanding to be able to connect such valuable tools to specific instruments, circuits, and experiments.

It is assumed that the reader will have had a course in a.c. circuit theory and electromagnetic theory. The mathematical background assumes a basic familiarity with Fourier series and transforms and uses the calculus and complex numbers, but none of this is essential since the results of the analysis are also stated. It is also assumed that the reader will have had a first course in electronics which will have covered such topics as passive a.c. circuits using the complex impedance, diode switching, binary logic, and basic transistor bias circuits and operation. Throughout the text proofs are not given but there is a concentration on principles. The field-effect transistor is usually used for examples in preference to the bipolar transistor since its operation is easier to follow. Circuits involving integrated circuits are described in general rather than with specific devices since no special properties are usually needed. An appendix describes specific common devices. Apologies are given that the sequence of topics may not be to everyone's taste but cross-references are given. Frequency and angular frequency are both used where it seems most appropriate. The abbreviations a.c. and d.c. are now widely used for any variable and no longer have their literal meaning reserved for currents. Since we discuss specifically frequency effects use has been made of zero frequency (z.f.) for d.c. where appropriate.

Chapter 1 reviews the circuit theory that is needed and introduces approaches to circuit analysis that are used later. The use of negative and positive feedback, especially round operational amplifiers, is described in chapters 2 and 3. The care that is needed to reduce interference and to increase the signal-to-noise ratio is described in chapter 4. Chapter 5 describes the digital circuits that are needed to interface the logic devices but is not intended to give a deep understanding of the internal operation of complex digital systems.

Chapter 6 describes the principles behind non-linear circuits and the manipulation of signals as frequencies. Chapters 7 and 8 describe the experiment itself with the use of bridge circuits, transducers, and the acquisition of the data into the electronic system. Signal processing to enhance the signal-to-noise ratio is described in chapter 9. The use of computers to control experiments using standardized techniques is outlined in chapter 10. Chapter 11 describes the special techniques needed when using high-frequency signals, and these are often needed since the bandwidth of integrated circuits is so large. The appendices are designed to be a useful collection of information that may be needed for frequent reference.

BIBLIOGRAPHY

P. Horowitz and W. Hill, *The Art of Electronics*, Cambridge University Press (1980).

B. E. Jones, *Instrumentation, Measurement and Feedback*, McGraw-Hill (1977).

J. Millman, *Microelectronics: Digital and Analog Circuits and Systems*, McGraw-Hill (1979).

R. J. Smith, *Circuits, Devices and Systems*, Wiley (1971).

R. J. Smith, *Electronics, Circuits and Devices*, Wiley (1980).

1 CIRCUIT THEORY

INTRODUCTION

Electronics is the study of the behavior of electrical currents and voltages. Electronic circuits and devices are preferred over mechanical and hydraulic systems to perform useful functions because of the wide range of values that the voltage and current variables can take, the ease by which they can be controlled, and the many nearly ideal devices that exist.

A few broad divisions can be made within all circuits. An *active circuit* is one in which there is the possibility of an increase in the signal power between the input and output by conversion from another energy source such as the direct current (d.c.) power supply. Note that a transformer can provide voltage or current gain but not power gain. Also a poorly constructed active circuit such as an amplifier could produce no net signal power gain, so that the definition assumes a sensible use of the circuit. In practice, the active amplifying devices are few and easily recognizable: bipolar and field-effect transistors (and perhaps vacuum tubes and high-frequency microwave devices) and combinations of these made into integrated circuits. In contrast, a *passive circuit* has no external source of energy.

A *linear circuit* or device has a constant factor of proportionality between the applied and resultant variables (e.g. voltage V and current I, V and dV/dt, V and $\int I \, dt$, or V_{in} and V_{out}). The full-curve in figure 1.1(a) thus represents a linear circuit element and the broken curves *non-linear* elements. The distinction between linear and non-linear circuits is very important, since the vast simplification methods of circuit analysis (complex impedance notation, Fourier analysis, and equivalent circuits), which are used almost automatically, are based on the principle of superposition and are valid only for linear circuits. Non-linear circuits are discussed further in chapter 6. Many non-linear circuits can be approximated to linear circuits provided that the circuit variables (e.g. V and I) are restricted to a range of values in which there is a proportional relationship for increments to the signals. Thus in figure

1

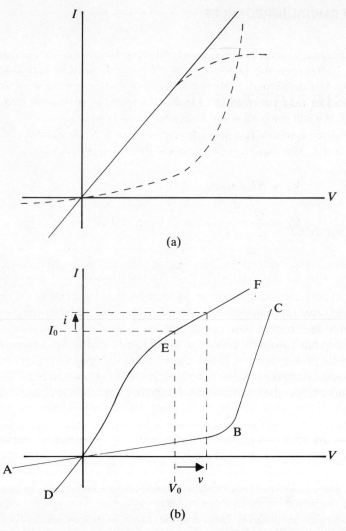

Fig. 1.1   (a) Linear (full curve) and non-linear (broken curves) characteristics. (b) A
non-linear characteristic ABC may be approximated by linear sections AB
and BC. On the linear part EF of the characteristic DEF, small signals, v and
i, are linearly related.

1.1(b) the characteristic ABC can be approximated by linear sections AB and
BC, and the curve DEF can be treated as a linear characteristic in the section
EF. In these cases the circuit is non-linear for the total voltage V and current I
but linear for small changes v and i from some fixed bias point V_0, I_0 on the
curve within the linear region, as shown. For these incremental values, the
convenient and powerful circuit analysis techniques are then applicable.

TWO-TERMINAL IMPEDANCES

The basic circuit element is the two-terminal passive impedance shown in figure 1.2. Between the two terminals a current I can flow and a voltage difference V is developed. Although it does not matter how these are set up, let us consider that a current $I = I_0\cos\omega t$ is applied at an angular frequency $\omega = 2\pi f$. We will use both ω and frequency f in this book.

The three common components are the resistor R, the capacitor C, and the inductor L. For these three ideal cases, the voltages developed are

$$V_R = RI_0\cos\omega t$$

$$V_C = \frac{Q}{C} = \frac{1}{C}\int I\,dt = \frac{1}{\omega C}I_0\cos(\omega t - \pi/2) \qquad (1.1)$$

$$V_L = L\frac{dI}{dt} = \omega L I_0\cos(\omega t + \pi/2)$$

For a sine-wave input there is a sine-wave output. The relationship between the current and voltage describes the characteristic of the component. The relationship has a magnitude $|V/I| \equiv |\mathbf{Z}|$, the *impedance*, and a phase ϕ, the phase angle of V relative to I. For a resistance, the impedance is R and the phase is zero. For a capacitance, the impedance is $1/\omega C$ and the phase is $-\pi/2$. For an inductance, the impedance is ωL and the phase is $+\pi/2$.

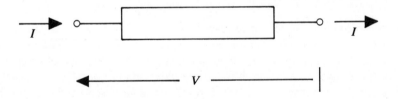

Fig. 1.2 A two-terminal circuit component.

Fortunately these three circuit elements, which involve the three time variations of the current, can each be easily manufactured over a wide range of values with high linearity and in nearly ideal form.

In a real circuit, signals over a wide range of frequencies may need to be considered at the same time. For several decades of frequency the circuit behavior may also change by several orders of magnitude, and this is best displayed on a $\log\omega$ plot as shown in figure 1.3. If $\log|V/I| = \log|\mathbf{Z}|$ is displayed, then the basic impedances above fall on straight lines. If a wide range of frequencies are involved, these rapid impedance variations indicate

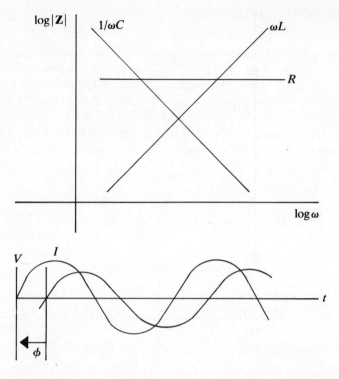

Fig. 1.3 The magnitudes of the basic impedances are illustrated as straight lines on a log $|\mathbf{Z}|$ versus log ω plot. The angle ϕ is the phase between the voltage and current sine waves.

that approximations can be readily made; at a given frequency some impedances will be negligible compared with others. Such approximations should be made with great facility in the initial or approximate analysis of a circuit. If one wishes to understand how a complex circuit operates at a certain frequency, then the full circuit can be simplified to just the significant impedances at that frequency by ignoring any much higher impedance in parallel with the significant impedance. Similarly small impedances in series can be replaced by a short circuit. This normally results in a great simplification of the circuit and allows easier conceptual analysis. Only in a few circuits is the choice of frequency for analysis critical within an order of magnitude, and then two impedances in series or parallel may have comparable magnitudes. These occur in oscillators, filters, phase-shifting circuits, and bridges. In general therefore the phase part of the impedances can also be ignored if only an understanding rather than an exact solution of the circuit operation is required.

In most circuits the exact values of many of the components are not important. For many, only the order of magnitude is required; for others,

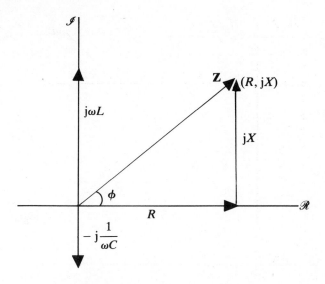

Fig. 1.4 The complex impedance **Z** can be represented in the complex plane using polar or Cartesian coordinates.

only a 20% accuracy is needed. The values of a few components need to be precise since they define a gain, attenuation or frequency, but often even then the precise value is adjusted using a variable impedance at a final calibration step. Although it is contrary to the precision and exactness stressed in the training of a scientist, facility is necessary during the analysis and construction of electronic circuits to make major, or even gross, approximations in the calculation of component values except in those few cases where high precision is in fact needed. Thus a resistance may be considered decreased by 17% or even 20% if an impedance five times its value is added in parallel.

The magnitude and phase relationship of impedances can be combined together as a single complex number **Z**. The properties of the three basic components are described in amplitude and phase by vectors along the positive and negative imaginary axes of the complex **Z** plane as shown in figure 1.4.

Any passive linear network between two terminals will have an electrical behavior that can be described by the $V/I = $ **Z** relationship in amplitude and phase at any frequency. This value, **Z**, can be described by polar coordinates $|\mathbf{Z}|$, ϕ or Cartesian coordinates R, jX. The latter representation shows that at any frequency such a network can be represented by a series combination of a resistance R and a reactance X which is either positive (inductive) or negative (capacitive). This is a major simplification and, if the frequency dependence is also added, i.e. $\mathbf{Z}(\omega) = R(\omega) + jX(\omega)$, then the performance of any complicated passive two-terminal circuit can be expressed in a very compact form.

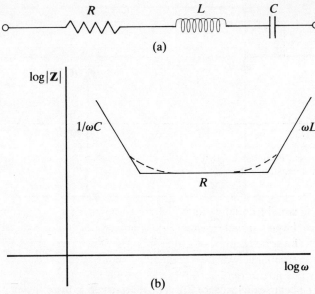

Fig. 1.5 The total impedance of a series RLC circuit (a) can be approximated in the log $|\mathbf{Z}|$ versus $\log\omega$ graph by three straight lines (b). The exact curve is shown by broken lines.

Consider the simple series resonant circuit shown in figure 1.5(a). The impedance is

$$\mathbf{Z} = R + j\omega L + \frac{1}{j\omega C} = R + j\left(\omega L - \frac{1}{\omega C}\right) \tag{1.2}$$

In figure 1.5(b) it can be seen that at low frequencies this can be approximated by the capacitance $1/\omega C$, at intermediate frequencies by the resistance R, and at high frequencies by the inductance ωL. To a reasonable approximation, the circuit impedance can be represented on the log $|\mathbf{Z}|$ versus $\log\omega$ graph by three straight lines, although the actual characteristics follow the broken curves near the corners.

Real two-terminal components are not perfectly ideal because of the way in which they are constructed. Consider the inductance shown in figure 1.6. There will be some series resistance since the wire of the coil will have some resistance. There will also be a parallel capacitance, since each conductor is near another conductor at a different potential and this constitutes a capacitance. In a more complete equivalent circuit, the resistance and capacitance would be distributed through the inductance with one element for each turn. Several different equivalent circuits are possible to describe a given real circuit, but the one usually chosen is that which most closely reflects what is actually causing the effect or has fewer frequency-dependent elements. In this

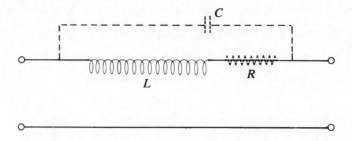

Fig. 1.6 A real inductance L will contain stray impedances such as the capacitance and resistance shown.

example, the small frequency-independent series resistance could have been replaced by a large parallel resistance but then it would have been frequency-dependent. The series representation easily gives the limiting zero-frequency (z.f. or d.c.) impedance which is just the resistance of the wire.

The *quality factor*, or Q, of the component is a rather crude measure of its quality and is the ratio of the ideal impedance and any stray, non-ideal, impedance. It is much larger than unity for a good device. Thus for a resistance of actual value $R + jX$ the quality factor is $Q = R/X$.

NETWORK THEOREMS

Electrical circuit analysis can be simplified by the use of several theorems.
Kirchhoff's laws state that:

The algebraic sum of the currents flowing into any junction or node is zero, i.e.

$$\sum_i I_i = 0 \qquad \text{for all nodes} \qquad (1.3)$$

This is a statement that charge is conserved and cannnot be stored in an ideal conductor.

The algebraic sum of the potential differences round any complete current path loop, or mesh, in a circuit is zero, i.e.

$$\sum_i V_i = 0 \qquad \text{for all meshes} \qquad (1.4)$$

This is a statement that electromagnetic forces are conservative.

A related theorem is *Tellegen's theorem* which states that:

The algebraic sum of the power dissipated in all the circuit elements is zero, i.e.

$$\sum_i V_i I_i = 0 \qquad \text{over all elements} \qquad (1.5)$$

This is a statement of the first law of thermodynamics.

The frequently used results of these theorems are that, if several impedances Z_i are connected in series, then the net impedance is

$$Z_{tot} = \sum_i Z_i \qquad (1.6)$$

and if several impedances Z_i are connected in parallel, then the net impedance is Z_{tot} where

$$(Z_{tot})^{-1} = \sum_i (Z_i)^{-1} \qquad (1.7)$$

In practice all circuits can be reduced by combining the elements in pairs, either in series or in parallel.

For linear circuits the *principle of superposition* states that the effect on a circuit of each signal source is independent of all the other sources and the resultant effect at any point is the sum of the effects of each source taken separately. This is of great help as all sources except one can be reduced to zero and the effect on the circuit can be calculated for each source in turn.

Fourier analysis allows the principle of superposition to be used to create waveforms of different shapes. Any waveform can be constructed from the summation of a set of sine waves with appropriate amplitudes and phase. Thus if a problem can be solved for a sine wave at all frequencies, it can be solved for an arbitrary waveform. This is used in chapter 6 and described in more detail in appendix 3.

Thévenin's theorem is a very useful theorem and extends the previous discussion of the two-terminal networks to include active elements.

Any linear circuit with two terminals may be represented, at any frequency, by an equivalent circuit consisting of an ideal voltage source V_0 and a series impedance Z_S.

Thus these two components can specify the behavior of any linear circuit, however complex, and enable such circuits to be considered in a much more simple way. The Thévenin equivalent circuit is shown in figure 1.7(a). An *ideal voltage source* generates a constant voltage irrespective of the current flowing through it. The *Thévenin equivalent impedance*, *internal impedance* or *output impedance* (Z_S) is zero for such a source. If the circuit being considered

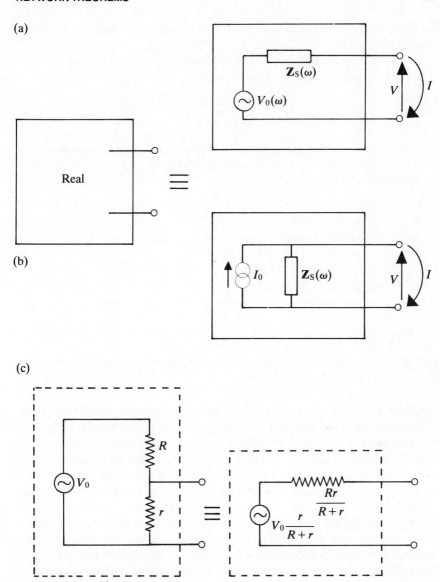

Fig. 1.7 A real, active, linear two-terminal circuit may be represented by (a) an equivalent Thévenin circuit or (b) an equivalent Norton circuit. (c) The real and Thévenin equivalent circuits of a simple potential divider.

is a receiving circuit, then the terminals are the input terminals and the impedance is called the *input impedance*.

An equivalent form of Thévenin's theorem is *Norton's theorem*, in which the generator is an ideal current generator I_0 and there is a parallel impedance

$\mathbf{Z}_S$ as shown in figure 1.7(b). An *ideal current generator* produces the same current irrespective of the voltage developed across it.

These theorems arise because in a linear circuit the terminal current and voltage (I, V) must be linearly related so that

$$V = V_0 - I\mathbf{Z}_S$$
$$I = I_0 - V/\mathbf{Z}_S \tag{1.8}$$

The constants in these equations are the Thévenin equivalent components.

These equivalent components can be found from a real circuit either experimentally or by a calculation by deriving one form of equation (1.8) and

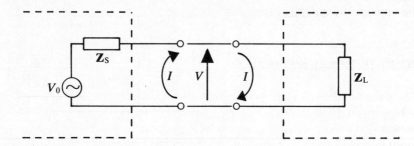

Fig. 1.8 The interconnection between two circuits can be illustrated by the connection of their equivalent circuits.

determining the two constants. The principle of superposition enables the calculation to be made easily. For example, each source within the circuit can be reduced to zero amplitude, while keeping its own internal impedance, so that V_0 will be reduced to zero. The impedance $\mathbf{Z}_S$ is then the total impedance between the terminals of this, now passive, circuit. Similarly the calculated, or measured, terminal voltage when no terminal current flows (the open-circuit voltage) is equal to the Thévenin source voltage V_0.

Consider the simple example of a resistive potential divider circuit shown on the left side of figure 1.7(c). If no current flows through the terminals the terminal voltage is $V_0 r/(R + r)$ determined either by calculation or measurement. The internal impedance can be calculated by imagining the source V_0 reduced to zero but retaining its zero internal impedance, that is it is replaced by a short circuit. Thus the internal impedance, seen from the terminals, is R and r in parallel, or $\mathbf{Z}_S = Rr/(R + r)$. The equivalent circuit is therefore as shown on the right of the figure.

Consider two circuits connected together as shown in figure 1.8. We can represent each circuit by its Thévenin equivalent circuit. The receiving circuit is often designed to generate no output voltage, so we will make its equivalent voltage source zero and denote its internal impedance by $\mathbf{Z}_L$, the load impedance.

If the signal to be transferred between the circuits is a voltage V_0, then we need this voltage to appear across the input terminals, or the load $\mathbf{Z}_L$. For the circuits to allow this, or to be '*matched*' or to not '*load*' each other, the necessary condition is that $|\mathbf{Z}_L| \gg |\mathbf{Z}_S|$. Similarly for a current signal there will be full signal transfer if $|\mathbf{Z}_L| \ll |\mathbf{Z}_S|$. A voltmeter has to have a very high input resistance and an ammeter a very low input resistance.

For *maximum power transfer* the condition is that $\mathbf{Z}_S$ and $\mathbf{Z}_L$ are complex conjugate, so that $\mathbf{Z}_S = R + j\omega X$ and $\mathbf{Z}_S^* = \mathbf{Z}_L = R - j\omega X$. Then $R_S = R_L$ and the reactances resonate at the signal frequency. If the reactance is non-zero, maximum power transfer will only take place at one frequency. Care should be taken in deciding which quantity, voltage, current or power, is the appropriate quantity in any particular case.

FOUR-TERMINAL NETWORKS

The basic building block of a circuit is the two-terminal component. However a bigger sub-unit that is often used in large circuits is the *four-terminal network*, *two-port network* or *two-terminal pair network*. This has a pair of input terminals and a pair of output terminals. Since the four terminals cannot be used independently to form pairs in any combination it is not a true four-terminal network. Many such networks have a common potential for the input and output so that they become three-terminal networks. As a logical extension of Thévenin's theorem, the input and output circuits can be represented by equivalent circuits as shown in figure 1.9. Norton equivalent circuits can also be used. The circuit will modify a signal applied to the input on its way to the output and this effect is incorporated into the equivalent circuit by making the output generator amplitude some linear function of the input (terminal) signal. Similarly a signal may be able to flow from the output to the input so that the input generator may be made dependent on the output voltage. The four elements of the network, the two impedances and the two

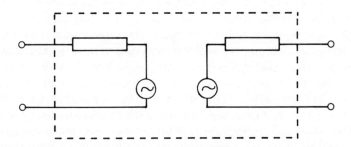

Fig. 1.9   A two-terminal pair network consisting of two Thévenin equivalent circuits.

generators, describe its behavior and therefore completely characterize it. These equivalent circuits enable large circuits to be analyzed in terms of smaller sub-units. There are six possible equivalent circuit representations of a four-terminal network and for each there is a matrix formulation. For the manipulation of these networks by this powerful technique, more detailed texts should be consulted.

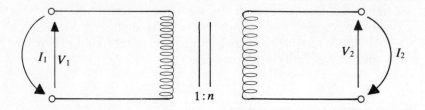

Fig. 1.10   A transformer with a turns ratio of n.

The *transformer* shown in figure 1.10 is a common four-terminal network. In its ideal form, with a secondary-to-primary turns ratio of n, it has the properties that

$$V_2 = nV_1$$

$$I_2 = \frac{1}{n}I_1$$

$$P_2 \equiv V_2 I_2 = V_1 I_1 \equiv P_1 \qquad (1.9)$$

$$\mathbf{Z}_{in} \equiv \frac{V_1}{I_1} = \frac{1}{n^2}\frac{V_2}{I_2} = \frac{1}{n^2}\mathbf{Z}_L$$

There is voltage amplification by n and current amplification by $1/n$. The power P is conserved and if a load $\mathbf{Z}_L$ is attached to the input it will have an effect at the input terminals as if it were an impedance $(1/n^2)\mathbf{Z}_L$. The transformer is thus a voltage, current or impedance transformer. Other uses will be described in chapter 4. In practice the transformer is not as valuable as might be expected. For good operation, it has to have a high-permeability core but this will be both lossy and non-linear. Also the stray impedances are relatively large so that the frequency range of operation of a given transformer is very limited.

FILTERS

Common circuit sub-units are filters, which are designed to attenuate some frequencies differently from others.

The simple RC low-pass (high cut-off) and high-pass (low cut-off) filters are shown in figure 1.11. The 3 dB point or characteristic frequency (see appendix 1) is given by $\omega_0 = 1/RC$.

Filters with the same responses can be made by changing the resistance R to an inductance L and the capacitance C to a resistance R and $\omega_0 = L/R$. On the log–log plot the circuit response $\mathbf{A}_V \equiv V_{out}/V_{in}$ is given approximately by two straight lines for both the magnitude $|\mathbf{A}_V|$ and the phase-shift, which is 0

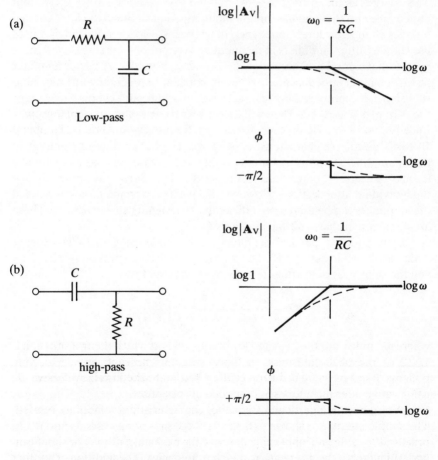

Fig. 1.11 The basic RC low-pass filter (a) and RC high-pass filter (b) together with their transfer characteristics if they are driven from an ideal voltage source and not loaded at the output.

or $\pm\pi/2$. The true response deviates from these simple approximations only near $\omega = \omega_0$, as shown by the broken curves.

Algebraically, for the low-pass filter

$$\mathbf{A_V} = \frac{1}{1 + j\omega/\omega_0} = \frac{1 - j\omega/\omega_0}{1 + (\omega/\omega_0)^2} \qquad (1.10)$$

and for the high-pass filter

$$\mathbf{A_V} = \frac{1}{1 - j\omega_0/\omega} = \frac{1 + j\omega_0/\omega}{1 + (\omega_0/\omega)^2} \qquad (1.11)$$

This analysis assumes that the network is fed from a source with a zero output impedance and the load has infinite input impedance. Since the filter characteristics change or deteriorate when the network is loaded, it is advisable to use simple buffer amplifiers at the input and output of filter stages, and these need to have good and accurately known characteristics. A buffer amplifier has a high input impedance, a low output impedance together with unity gain. If a sharp or complex filter characteristic is required, several single-stage filters may be cascaded. They will interact with each other in a complex way since the input and output impedances are frequency-dependent. To obtain an easily calculable characteristic, the stages can be separated by unity-gain buffer amplifiers to prevent mutual loading. In this case the final characteristic is the product of the magnitudes of the gains and the sum of the phase-shifts of the individual filter sections. However, if a particular characteristic is needed the amplifiers can be used more efficiently by designing an active filter. These are discussed in chapter 2 and appendix 6.

Band-pass and band-reject filters can be made using an LCR resonant circuit as shown in figure 1.12. The characteristic frequency is $\omega_0 = 1/\sqrt{(LC)}$ and the sharpness of the filter is given by the quality factor

$$Q = \frac{\omega_h - \omega_l}{\omega_0} = \frac{1}{R} \sqrt{\left(\frac{L}{C}\right)}$$

where ω_h and ω_l are the high and low frequencies at which the transmission is $1/\sqrt{2}$ of the peak transmission. Since inductors are not very ideal components, band-pass and band-reject filters below about 100 kHz are best made using active filter techniques as described in appendix 6.

A circuit with a particular frequency characteristic is sometimes needed. The simple attenuator shown in figure 1.13 consists of resistors R_1 and R_2. In practice the cable and input capacitance of the next stage C_2 may be significant and will increase the attenuation at high frequencies. The addition of another capacitance C_1, which can be adjusted so that $R_1 C_1 = R_2 C_2$, will ensure a frequency-independent attenuation.

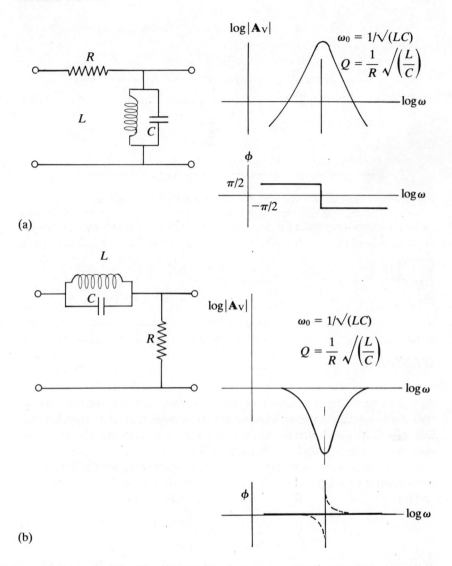

$$\omega_0 = 1/\sqrt{(LC)}$$

$$Q = \frac{1}{R}\sqrt{\left(\frac{L}{C}\right)}$$

(a)

$$\omega_0 = 1/\sqrt{(LC)}$$

$$Q = \frac{1}{R}\sqrt{\left(\frac{L}{C}\right)}$$

(b)

Fig. 1.12 The basic *RCL* band-pass (a) and band-reject (b) filters with their characteristics.

A special class of filters are the *all-pass networks* or *constant-amplitude phase-shift networks*. These have a frequency-independent amplitude response but have a frequency-dependent phase-shift. They are often used with variable components so that the phase of a single-frequency, sine wave, signal may be varied without changing the amplitude. A typical circuit is shown in figure 1.14(b). The phase-shift depends on the value of *RC* and can

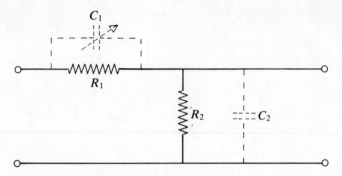

Fig. 1.13   A resistive attenuator $R_1 R_2$ may need to include a variable capacitance C_1 to preserve a frequency-independent attenuation if the circuit includes a stray capacitance C_2.

vary between $-\pi/2$ and $+\pi/2$. The circuit requires equal and opposite input signals, $+V_{in}$ and $-V_{in}$. The circuits of figure 1.14(a) show three methods of producing these. An active all-pass network is also shown in appendix 7.

BIASING

Any particular electronic device has to be set into the proper electrical state so that it will operate in the desired manner. It has to be put into a circuit which sets its voltages and currents to suitable values. Consider the two-terminal, non-linear device D, shown in figure 1.15. The bias circuit is a resistance R_L in series with it across a voltage supply V^+. The current through the device and R_L is I and the voltage across the device is V. Then

$$V^+ = V + IR_L \qquad \text{or} \qquad I = \frac{V^+}{R_L} - \frac{1}{R_L}V \qquad (1.12)$$

If the device characteristic is $I(V)$ as shown in the figure, then the equilibrium values of I and V (V_0, I_0) are found as the solution of the equations $I(V)$ and (1.12). Graphically, this is the intersection of the characteristic and the line representative of equation (1.12), the *load line*. To define the *bias point* (V_0, I_0) well, the two lines should intersect at a large angle. If the device characteristic is very curved, care should be taken that the lines only intersect at one point.

The power dissipated in the device is $P = IV$ and lines of constant power are hyperbolas, one of which is shown. The normal device limitations are defined by maximum values of V, I, and P, which thus defines a region of the

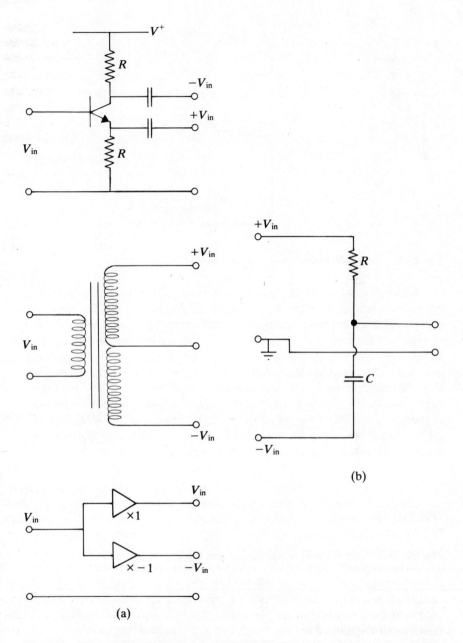

Fig. 1.14 The passive all-pass networks shown in (b) needs antiphase input signals. Methods of producing these are shown in (a).

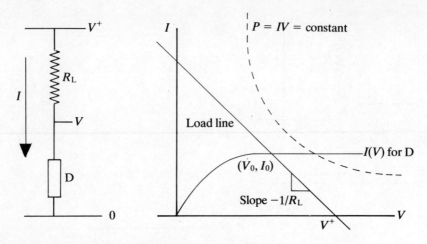

Fig. 1.15   The simple series bias circuit for device D.

characteristic in which a bias point may be chosen. If the device characteristic depends on temperature and hence the power dissipated in it, the bias point will move along the load line as the device warms up. The direction of the motion will depend on the properties of the device, but semiconductor devices normally pass more current on heating so the bias point moves up the load line. The maximum power dissipated in the device occurs when it has $V^+/2$ dropped across it. The bias point will be stable or unstable with temperature depending on which side of this point the initial bias point is chosen. In the semiconductor example, if the initial point were at $V > V^+/2$ then the self-heating would drive the bias point nearer $V = V^+/2$ and to higher power dissipation levels and hence more self-heating.

THE DIODE

The diode is the basic non-linear device and has the characteristic

$$I = I_{00} \left[\exp\left(\frac{eV}{kT}\right) - 1 \right]$$

which can be simplified to

$$I \simeq I_{00} \exp\left(\frac{eV}{kT}\right) \qquad \text{since usually } I_{00} \ll I \qquad (1.13)$$

The current–voltage relationship is thus exponential and may be used for analog computation as described in chapter 2. The shape of the characteristic

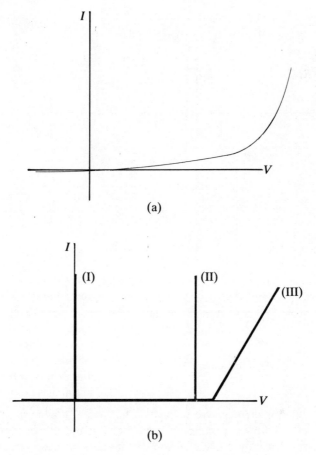

Fig. 1.16 The actual diode characteristic (a) may be approximated by one of the simple linear forms shown in (b) for large-amplitude signals.

is shown in figure 1.16(a). If the diode is biased at some point (V_0, I_0) then, for a small signal $(v \ll kT/e)$ about this point, the characteristic has a conductance

$$\frac{\mathrm{d}I}{\mathrm{d}V} \equiv \frac{i}{v} = I_{00}\frac{e}{kT}\exp\left(\frac{eV}{kT}\right) = \frac{eI_0}{kT}$$

so that the diode behaves as a conductance controlled by the bias current. For larger signals the characteristic about the bias point can no longer be considered linear; the non-linearity will introduce distortion with harmonic generation and frequency mixing effects as described in chapter 6. For very large-voltage signals $(V \gtrsim 0.6\,\mathrm{V})$, the diode can be approximated by a voltage-controlled switch with characteristics as shown in figure 1.16(b). In the simplest approximation (I) the diode conducts perfectly for positive voltages

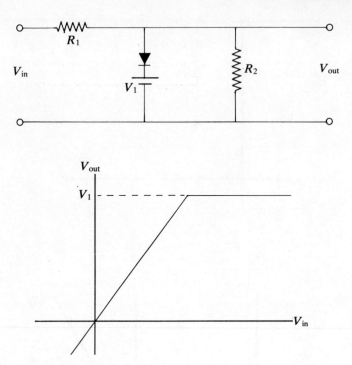

Fig. 1.17   The diode limiter circuit.

but is an insulator for negative voltages. The current flow in practice is not large below 0.6 V for the common silicon diodes, so the approximation (II) is more accurate. Usually a diode has some series resistance, so a linear voltage drop above +0.6 V as shown in approximation (III) is realistic. The diode is used to rectify large signals and this is described more fully in chapter 6.

A useful diode circuit is the *clipper* or *limiter*, which prevents signals becoming greater than a certain value. This is shown in figure 1.17. If $R_2 > R_1$ and the diode resistance is negligible compared with R_1 and R_2, we can use the approximation (I) of figure 1.16(b). For V_{in} negative or positive and less than V_1 the diode does not conduct and takes no part in the circuit so that the signal is passed unchanged. However for $V_{in} > V_1$ the diode conducts with negligible voltage drop and V_{out} is V_1. In practice the potential V_1 is supplied by a low internal impedance voltage source derived from some power supply, the diode resistance does not change sharply with voltage, and there is a small voltage drop across the forward-biased diode.

The *diode clamp* will add a suitable voltage to any a.c. signal or series of pulses so that the total signal is only positive (or negative) in sign. The circuit is shown in figure 1.18. If the voltage V_{in} is positive, the diode does not conduct and all the input signal appears across R_2 if $R_1 < R_2$. For negative V_{in}

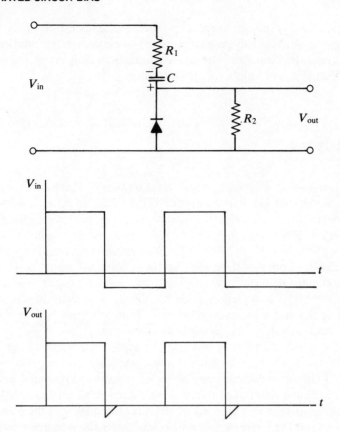

Fig. 1.18 The diode clamp circuit.

the diode conducts and the capacitor rapidly charges, with a time constant $R_1 C$, to the maximum negative voltage of the signal. The capacitor holds this voltage over a time $R_2 C$ so that V_{out} is equal to V_{in} plus this capacitor voltage. This circuit is useful to obtain an output value equal to the input peak-to-peak value or to make the signal of all one sign. Because the capacitor will discharge a certain amount during each cycle, there is a rapid recharging whenever V_{in} becomes negative, which results in V_{out} becoming negative for a very short time.

INTEGRATED CIRCUIT BIAS

Integrated circuits are designed so that they are easy to use and usually require little special bias arrangements other than the correct power supplies.

There are usually voltage, current, power, and temperature limits to the circuit operation. These limits may be on the whole circuit or on the input or output terminals. Care should be taken in interconnecting integrated circuits using different power supply voltages or sources.

TRANSISTORS

The basic solid-state amplifying device is the transistor. There are two types of devices, the bipolar junction transistor (BJT) and the unipolar or field-effect transistor (FET). Of the latter there are two varieties, the junction field-effect transistor (JFET) and the insulated gate or metal oxide semiconductor field-effect transistor (IGFET or MOSFET). Each comes in versions for positive or negative voltage polarity depending on the relative use of n-type or p-type semiconducting material. As well as the normal enhancement-mode MOSFET there is a depletion-mode MOSFET. The latter has a physical conducting channel between the source and drain, whereas the former has no channel until the gate voltage is applied to form one.

It is not the intention of this book to explain transistor action or the details of transistor use. In general most functions can be performed by integrated circuits, which are assemblies of transistors combined in a well engineered circuit that is easy to use. Thus there will be few occasions when individual transistors will be needed. However the quality of the transistors that can be used in integrated circuits is limited by the requirements of the method of manufacture and in such qualities as frequency response, power, current or voltage limits, and leakage current, so that for special circuits or for particular parts of a circuit (such as the low signal level input stage or the high signal level output stage) discrete transistors may be needed.

Here the use of transistors will be reviewed both for completeness and so that some particular applications of individual devices can be introduced. It will be assumed that a positive power supply is used and that the transistors are either n-p-n bipolar or n-channel field-effect so that a positive voltage on the control terminal, the base for bipolar transistors and the gate for field-effect transistors, will increase the current flow through the device (I_C or I_D). The terminal notation is shown in figure 1.19.

For each device a small power signal applied to the base or gate control electrode causes a large power change in the main current flow through the device, the collector–emitter current or the drain–source current. There is thus power gain. The characteristics in each case are non-linear such that, except at small output voltages (V_{CE} or V_{DS}), the device acts like a constant current source which has its magnitude altered by the control signal.

The main distinction between the performance of the devices is that the

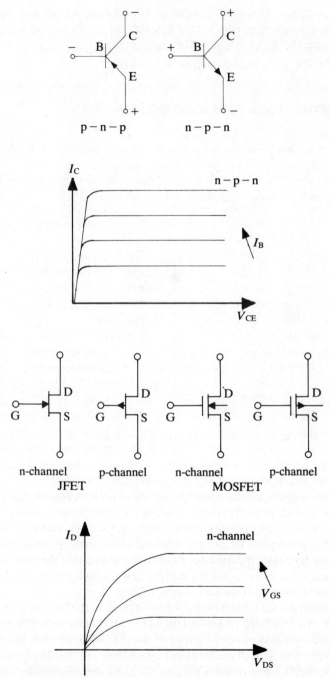

Fig. 1.19 The symbols and typical *I–V* characteristics for bipolar and field-effect transistors.

bipolar transistor has a low (non-linear) input resistance, so that there is a significant input current, whereas the field-effect transistors have a high input resistance and hence have a negligible input current.

TRANSISTORS USED FOR LARGE SIGNALS

For large signals a transistor acts like a switch and supplies either a large or a small output current. If the load is connected in series with the device, the load line is as shown in figure 1.20 and the current switches between points 1 and 2 depending on the magnitude of the input signal, V_G.

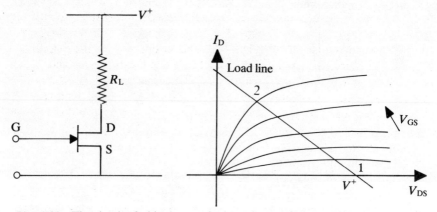

Fig. 1.20 The circuit of a bipolar transistor used as a switch.

In this circuit we use the notation V^+ for the positive supply voltage. More conventional usage is V_{DD}, V_{CC}, V_{SS}, etc., for the supply potential appropriate to the relevant terminal, namely drain, collector, source, etc.

SMALL-SIGNAL BIAS CIRCUITS

If small-amplitude signals are applied to the device, the response and characteristics of the device will depend on the part of the non-linear characteristics at which the device is biased. The bias conditions are the d.c. or constant conditions before any small signal is applied and they set the device into a state such that it will respond appropriately to a small-amplitude signal. The bias point is set by the device voltage and current (I_D, V_{DS} or I_C, V_{CE}) and the control voltage or current (V_{GS} or I_B) necessary to produce these conditions.

The choice of bias condition will depend on the type of device being used and the properties of the circuit which are to be optimized. Thus the circuit may be used for high voltage gain, low noise, high output signal voltage, current or power, or low device power dissipation. The choice of the particular type of device (for example bipolar or field-effect transistor), the particular model of device from the manufacturers' lists, and the particular bias point is one of great complexity and considerable experience is needed. In general the manufacturers give advice, supply specifications, and suggest suitable bias conditions to optimize the use of their devices.

The bias circuit is determined by the device used and the bias point desired. The general principles are one of simplicity and stability of the bias point against changes in temperature and device properties with time. A circuit design should also consider the constancy of the bias point and hence circuit performance when changing the transistor for another with nominally the same, but usually slightly different, characteristics. The properties of individual devices are not guaranteed with high precision.

Usually it is the device gain that needs to be stabilized. This is governed largely by the output characteristics. Therefore bias circuits are designed so that the output current is stabilized, rather than the input control variables. This is done by using a simple negative feedback arrangement.

The major difference between the bias circuits for field-effect and bipolar transistors is that the former require only a gate voltage with negligible current, so that a high internal impedance voltage source may be used, whereas the bipolar transistor requires a base voltage and current so that a much lower source impedance is necessary.

The basic bias circuit for a field-effect transistor is shown in figure 1.21(a) and the device characteristics and load line in figure 1.21(b). To operate an n-channel JFET requires a small negative voltage on the gate, relative to the source. Since a negative power supply is not usually readily available, this is achieved by holding the gate at zero potential by connecting it to earth and making the source potential positive by making the device current flow through a small resistance R_S. This is shown in figure 1.21(c). Since negligible gate current flows, the connection of the gate to earth potential can be made with a large (~ 1 MΩ) resistance R_G. If no (bias) current flows through this there will be no potential drop across it. The signal will be applied to the gate. If R_G was not large there would be a low input impedance to earth with consequent loading of the signal source.

The chosen bias point specifies the values of V_{GS}, I_D, and V_{DS}. A resistance R_S in series with the source is chosen so that $I_D R_S = V_S = -V_{GS}$. The equation for the device current is then

$$V^+ = I_D R_L + V_{DS} + I_D R_S$$

which allows the completion of the design by the choice of V^+ and R_L. Normally V^+ is fixed by an initial choice for the whole circuit. The load line

EER–B*

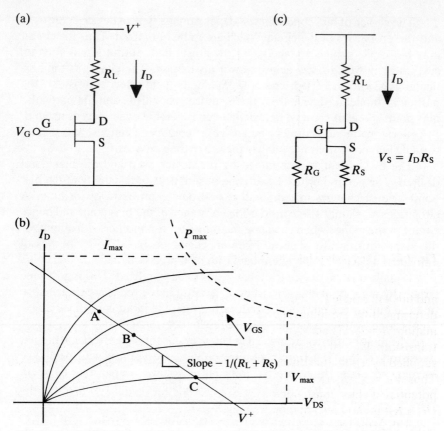

Fig. 1.21   (a) The small-signal bias circuit for an n-channel JFET, (b) the character-istic curves and the determination of the bias point, and (c) the practical circuit if a negative gate bias voltage is needed.

slope is determined by $(R_L + R_S)$ but R_S is usually much smaller than R_L and for a.c. signals we shall see that R_S is bypassed and has no effect on the a.c. gain.

    The bias circuit for the bipolar transistor uses the same principles and is shown in figure 1.22. The n-p-n bipolar transistor requires a small positive voltage on the base and, since its input impendance is low, this must come from a source with a fairly low internal impedance. The chosen bias point specifies values of V_{BE}, I_B, I_C and I_E, and V_{CE}. An emitter resistance R_E is chosen in a fairly arbitrary way. It needs to be large to provide good bias point stabilization but it should be much less than R_L (say $R_L/4$) since R_L will provide the voltage gain. The total series resistance $(R_L + R_E)$ provides the bias point load line. The device current equation is then

$$V^+ = I_C R_L + V_{CE} + I_E R_E \approx V_{CE} + I_C(R_L + R_E)$$

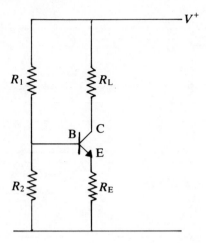

Fig. 1.22 The practical bias circuit for an n-p-n bipolar transistor.

and this will enable V^+ and $(R_L + R_E)$ to be chosen. Again V^+ will normally be determined by the initial choice for the whole circuit. As another approximation $I_C \approx I_E$. Then V_B is chosen so that $V_B = V_{BE} + I_E R_E$. For silicon transistors $V_{BE} \approx 0.6 \, \text{V}$ under most conditions. The base bias voltage is supplied by a potential divider of R_1, R_2 derived from the supply voltage V^+. Thus $V_B = V^+ R_2/(R_1 + R_2)$. This must be a constant voltage so that the potential divider must not be loaded by the transistor. To achieve this $(R_1 + R_2)$ is chosen so that the current through them, $V^+/(R_1 + R_2)$, is much larger than the base bias current I_B.

It was stated earlier that these bias circuits are negative feedback circuits that stabilize the device output bias current. In each case the control voltage is kept constant. If the device characteristics change so that the device current, I_D or I_C, increases then the voltage drop across R_S or R_E, and hence V_S or V_E, increases. The control voltage across the device, V_{GS} or V_{BE}, therefore decreases and the device responds by reducing the current. Thus the circuit will tend to keep the device output bias current constant if it deviates for any reason.

Other bias circuits are possible but the types described above will be suitable for most requirements.

TRANSISTOR EQUIVALENT CIRCUITS

The particular bias point chosen will determine how the device itself will behave for small-amplitude signals applied to it. This behavior can be

(a)

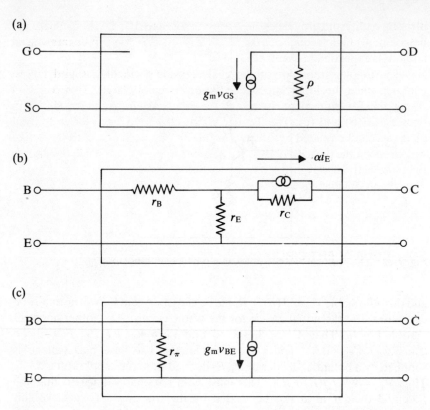

Fig. 1.23 The low-frequency equivalent circuit for an FET (a) and the Tee (b) and Pi (c) equivalent circuits for a bipolar transistor.

described with a linear equivalent circuit if the signal is small so that all variables are proportional to each other. The response of the total circuit is then the response of the biased device, represented by its equivalent circuit for that bias point, with the addition of the bias circuit components.

The simplified, low-frequency small-signal equivalent circuit for an FET is shown in figure 1.23(a). The input impedance is high, shown here as infinite. The Norton equivalent circuit is used since the device acts like a voltage-controlled current generator. The output resistance ρ is usually very large. The voltage-controlled current generator provides the link between the output and input equivalent circuits. There is no reverse signal flow so that there is no signal generator in the input equivalent circuit. The magnitudes of the quantities g_m (the mutual conductance) and ρ, which describe the behavior of the device to small signals, will depend on the bias point. Other equivalent circuits are possible, for example, with a Thévenin equivalent output circuit, but the Norton configuration corresponds most closely to physical reality and provides simple constants g_m and ρ which characterize the behavior. At high frequencies the device capacitances have to be introduced and this is expanded in chapter 11.

The bipolar transistor small-signal equivalent circuit is slightly more complex since the input impedance is not extremely large. Two common forms, the Tee equivalent circuit and the Pi equivalent circuit are shown in figures 1.23(b) and (c). The Tee circuit is often used since the individual elements can be related to the physical device impedances and to the actual way in which the device works. The constants r_B, r_E, r_C, and α will depend on the bias point. However r_B and α change little and r_B is small and can often be neglected. The Pi equivalent circuit is the more conventional form.

FULL EQUIVALENT CIRCUIT

The device, set into a working state by means of its bias circuit, is now ready to be used to amplify small-amplitude signals. The full circuit consists of the device equivalent circuit plus the bias circuit components. Many of the circuit components can be approximated to zero or infinite impedances at the signal frequency and hence a simple approximate full equivalent circuit may be easily obtained. There are many ways in which a biased device may be included in a full circuit. Some will be considered next. As an example consider the common emitter bipolar transistor amplifier shown in figure 1.24(a).

The bias circuit consists of $R_1 R_2 R_L R_E$. As the device is in the common emitter configuration (which will be explained more fully shortly), the emitter must be at zero potential for the small-amplitude a.c. signals. Usually the signal is alternating with frequency components above some minimum value ω_{min}. The emitter can be set at zero potential (for the a.c. signal) by connecting a *decoupling capacitor* C_E across R_E so that $1/\omega_{min} C_E \ll R_E$. The bias circuit is at z.f. (d.c.) and the signal circuits connected to the bias circuit should not conduct at z.f. and hence alter the bias circuit conditions. *Coupling capacitors*, or *blocking capacitors*, C_{C1} and C_{C2} are used to allow the a.c. signal to pass into, and out of, the circuit but prevent any z.f. current flow. The impedance $1/\omega_{min} C_C$ must be much less than the input impedance of its following stage so that no signal voltage is lost across it.

For the a.c. signal the power supply potentials are zero since the power supply has a low internal impedance to earth for a.c. signals and usually has a large capacitance across it. The full small-signal equivalent circuit is thus as shown in figure 1.24(b) and the approximate simplified form when all negligible impedances at the signal frequency are neglected is shown in figure 1.24(c). The capacitors C_C and C_E together with the significant series or

(a)

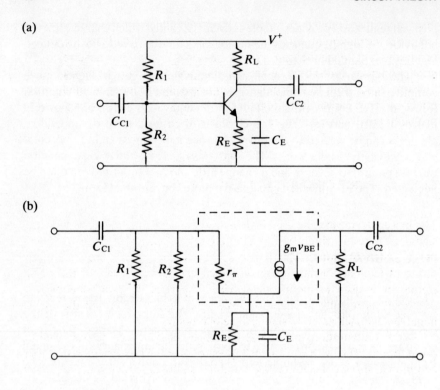

(b)

(c)

Fig. 1.24 (a) The biased bipolar transistor connected as a common emitter amplifier, with the full (b) and approximate (c) equivalent circuits for the device and its bias components.

parallel resistors form RC filters which usually provide the low-frequency limit to the performance of the circuit. This approach to the circuit design assumes that the z.f. (d.c.) bias circuit can be separated from the a.c. signal circuit. If the signal is also at z.f. or is very slowly varying so that its frequency components are very low, then this separation cannot be made and other techniques must be used. In general the properties of devices vary slowly due to changes in temperature or to aging effects. In a z.f. circuit a slow change in the device properties, and hence the bias point, will appear as a signal whereas in a capacitive coupled circuit which only amplifies a.c. signals the slow change in the bias point will result in only a very small change in the a.c. device properties and hence the gain. For this reason z.f. amplifiers have relatively poor properties and should be avoided if an a.c. amplifier can be used. The high-frequency limit to the amplification is usually produced by the filtering effect of stray capacitances together with the relevant resistances. These problems are discussed in more detail in chapter 11.

SINGLE-DEVICE CIRCUIT CONFIGURATIONS

The biased device may be used in many ways to amplify small-amplitude a.c. signals. There are three basic single-device configurations and many two-device configurations. The single-device configurations are essentially different feedback arrangements in which negative feedback at the signal frequency is used to modify the device properties. Negative feedback is described more fully in chapter 2. We have already described the use of negative feedback at z.f. to stabilize the bias point.

The configurations are called *grounded*, or *common*, *source*, *gate* or *drain* for the FET, with equivalent expressions for the bipolar transistor. The common drain or collector configuration is usually called the *source follower*

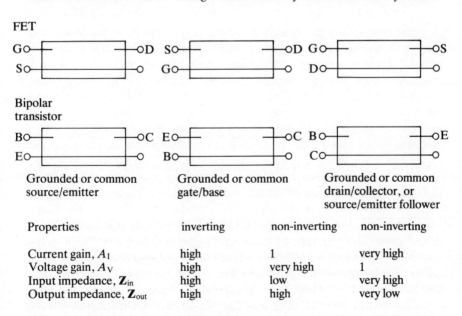

Properties	inverting	non-inverting	non-inverting
Current gain, A_I	high	1	very high
Voltage gain, A_V	high	very high	1
Input impedance, Z_{in}	high	low	very high
Output impedance, Z_{out}	high	high	very low

Fig. 1.25 The connections and basic properties of the three circuit configurations of bipolar and field-effect transistors.

or *emitter follower* configuration. The circuits are shown in figure 1.25 together with the main properties that are emphasized for each configuration.

The common source (common emitter) configuration is the most common circuit since it has high voltage gain with reasonably high input impedance and reasonably low output impedance, so that little of the voltage gain is lost by loading when similar stages are connected one after the other. This configuration was used in the example shown in figure 1.24. The signal is applied between the base and emitter and is taken out between the collector and emitter. The emitter is thus a common potential reference point or earth for both the input and output signals.

The common gate (common base) configuration has a very high voltage gain but this benefit is often devalued since there is usually voltage lost by loading if similar stages are cascaded because of the low input impedance and high output impedance. It is used in high-frequency circuits since it has a low input capacitance because it does not exhibit the Miller effect (chapter 11).

The source follower (emitter follower) configuration is a unity-gain buffer amplifier which is used to prevent loading between sections of circuits since it has a very large input impedance and a small output impedance.

TWO-DEVICE CIRCUIT CONFIGURATIONS

A simple two-device configuration for bipolar transistors is the *Darlington configuration* in which the emitter current of one transistor is used as the base current of a larger transistor as shown in figure 1.26. The circuit behaves as a single transistor with an extremely high gain and can be obtained as a simple integrated circuit consisting of a small and a large transistor made and packaged together. The circuit is often used in the emitter follower configuration and has a large input impedance, a low output impedance, and a large current handling capacity. It has the disadvantage that any change in the properties of the first transistor will be amplified by the following device and this is true for both the a.c. and the bias properties. It therefore has properties that are not very stable with temperature or time and it is usually used only within a negative feedback loop so that the bias conditions are strongly stabilized. Improved versions exist which reduce the temperature sensitivity of the circuit. If the temperature increases, the emitter current of the first transistor will increase. To prevent this increase being amplified by the second transistor, an increasing current is removed by a subsidiary temperature-dependent circuit shown schematically with broken lines in figure 1.26.

The *current mirror* is shown in figure 1.27. A current I_{out} is produced which is equal to the input current I_{in}. The advantage of the circuit is that the output circuit acts as a nearly ideal current source although the input current

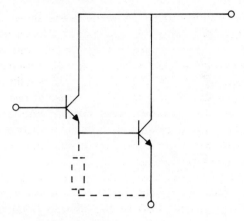

Fig. 1.26 The Darlington configuration using two transistors with the optional stabilizing circuit shown schematically with broken lines.

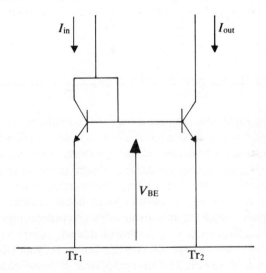

Fig. 1.27 The current mirror circuit.

may be derived from a simple circuit. The current I_{in} flowing through transistor Tr_1 changes its V_{BE} which in turn becomes the input voltage for Tr_2 to produce I_{out}. The use of two transistors results in a circuit that is quite temperature-insensitive. The circuit works best if the transistors are identical and kept in the same environment, as happens if they are on the same piece of silicon in the same integrated circuit. The output current can be controlled easily by controlling I_{in}. Since V_{BE} is small and fairly constant an input voltage

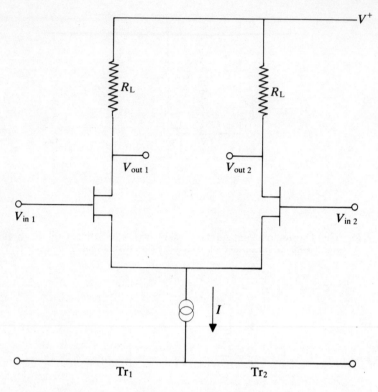

Fig. 1.28 The long-tailed pair differential amplifier circuit.

V_{in} applied to a large resistance R will produce an input current $I_{in} = (V_{in} - V_{BE})/R \approx V_{in}/R$ to make a voltage-controlled current source $I_{out} \approx V_{in}/R$. A single transistor Tr_1 can control the same current $I_{out} = I_{in}$ in several output transistors if its V_{BE} is applied to each base-emitter junction. If identical transistors are used and their collector currents are added, then accurate ratios I_{out}, $2I_{out}$, $3I_{out}$, etc., may be produced.

The *long-tailed pair* differential amplifier shown in figure 1.28 is the basic differential amplifier circuit. The current source I is the "long tail" and consists of a current source such as the current mirror just described or a resistance large enough so that most of the supply voltage V^+ is dropped across it. The circuit relies on the two transistors being matched or having the same properties. Thus the transistors should preferably be a pair constructed simultaneously on the same piece of silicon. The total current I is split between the two transistors Tr_1 and Tr_2. If the circuit is balanced, the division of the current will not be affected by a voltage applied equally to both input terminals but will depend on the difference in the input voltages. The transistor currents flowing through the equal load resistances R_L produce the output voltages. Thus $(V_{out\,2} - V_{out\,1})$ is proportional to $(V_{in\,2} - V_{in\,1})$. Another

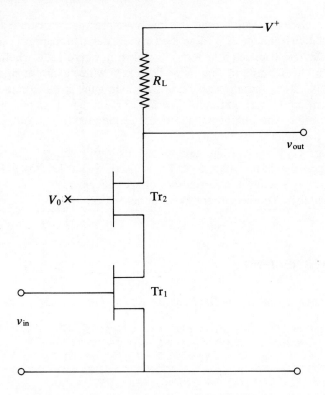

Fig. 1.29 The two-transistor cascode circuit.

advantage is that a differential input signal applied asymmetrically with respect to earth produces a differential output signal which is symmetrical with respect to earth since changes in the current through Tr_1 and Tr_2 must be equal and opposite.

Because this circuit is insensitive to the properties of the devices provided that they are matched, it is a valuable z.f. (d.c.) amplifier. It can also be considered as a two-stage circuit. Consider a signal $V_{in\,1}$ applied to Tr_1 while $V_{in\,2}$ is kept constant. Transistor Tr_1 is thus a source follower with a high input impedance but no voltage gain between the gate and source. The voltage common to both sources provides the input signal to Tr_2 which is held in the common gate configuration by the constant $V_{in\,2}$ and has a high voltage gain. The very low output impedance of Tr_1 is not loaded by the low (but larger) input impedance of Tr_2. Thus the combination of an emitter follower and a common base circuit produces a high input impedance and reduces the loading between stages so that the full voltage gain of the second stage may be used. The advantages of modifications to this configuration for use at high frequencies are described in chapter 11.

The *cascode* circuit is used as a low-noise preamplifier circuit and is also useful at high frequencies, as described in more detail in chapter 11. It consists of two devices connected in series as shown in figure 1.29, where the bias circuit has been omitted. Transistor Tr_2 is kept with a constant gate voltage. Transistor Tr_1 is therefore working with high gain in the common source configuration. Its current output flows into Tr_2 in the high-gain common gate configuration. The output voltage signal is obtained by the output current flowing through the load R_L.

Since Tr_2 has a constant gate voltage its source voltage is also constant and hence the drain voltage of Tr_1 is fixed. Since Tr_2 has a low input impedance it is acting as a current-to-voltage converter.

In all these circuits either bipolar or field-effect transistors may be used.

FURTHER READING

P. M. Chirlian, *Analysis and Design of Integral Electronic Circuits*, Harper and Row (1981).
P. Horowitz and W. Hill, *The Art of Electronics*, Cambridge University Press (1980).
B. Jones, *Circuit Electronics for Scientists*, Addison-Wesley (1974).
J. Millman, *Microelectronics: Digital and Analog Circuits and Systems*, McGraw-Hill (1978).
R. J. Smith, *Circuits, Devices and Systems*, Wiley (1984).
R. J. Smith, *Electronics, Circuits and Devices*, Wiley (1980).

2 OPERATIONAL AMPLIFIERS AND NEGATIVE FEEDBACK

INTRODUCTION

The operational amplifier is the general-purpose active circuit element, and is specifically designed to be used in a wide variety of ways. In integrated circuit form they are cheap and designed to be very easy to use, so that they can be considered for use in circuits almost in the same way as the common passive components, resistors, capacitors, and inductors. An active circuit incorporating an operational amplifier has a performance that is easily calculated to a high degree of precision. In general, the presence of the amplifier will enable a particular operation to be performed on a signal with a much higher precision than if only passive components had been used. There will also be far less interaction with the preceding and following stages of the circuit.

Practical operational amplifiers all have very similar performances and differ only in the optimization of one or more of their specific parameters, such as gain, high-frequency response, large voltage range or low noise. The analysis of the circuits presented here is therefore quite general. The amplifiers can be used to perform different functions by applying different types of feedback. In a feedback circuit the output signal is taken, modified in amplitude and phase by a feedback network, and then added to, or subtracted from, the input signal. Under these circumstances the net result is usually determined by the properties of the feedback network rather than by those of the amplifier. Since the feedback network can be made of precise, stable, and well characterized passive components, the circuit will have these properties rather than the poorer properties of the active elements in the amplifier itself.

Another way of considering operational amplifier circuits is that they are control circuits or servo-circuits in which all the elements and variables are electrical. The operational amplifier circuit thus keeps certain voltages or currents constant. This aspect will be expanded at the end of the chapter.

The name 'operational amplifier' was introduced since they were originally used in analog computation circuits to perform specific mathematical operations on voltages. In such circuits the voltages represent the magnitude of some experimental variable which is manipulated by the circuit to calculate some mathematical function. For such use digital computers are now usually better. The term 'operational amplifier' is now used for general-purpose amplifiers specifically designed for use with feedback.

GENERAL FEEDBACK

The basic principles involved in applying feedback to an amplifier can be described by considering the idealized voltage feedback circuit shown in figure 2.1. Here an ideal differential voltage amplifier with infinite input impedance, zero output impedance, and characteristic

$$V_2 = \mathbf{A}V_1 = \mathbf{A}(V_+ - V_1) \tag{2.1}$$

is used. The voltage transfer function $\mathbf{A}$ gives the gain and phase response. The voltage at the non-inverting input is V_+ and that at the inverting input is V_-. This notation and the $+$ and $-$ symbols on the amplifier terminals only represent the *relative* polarities of the signals and not the absolute voltages. It should be emphasized that the analysis applies to any amplifier, such as a single-transistor amplifier, provided that the appropriate equivalent circuit is used and account is taken of the actual input and output impedances. The

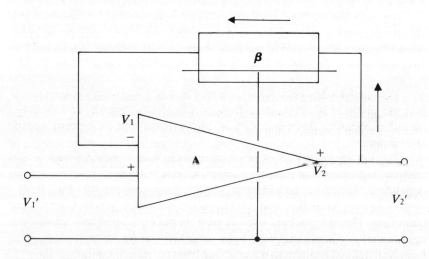

Fig. 2.1 The general feedback circuit with the fed-back signal taken to an inverting input.

feedback signal is provided by a network with a voltage transfer function β so that the output signal V_2 is modified to βV_2 and fed to the inverting input terminal. Therefore

$$V_- = \beta V_2 \qquad (2.2)$$

The network β is usually a three-terminal passive network, although active, non-linear, and more complex networks may be used.

The circuit with feedback has an input signal V_1' and output signal V_2', where the primes indicate the closed-loop condition, and the total voltage transfer function is $\mathbf{A}' \equiv V_2'/V_1'$. From the circuit it can be seen that

$$\begin{aligned} V_1' &= V_+ \\ V_2' &= V_2 \end{aligned} \qquad (2.3)$$

so that with equations (2.1) and (2.2) we get

$$V_2' = V_2 = \mathbf{A}(V_+ - V_-) = \mathbf{A}(V_1' - \beta V_2')$$

or

$$\mathbf{A}' \equiv \frac{V_2'}{V_1'} = \frac{\mathbf{A}}{1 + \mathbf{A}\beta} \qquad (2.4)$$

This general feedback equation is sometimes presented in different forms if, instead of a differential amplifier, an adding or subtracting network is assumed before a simple inverting or non-inverting amplifier. Sometimes a different sign convention is used. The terminology used here is that $\mathbf{A}'$ is the *closed-loop gain*, $\mathbf{A}$ is the *open-loop gain*, and $(-\mathbf{A}\beta)$ is the *loop gain*. The last is the net gain experienced by a signal passing round the feedback loop from any point back to the start and its size and phase determine the behavior of the circuit.

This analysis has been done assuming that the signals are voltages and that the amplifier is a voltage device with a high input impedance and a low output impedance. A similar analysis can be carried out for current signals and circuits.

The full equation (2.4) is not easy to investigate in general since it is a complicated function of complex quantities, each of which may be frequency-dependent. However, considerable understanding can be had by initially neglecting the phase-shifts and treating $\mathbf{A}$ and β as frequency-dependent real quantities. The analysis here so far is general, but most feedback circuits use operational amplifiers that have been specifically designed for such use and have well defined characteristics enabling them to be used easily.

An ideal operational amplifier has a linear characteristic, as shown in figure 2.2(a); this continues up to some saturation values $V_{\text{sat}}^{\pm}$ which are just

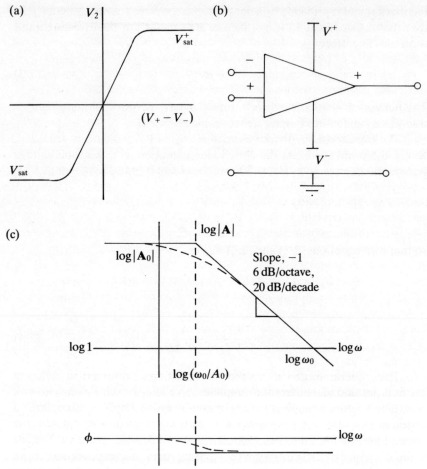

Fig. 2.2 The characteristics of an ideal operational amplifier. The transfer characteristics (a) show a high gain and saturation at $V_{sat}^{\pm}$. The schematic diagram (b) and the magnitude and phase of the open-loop gain (c).

less than the power supply voltages, $V^{\pm}$. In many integrated circuit operational amplifiers, the earth potential is not defined within the amplifier but by the earth of the power supply, as shown in figure 2.2(b). Thus three voltages are supplied to the circuit, namely 0 and $V^{\pm}$, but there is no direct connection of the potential $V = 0$ to the amplifier itself. The input signal is applied relative to the circuit or power supply earth ($V = 0$) and the output signal appears relative to this potential. Most linear integrated circuit operational amplifiers operate at 0 and ± 15 V. The operational amplifier has a response for small-amplitude signals in the frequency range from d.c. (or zero frequency (z.f.)) upwards. The high-frequency decrease in gain is specially controlled internally in most amplifiers (internally compensated) to have a frequency response corresponding to that of a single RC low-pass filter. This makes the design of stable feedback circuits easier, and the reason will be described in chapter 3. Some amplifiers are not internally compensated so that their A–f response is not a simple function. These require special feedback paths to be added externally to give the amplifier a suitable gain–frequency response before the normal feedback path β is added. These amplifiers can usually be used at higher frequencies than those which are internally compensated, and they are more flexible in use but require more skill and experience in order to achieve stable operation.

The gain–frequency curve of a typical compensated operational amplifier is shown in figure 2.2(c). To enable all frequencies of interest to be displayed, a log–log plot is shown. The (linear–log) phase–frequency graph is also shown. On such displays the response can be approximated by straight lines with significant deviations from the true response only near changes of slope. This straight-line approximation can usually be used for most analyses. This is the small-amplitude gain, since for large-amplitude signals the high-frequency gain is more limited. This will be described later in this chapter.

The characteristic is that of an amplifier with a low-frequency gain A_0 in series with a low-pass filter of characteristic (angular) frequency ω_0/A_0, so that at high frequencies the gain decreases as $1/f$ or $1/\omega$ to give a gain of unity at ω_0. The amplifier can thus be described by the d.c. (z.f.) gain A_0 and the unity-gain frequency or the constant gain–bandwidth product $f_0 = \omega_0/2\pi$. The $1/\omega$ decrease in gain corresponds to a slope of -1 on the graph or -6 dB per octave of frequency (a frequency ratio of 2) or -20 dB per decade of frequency (a frequency ratio of 10). The phase-shift through the amplifier is zero at low frequencies but $-\pi/2$ at frequencies above ω_0/A_0. Typical values of A_0 are 10^5–10^6 and $f_0 = \omega_0/2\pi$ lies between 10^6 and 10^7 Hz. The input resistance is between 10^6 and 10^{14} Ω while the output resistance may be 10–100 Ω.

The general feedback equation (2.4)

$$\mathbf{A}' = \frac{\mathbf{A}}{1 + \mathbf{A}\beta}$$

can now be considered in the approximation that $\mathbf{A}$ and β are frequency-dependent quantities but the phase-shifts are ignored except to give the sign of the loop gain $(-\mathbf{A}\beta)$.

If $(-\mathbf{A}\beta) = 0$, then $A' = A$, the loop is broken, and the closed-loop gain equals the open-loop gain.

If $(-\mathbf{A}\beta)$ is small and positive, $|\mathbf{A}'| > |\mathbf{A}|$, and there is an increase in gain. This is positive feedback or regeneration and was a valuable condition when amplifiers had only low gain. However, now gain is a cheap and readily available quantity, such techniques are not necessary. Also such feedback reduces the performance of the amplifier in other important respects such as input and output impedance, bandwidth, and stability.

As $(-\mathbf{A}\boldsymbol{\beta})$ increases in size, while remaining positive, a point is reached when $(-\mathbf{A}\boldsymbol{\beta}) = +1$. Here $\mathbf{A}' \to \infty$ and oscillation occurs. A signal in the system can circulate round the feedback loop without decreasing in size. In general this condition will occur at only one frequency as $|-\mathbf{A}\boldsymbol{\beta}|$ is increased, so that the circuit will act as an oscillator, or source of power, at that frequency. This condition will be considered in more detail in chapter 3.

If $(-\mathbf{A}\boldsymbol{\beta})$ is small and negative, the gain is reduced. At the same time other important properties of the amplifier improve. This improvement of some desirable properties at the expense of a reduction in gain reaches a limit when $(-\mathbf{A}\boldsymbol{\beta})$ is very large $(|-\mathbf{A}\boldsymbol{\beta}| \gg 1)$ and negative. This is the condition of negative feedback for which operational amplifiers are designed.

In the limit $|-\mathbf{A}\boldsymbol{\beta}| \gg 1$ and $(-\mathbf{A}\boldsymbol{\beta})$ is negative, then

$$\mathbf{A}' \to \frac{\mathbf{A}}{A\beta} = \frac{1}{\beta} \tag{2.5}$$

so that the characteristics of the closed-loop amplifier are governed by the feedback circuit and are influenced little by the characteristics of the amplifier itself. This is particularly valuable, as an active device (even a well designed integrated circuit operational amplifier) will have characteristics, such as the gain and the input and output impedances, that are not reproducible from one particular device to another and may change with temperature, time, and power supply voltage. The external feedback circuit β on the other hand will in general be made of passive components, which can be precise and stable. The circuit performance with feedback can therefore be designed accurately and its characteristics can be calculated precisely. Although the closed-loop characteristics are determined by the (passive) feedback network, the performance is better than could be achieved by passive components alone.

In the rest of this chapter, large negative feedback will be assumed. For a given circuit, this condition can be verified approximately by calculating the magnitude of the gain round the loop $(|\mathbf{A}\boldsymbol{\beta}|)$ and by verifying the sign by imagining a small positive departure from the equilibrium voltage at one point in the loop, say the output, and determining the sign of this departure after each stage in the loop until it returns to the starting point. If the sign of the fed-back signal is negative, so as to restore equilibrium, then the feedback is negative. Since $\mathbf{A}$ and β can be frequency-dependent, this check should be carried out at all significant frequencies.

ANALYSIS OF NEGATIVE FEEDBACK

A circuit with negative feedback may be analyzed in different ways depending on the approximations that may be permitted. In general the very approximate methods can usually be used since the actual amplifier gain, and hence the feedback loop gain, is large and the accuracy is limited by the tolerance that can easily be obtained in the passive feedback components. We will consider three methods of analysis.

(a) The full analysis requires that all the circuit components, or equivalent circuit elements, be introduced together with the amplifier equation $V_2 = A(V_+ - V_-)$ and the circuit response is then calculated. This is the approach that was taken in the algebraic derivation of equation (2.4). In principle it is also possible to take equation (2.4) and to substitute in it expressions for A and β, but these are often not easy to evaluate separately so that analysis from first principles is better. For negative feedback circuits the full expression can then be simplified by ignoring small terms or taking the limit as $|A\beta|$ or A tends to infinity.

(b) If the circuit is such that β can be identified clearly to a sufficiently good approximation, then the approximate form of the general feedback equation (2.4), namely equation (2.5), $A' \simeq 1/\beta$, which holds for large negative feedback, may be used directly.

(c) For most purposes it may be assumed that practical amplifiers have a large gain and a high input impedance, so that the following approximations can be made:

$$V_+ \simeq V_-$$

$$(2.6)$$

$$I_\pm \simeq 0$$

The first of these equations says that, if the amplifier gain is large, then for a finite output signal $(V_2 = V_2')$ the differential input signal $V_+ - V_-$ is negligible. In the large negative feedback, large amplifier gain approximation one can consider the circuit in figure 2.1 as a servo-system. The amplifier has to adjust the output voltage at all times to be of such a value that when modified by β it equals the input signal to give no net differential input signal to the amplifier.

The second approximation in equations (2.6) follows if the input impedance is large and if $V_+ - V_-$ is small, so that there is little potential to cause a current $I_\pm$ to flow through the input impedance.

Equations (2.6) allow negative feedback circuits to be analyzed very rapidly provided that the user is aware of the approximations that have been made. In the examples that follow, it will be seen that for particular types and configurations of circuits these approximations can be replaced by alternative but equivalent forms.

ADVANTAGES OF NEGATIVE FEEDBACK

The use of amplifiers, together with passive components, in negative feed-back circuits can produce circuits with many desirable features. By introducing negative feedback, the gain is reduced but other properties are improved. Circuits containing only passive components, followed or preceded by an amplifier to give gain, can perform similar functions to amplifier circuits using passive components in a negative feedback loop. However, the feedback circuit will usually be more precise, easier to design, and produce less interference by loading with other sections of the circuit. The cost will often be less for the same performance and the components smaller in value and size.

With large negative feedback the closed-loop gain $\mathbf{A}' \simeq 1/\beta$ is independent of $\mathbf{A}$. For finite-loop gain we can calculate the gain stability, which is a measure of the extent to which the closed-loop gain is susceptible to changes in the open-loop gain, $\mathbf{A}$. From the general feedback equation (2.4), $\mathbf{A}' = \mathbf{A}(1 + \mathbf{A}\beta)$, we can neglect the phases and obtain

$$\frac{\mathrm{d}A'}{A'} = \frac{\mathrm{d}A}{A} \left(\frac{1}{1 + A\beta} \right) \tag{2.7}$$

Since $|\mathbf{A}\beta|$ is large, the fractional change in gain of the amplifier in closed-loop form is much less than that of the amplifier itself. Changes in the gain of the active element are reduced, and this is valuable since transistors and other active devices have properties that are sensitive to temperature, time, and power supply variation. Perhaps of more importance is the variation in manufacturing tolerance between devices of nominally the same specification. The use of feedback enables a circuit to be designed which will have accurately the same performance for almost any particular amplifier that is used in it. The factor of improvement is $(1 + A\beta) = A/A'$, which is the reduction in gain. For large negative feedback this may be approximated by the magnitude of the loop gain, $|-\mathbf{A}\beta|$.

The *differential input impedance* is also improved or increased by negative feedback. Consider a feedback amplifier with differential input impedance $\mathbf{Z}_{in}$ as shown in figure 2.3.

We can define the closed-loop input impedance by $\mathbf{Z}'_{in} = V_{in}/I_{in}$ since the Thévenin voltage source of the amplifier input is zero. ($V_+ = 0$ if this input is open circuit.) Now $V_{in} = V_1'$ and, using the amplifier equation,

$$I_{in} = I_{\pm} = (V_+ - V_-)/\mathbf{Z}_{in} = V_2'/\mathbf{A}\mathbf{Z}_{in}$$

Thus,

$$\mathbf{Z}'_{in} = \frac{V_1'}{V_2'}\mathbf{A}\mathbf{Z}_{in} = \mathbf{Z}_{in}\frac{\mathbf{A}}{\mathbf{A}'} = \mathbf{Z}_{in}(1 + \mathbf{A}\beta) \tag{2.8}$$

Again the input impedance is improved or increased by the same factor $(1 + \mathbf{A}\beta) \simeq \mathbf{A}\beta$.

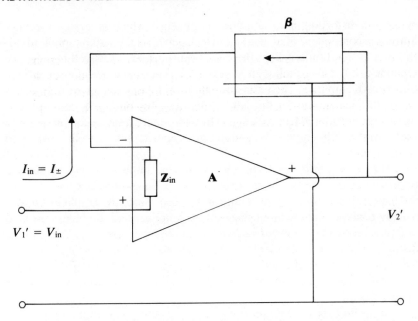

Fig. 2.3 Negative feedback increases the differential input impedance.

It should be noted that there is no improvement in the (common-mode) input impedances between each input and the circuit earth. In general these will limit the actual performance of the circuit.

Physically, the reason for the high input impedance is that only a small current flows for a given input signal. The current flows through Z_{in} and it is less than V_{in}/Z_{in} because the voltage at the other end of the input impedance Z_{in} is forced to follow V_{in} by the feedback action of the amplifier.

The closed-loop *output impedance* is less than the open-loop output impedance by the same factor, $(1 + A\beta)$. Thus $Z'_{out} = Z_{out}/(1 + A\beta)$. The analysis is very similar to the above. The result should appear reasonable since the actual output impedance produces a voltage drop inside the amplifier if an output current flows. This voltage drop could be interpreted as a reduction in open-loop amplifier gain, A, but we have seen that the closed-loop gain is very insensitive to this quantity. Thus the closed-loop output voltage is not affected much by the output current flowing.

The *distortion* in an amplifier is also often improved or reduced. There are many forms of distortion, and most are generated at the output stage of the amplifier where the signal amplitude is large. Some are produced by the absolute limitations of the amplifier; for example, the saturation at large amplitudes shown in figure 2.2(a). For the same level of output signal this type of distortion is not affected by the use of negative feedback since voltages above the saturation value are not available to the amplifier. However, consider a distortion in the amplifier output stage which generates a second-harmonic component of an amount that depends on the output amplitude. If the output amplitude is kept the same and the gain is reduced by negative feedback, but the overall gain is kept the same by the addition of a (low-distortion) amplifier, then the distortion will be reduced by the factor $(1 + \mathbf{A}\boldsymbol{\beta})$. The reason for this is that, although the output stage is still distorting the signal, the feedback signal has introduced a signal component into the output nearly equal in magnitude but opposite in sign to the distortion component.

The *noise* performance of an operational amplifier is not in general improved by the addition of negative feedback. This will be discussed further in chapter 4, but the general result can be seen. Since the amplifier noise is usually generated at the input stages of the amplifier and can be represented as equivalent voltage and current sources at the input terminals, it cannot be distinguished by the amplifier from the signal itself so that the signal and noise will be amplified and affected equally by the negative feedback. The signal-to-noise ratio will not be improved by negative feedback but can sometimes be made worse.

As well as these general principles, the examples given later will show that negative feedback circuits have considerable advantages over the equivalent passive circuits in many other ways specific to each circuit.

NEGATIVE FEEDBACK CIRCUITS

The examples given in this section are some of the most common circuits and are used here to illustrate the analysis and description given so far and to introduce new methods of analysis and ways of looking at circuits. Using these approaches it should be possible to analyze or design any negative feedback circuit. A collection of commonly used circuits is given in appendix 7 without a detailed description of their characteristics.

Voltage follower

The simplest negative feedback circuit is the *voltage follower, buffer amplifier* or *unity-gain, non-inverting amplifier*. The circuit is shown in figure 2.4 and involves a feedback of all the output signal to the inverting input so that $\beta = 1$. In a typical operational amplifier $|\mathbf{A}| \approx 10^5$, so that $|\mathbf{A}.\boldsymbol{\beta}| \approx 10^5$. Using the approximation of equation (2.5), $\mathbf{A}' = 1/\boldsymbol{\beta}$, we get $\mathbf{A}' = 1$.

Using the voltage approximation of equations (2.6)

$$V_1' = V_+ \simeq V_- = V_2' \qquad \text{so that } \mathbf{A}' \equiv \frac{V_2'}{V_1'} = 1$$

(a)

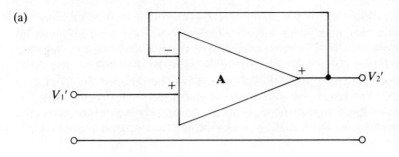

(b)

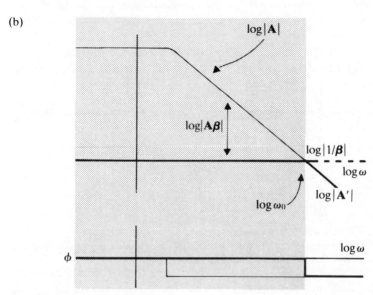

Fig. 2.4 The unity-gain, non-inverting amplifier (a) and its transfer characteristics (b). The frequency range over which there is large negative feedback is shaded.

Using the full analysis, equations (2.4),

$$V_1' = V_+ \qquad V_2' = V_2 = V_-$$

$$V_2' = V_2 = \mathbf{A}(V_+ - V_-) = \mathbf{A}(V_1' - V_2')$$

so that

$$\mathbf{A}' \equiv \frac{V_2'}{V_1'} = \frac{\mathbf{A}}{1 + \mathbf{A}} = \frac{1}{1 + 1/\mathbf{A}} \tag{2.9}$$

The frequency and phase response of a real amplifier, $\mathbf{A}$, is also shown in figure 2.4 together with $\log|1/\boldsymbol{\beta}|$. A convenience of this log–log graph is that the graphical distance between the $\log|\mathbf{A}|$ and $\log|1/\boldsymbol{\beta}|$ curves at any frequency represents $\log|\mathbf{A}\boldsymbol{\beta}|$, so that the magnitude of the loop gain can be easily seen. Although the loop gain, and hence the factor of improvement in Z_{in}, Z_{out}, etc., is large at low frequencies, it decreases to zero at some frequency, in this case the unity-gain frequency $f_0 = \omega_0/2\pi$. At, and above, this frequency the large negative feedback analysis is not valid and the loop gain becomes small,

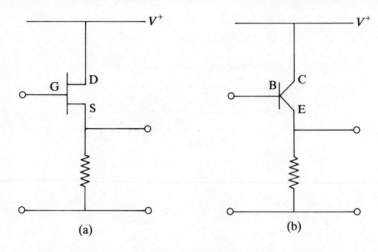

(a)   (b)

Fig. 2.5   The single-transistor versions of the unity-gain, non-inverting amplifier: the source follower (a) and the emitter follower (b).

so the net effect is that the amplifier is effectively open loop. The resulting gain $|\mathbf{A}'|$ is thus unity below f_0 and then drops with the amplifier open-loop gain above f_0. The phase-shift is zero below this frequency and then changes to $-\pi/2$. The frequency region below f_0 where the circuit has large negative feedback is shown shaded to emphasize that the properties are only improved in this region but are equal to the open-loop properties elsewhere.

The voltage follower has a high input impedance and low output impedance as well as a wide bandwidth. It is used as a buffer between two circuit stages so that the first stage is not loaded and the following stage does not load the preceding stage. Since the output voltage follows the input and the output impedance is low, it also acts as a good voltage source which can have a value derived from a voltage source that is very stable but cannot supply much current.

The single-transistor amplifier versions of this circuit are the source follower (FET) and the emitter follower (bipolar transistor) shown in figures 2.5(a) and (b). The similarity with the operational amplifier circuit can be seen since each transistor is a differential amplifier with input terminals G,S and B,E and with outputs S and E.

Non-inverting amplifier

The voltage follower can be modified to give gain if only a fraction of the output voltage is fed back to the input. This is shown in figure 2.6 using a

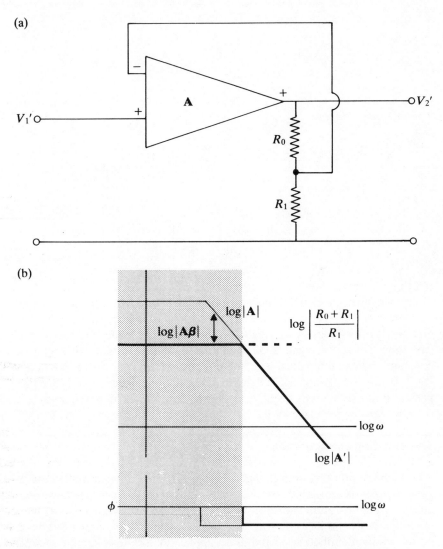

Fig. 2.6 The non-inverting amplifier (a) with its transfer characteristics (b).

resistive voltage divider as the feedback network. With suitable choice of the divider component values there should be no loading of the amplifier output by R_0 and R_1 or loading of the voltage divider by the input of the amplifier so that $\beta = R_1/(R_0 + R_1)$. Using the approximation (equation (2.5)) that $A' = 1/\beta$ we get $A' = (R_0 + R_1)/R_1$. Using the voltage approximation (equations (2.6)) we get

$$V_1' = V_+ \simeq V_- = \frac{R_1}{R_0 + R_1}V_2'$$

so that

$$A' \equiv \frac{V_2'}{V_1'} = \frac{R_0 + R_1}{R_1} \tag{2.10}$$

The full analysis gives

$$V_2' = V_2 = A(V_+ - V_-) = A\left(V_1' - V_2'\frac{R_1}{R_1 + R_2}\right)$$

so that

$$A' \equiv \frac{V_2'}{V_1'} = \frac{R_0 + R_1}{R_1}\left[1 + \frac{1}{A}\left(\frac{R_0 + R_1}{R_1}\right)\right]^{-1} \tag{2.11}$$

which becomes the previous approximate result when $AR_1/(R_0 + R_1) \gg 1$.

Once more the gain is frequency-independent up to a frequency at which the loop gain decreases to zero, and above this frequency the amplifier is effectively open-loop. By altering R_0/R_1 the gain can be made variable. In this case the product of the gain and the bandwidth of the constant-gain region is constant and equal to $f_0 = \omega_0/2\pi$, the unity-gain frequency for the amplifier itself. It should be noted again that the loop gain (and hence the value of the various improvements by negative feedback) decreases at high frequencies.

The inverting configuration

Although the non-inverting configuration just described fits in well with the general analysis, it is not the most commonly used connection. The *inverting* amplifier configuration shown in figure 2.7 comprises, at its simplest, two impedances Z_1 and Z_2 as shown. Here the voltage feedback circuit β cannot be so readily identified, so that a direct application of the general feedback equation cannot be made. The full analysis using the amplifier voltage

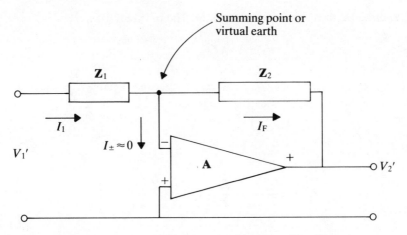

Fig. 2.7 The basic inverting configuration of an operational amplifier.

equation and normal network theorems can be performed. The approximate analysis for large negative feedback can be done using equations (2.6).

$$V_+ \simeq V_-$$

$$I_\pm \simeq 0$$

In this approximate analysis the inverting input terminal takes on a particular significance. The amplifier acts to keep $V_- \simeq V_+ = 0$ in this case. If $|A|$ is large then to a good approximation the inverting input terminal is at earth potential although it is not connected to the circuit earth. It is called a *virtual earth*.

Using this principle the approximate analysis is to use Kirchhoff's current sum equation on the node at the inverting input terminal, remembering that the current $I_\pm \simeq 0$. Because of this method of analysis the node is also called the *summing point*. Since the analysis is now in terms of currents, we can say that the amplifier acts by changing the output voltage so that a current $-I_F$ is forced through the feedback impedance Z_2 to cancel the other currents flowing into the summing point. Equating the currents and remembering that $V_- \simeq 0$

$$\frac{V_1'}{Z_1} = I_1 = I_F = -\frac{V_2'}{Z_2}$$

so that

$$A' \equiv \frac{V_2'}{V_1'} = -\frac{Z_2}{Z_1} \tag{2.12}$$

The circuit is thus an inverting amplifier. The full analysis is

$$V_- = V_1' + \frac{(V_2' - V_1')\mathbf{Z}_1}{\mathbf{Z}_1 + \mathbf{Z}_2}$$

$$V_2' = \mathbf{A}(V_+ - V_-) = -\mathbf{A}V_- = -\mathbf{A}\frac{(V_1'\mathbf{Z}_2 + V_2'\mathbf{Z}_1)}{\mathbf{Z}_1 + \mathbf{Z}_2}$$

and

$$\mathbf{A}' \equiv \frac{V_2'}{V_1'} = -\frac{\mathbf{Z}_2}{\mathbf{Z}_1}\left[1 + \frac{1}{\mathbf{A}}\left(\frac{\mathbf{Z}_1 + \mathbf{Z}_2}{\mathbf{Z}_1}\right)\right]^{-1} \tag{2.13}$$

It is particularly important to note that, although the output impedance and other features are improved by negative feedback, in this configuration the input impedance is $\mathbf{Z}_1$ and this is usually low if the gain $\mathbf{Z}_2/\mathbf{Z}_1$ is to be greater than unity since there is a practical limit to the size of $\mathbf{Z}_2$. The input impedance will also be reactive if $\mathbf{Z}_1$ is a reactance.

If we consider the special case of the inverting configuration in which both impedances are resistors, we obtain the inverting amplifier shown in figure 2.8. The gain is $-R_2/R_1$. The gain–frequency response can be plotted as before. The curves of $\log|\mathbf{A}|$ and $\log|\mathbf{A}'|$ cross and at that point $\log|\mathbf{A}/\mathbf{A}'| = \log|1 + \mathbf{A}\boldsymbol{\beta}|$ becomes zero and the loop gain is no longer large, so that the amplifier is effectively open loop at higher frequencies. Since there is also inversion, the phase change is from π to $\pi/2$ at $f = f_0 R_1/R_2$.

This configuration shows many significant features. Consider the circuits shown in figure 2.9. Here the input signal is a current and the amplifier acts so as to force an equal current through the feedback impedance $\mathbf{Z}_2$ in (a). If $\mathbf{Z}_2$ is a resistance, as in (b), then $V_2' = -I/R_2$ so that the circuit acts as a *current-to-voltage converter*. This is a particularly valuable circuit to use with two-terminal devices (such as photodiodes and photomultipliers) or three-terminal amplifiers (such as bipolar or field-effect transistors) which have a current output. The converter then produces a voltage output.

For use as a current meter, a low input impedance is desirable to prevent loading. The input impedance of this circuit is

$$\mathbf{Z}_{\text{in}} = \frac{V_{\text{in}}}{I} = \frac{V_-}{I} = \frac{V_-}{(V_- - V_2')/\mathbf{Z}_2}$$

But $V_2' = -AV_-$ so that

$$\mathbf{Z}_{\text{in}} = \frac{\mathbf{Z}_2}{A + 1} \tag{2.14}$$

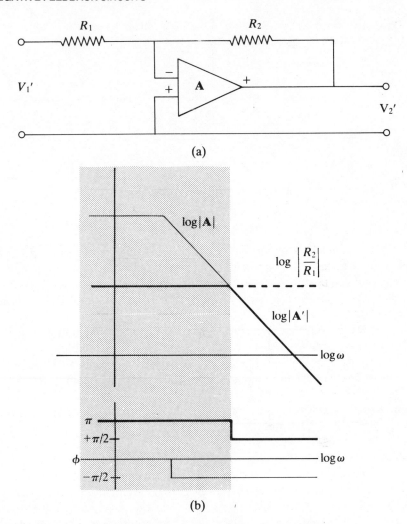

Fig. 2.8 The inverting amplifier (a) with its transfer characteristics (b).

For large values of A this produces the significant result that the circuit of figure 2.9(b) has a very low input impedance. If the feedback impedance $\mathbf{Z}_2$ is a capacitance C_2 with impedance $1/j\omega C_2$, the input impedance becomes $\mathbf{Z}_{in} = -1/j\omega(A + 1)C_2$ and the circuit acts, as far as it is seen through the input terminals, as a capacitor of value $(A + 1)C_2$, as shown in figure 2.9(c). This is a *capacitance multiplier*, in which a large capacitance can be simulated using a small capacitance and an amplifier. This effect is of particular importance in high-frequency circuits where a small stray capacitance C_{BC} between the collector and base, or output and inverting input, of a transistor used in the common emitter configuration acts effectively as a capacitance

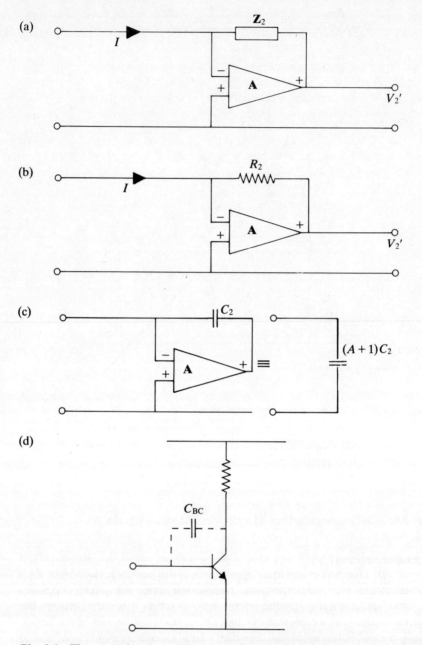

Fig. 2.9 The operational amplifier with just a feedback impedance (a) acts as a current-to-voltage converter (b) with resistive feedback or simulates an enhanced capacitance with a capacitive feedback (c). For a single-transistor amplifier (d) the enhanced input capacitance due to the stray capacitance C_{BC} is called the Miller effect.

$(A + 1) C_{BC}$ across the input. The high-frequency gain can be restricted by the signal passing through this effective capacitance to earth rather than into the transistor base terminal. This is called the *Miller effect*.

The virtual earth concept can be extended since the non-inverting input terminal need not be at earth potential. If it is kept at some fixed reference potential V_{ref} the inverting input will follow it. In this case the input terminal of the current-to-voltage converter will always be at the potential of V_{ref} and

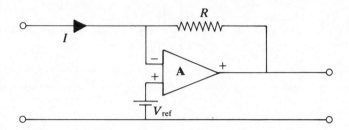

Fig. 2.10 The voltage clamp.

the system acts as a voltage-stabilizing circuit at the input terminal. The circuit is shown in figure 2.10. For any value of the input current the input terminal potential will be kept constant. The circuit is called a *voltage clamp* and is often used in electrochemical measurements.

The adder

The current summing analysis can be used for multiple input signals in the *adder* circuit shown in figure 2.11(a). Here the approximate analysis gives

$$\frac{V_{11}'}{R_{11}} + \frac{V_{12}'}{R_{12}} + \frac{V_{13}'}{R_{13}} = -\frac{V_2'}{R_2} \tag{2.15}$$

If the resistances are equal, $R_2 = R_{11} = R_{12} = R_{13}$, then this is an analog summing circuit with $V_2' = -(V_{11}' + V_{12}' + V_{13}')$.

If $3R_2 = R_{11} = R_{12} = R_{13}$, then this is an analog average circuit with $V_2' = -\frac{1}{3}(V_{11}' + V_{12}' + V_{13}')$. Similarly weighted averages can be computed.

The value of the feedback circuit for accurately performing an operation can be illustrated by comparison with the passive adding circuit shown in figure 2.11(b). Here $R_S \ll R_{11}$, R_{12}, R_{13} and each input voltage generates a current $V_1/(R_1 + R_S)$ through its input resistor. These currents all flow through R_S, so that the voltage across R_S is a measure of the total current. An amplifier is used to enlarge this small signal. The accuracy of the summation operation increases as R_S is made small compared with

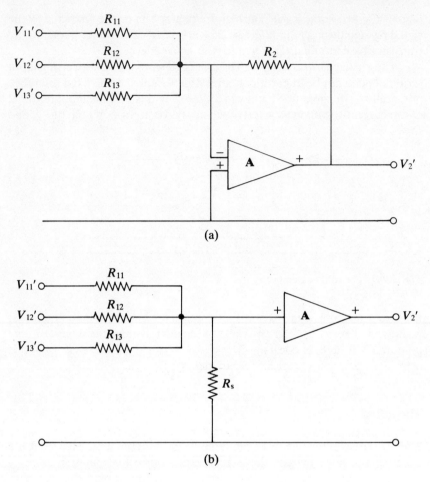

Fig. 2.11 The active operational amplifier adder circuit (a) compared with the passive resistive adder circuit (b).

R_{11}, R_{12}, R_{13}. As the approximation is made better in the passive circuit by reducing R_S, the voltage signal across R_S reduces and the amplifier gain **A** has to be increased to restore the value. In this case, however, the signal-to-noise ratio is inevitably reduced. Since an amplifier is part of both the feedback and the passive adding circuit, a signal applied at the output terminal will not reach any of the input terminals. However, in the passive circuit a signal applied to any one of the input terminals will produce a signal at all other input terminals so that there is interaction, or poor isolation, between the inputs. This effect is considerably improved in the feedback circuit because the summing point is a virtual earth, so that this potential is fixed and a current flowing through one input resistor will not cause currents to flow in any other input resistor. If **A** is finite the virtual earth is not ideal. The errors introduced can be calculated, since the effective resistance from the summing point to earth is $R_2(A + 1)$, which may be compared with R_S in the passive circuit.

Digital–analog converter

The digital–analog (DA) converter changes a digital signal into an analog signal of the appropriate size. The reverse operation of analog–digital (AD) conversion is described in chapter 8 and digital signals in chapter 5. The digital signal is usually in binary form and thus can take two values, logic 0 and logic 1. The voltages corresponding to these signals are usually 0 and V^+, the power supply voltages of the circuit. In digital form the value of an analog voltage will be described by a series of several digital bits, each of which will have a weight. Thus in the most common system, that of pure binary, the value of bit n indicates the presence or absence of a voltage with weight 2^n. The weighting of the bits is $2^3 2^2 2^1 2^0$ or 8421, so that the number 12 is represented as 1100.

The circuit is shown in figure 2.12(a). The switches are usually transistors. In some integrated circuits weighted current sources are used instead of the voltage source and weighted resistors. This is shown in figure 2.12(b). Although feedback principles are not used, a popular DA converter circuit uses the ladder network shown in figure 2.13. By standard analysis (using the superposition theorem) it can be shown that the voltage developed across R_L depends on the reference voltage V_{ref} and on the position of the binary switches with weighting 8421. The value of this circuit is that it involves resistances of only two values (R and $2R$) and can be extended easily for any number of bits. The circuit previously described has resistance values with weighted $2^0, 2^1, 2^2$, etc., so that a very wide range of accurately matched resistance values would be needed for a multi-bit DA converter.

The DA converter circuits of figures 2.12(a) and 2.13 can be used with values for V_{ref} of either sign. If an external voltage is used for V_{ref}, the circuit becomes that of a *multiplying digital–analog converter* (MDAC). The output voltage is the product of an analog and a digital input signal. Since it has analog input and output signals it could also be considered as a *digital attenuator*. It can be used for an a.c. input signal of any waveform.

Although the DA converter has an analog output, this can only take the certain discrete values specified by the digital input, as shown in figure 2.14. The fineness of these steps is described by the *resolution*, which is governed by the number of bits in the digital input. These bits control the resolution with respect to the full-scale voltage, so that the absolute voltage resolution, or voltage step size, depends on the full-scale voltage. The absolute accuracy of the output voltage depends on the accuracy of the resistor network and on the accuracy of the reference voltage. Usually devices are made to have $\pm \frac{1}{2}$ bit

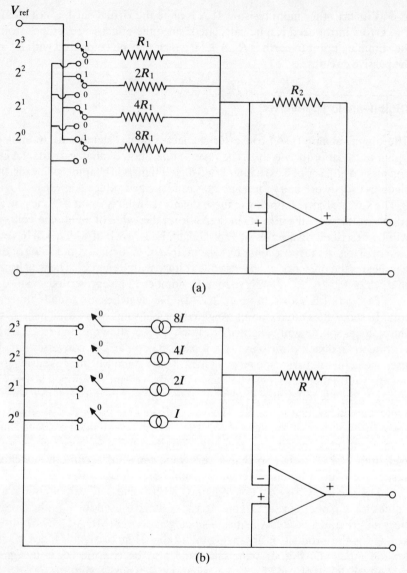

Fig. 2.12 The digital–analog converter using a weighted adder (a) and weighted current sources (b).

accuracy so that the steps are always in the correct order and hence the transfer function in monotonic. A more accurate resistor network can give higher absolute accuracy than resolution. The converters also have dynamic errors described by the speed of response and settling time. In general DA converters are more accurate and less expensive than AD converters.

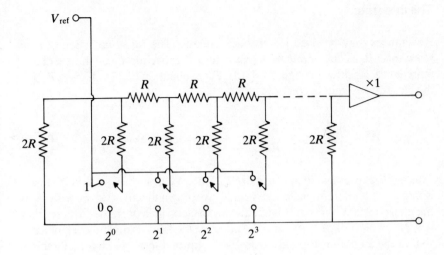

Fig. 2.13 The digital–analog converter using a ladder network of R and $2R$ resistors.

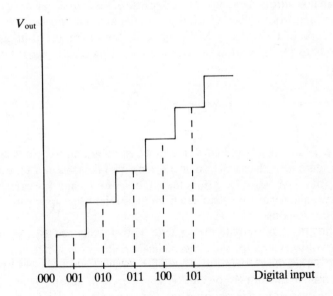

Fig. 2.14 The transfer characteristic of a digital–analog converter showing the inherent loss of resolution due to the steps.

The integrator

Reactances may be used in feedback circuits. The *integrator* circuit has a resistance R as the input impedance and a capacitor C as the feedback impedance, as shown in figure 2.15(a). From equation (2.12), $\mathbf{A}' = -\mathbf{Z}_0/\mathbf{Z}_1$, the closed-loop gain becomes

$$\mathbf{A}' \equiv \frac{V_2'}{V_1'} = -\frac{1}{j\omega RC} = -\frac{\omega_0}{j\omega} \qquad \text{where } \omega_0 = \frac{1}{RC} \qquad (2.16)$$

This has the response shown in figure 2.15(b). When $\omega = \omega_0 = 1/RC$ the gain is unity. At high frequencies the gain is inverting and varies as $1/\omega$ with ω_0 as the gain constant. At some low frequency the loop gain decreases to zero, that is $A'/A = 1/(1 + A\beta) \to 1$, and the negative feedback is no longer significant so that the amplifier responds to its open-loop characteristic. Normally this is at a very low frequency. The phase-shift corresponds to the combination of the inversion and the reactive phase-shift due to the RC combination.

Physically this is an integrator since the input voltage creates a current V_1'/R into the summing point. The amplifier adjusts its output voltage so this current can flow through the capacitor. Because of the virtual earth the output equals the capacitor voltage, which is proportional to the capacitance charge or the integral of the voltage. Mathematically the operation of integration corresponds to multiplication by a factor $1/j\omega$. Consider a signal equal to $Ve^{j\omega t}$, then

$$\int Ve^{j\omega t}dt = \frac{1}{j\omega}Ve^{j\omega t}$$

A z.f. (d.c.) signal applied to the input is integrated to give a ramp as shown in figure 2.16. This will be a linear ramp if it takes place in a time much less than $1/\omega_1 = A_0/\omega_0$, where A_0 is the z.f. open-loop gain. Frequency ω_1 is the break frequency and is calculated from the straight-line approximation of the amplifier response.

In a practical ramp circuit the capacitor voltage will need to be set to zero at the start of such a ramp, and a mechanical or electronic switch is normally connected across the capacitor to accomplish this.

The use of the integrator can be considered in several ways. It will perform the operation of integration on a time-varying signal, it can produce a ramp, or it can act as a low-pass filter. As a filter the integrator has gain and a characteristic frequency $\omega_1 = (A_0RC)^{-1} = \omega_0/A_0$ at which its gain drops by a factor of 2 below the low-frequency gain.

A passive filter with the same characteristic frequency would require components with an RC product that is A_0 times larger than in the equivalent

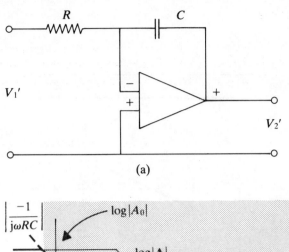

(a)

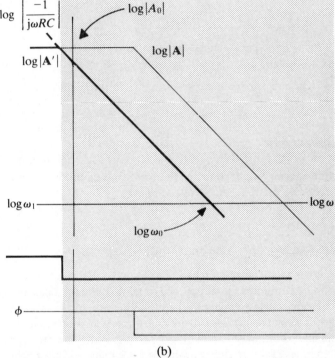

(b)

Fig. 2.15 The integrator circuit (a) and its transfer characteristic (b).

feedback circuit. In practice this means that much smaller capacitors need be used if feedback techniques are utilized.

Practical, compensated, operational amplifiers have an open-loop gain that varies as $1/\omega$ at high frequencies. They thus have an integrator response. This is achieved by including one dominant RC low-pass filter within the circuit. This integrator characteristic enables the operational amplifier to be used easily.

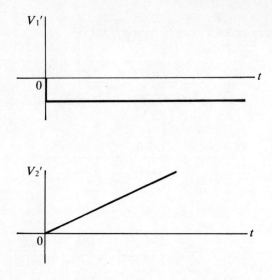

Fig. 2.16   The integrator produces a ramp output for a constant input signal.

The differentiator

The differentiator circuit shown in figure 2.17(a) has an input capacitance C and a feedback resistance R. Its response is

$$\mathbf{A}' \equiv \frac{V_2'}{V_1'} = - j\omega RC = -j\frac{\omega}{\omega_0} \qquad \text{where } \omega_0 = \frac{1}{RC} \qquad (2.17)$$

and this is shown in figure 2.17(b).

The differentiator performs the analog mathematical operation of differentiation, corresponding to the multiplication of the input function by $j\omega$. There is also inversion. It will only perform this operation for signals with all significant Fourier components occurring in its low-frequency region where $A' \sim \omega$. In this frequency range it has a high-pass filter characteristic. At some frequency the loop gain decreases to unity and the closed-loop response becomes the open-loop integrating response for higher frequencies. At intermediate frequencies the circuit acts as a low-Q band-pass filter.

The differentiator circuit has several inconvenient properties. Since the gain of all amplifiers will drop at high frequencies, the differentiating frequency range is restricted. The input impedance is the capacitor C, which is reactive and hence frequency-dependent. A property that can be solved is that the circuit as described is actually unstable and may oscillate at the frequency corresponding to its peak gain. In chapter 3 the analysis of and

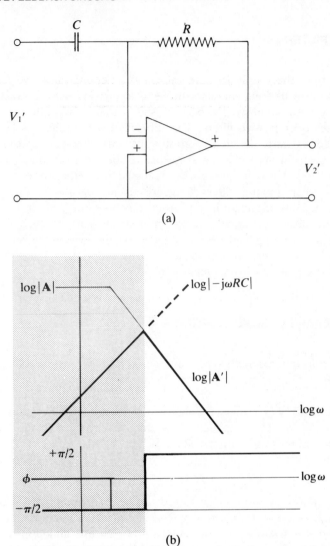

Fig. 2.17 The differentiator circuit (a) and its transfer characteristic (b).

remedy for such instabilities will be described. In this particular case the stabilization can be achieved by placing a small resistance r in series with C. In practice the output impedance of the previous stage may supply a large enough value of r. If the frequency of the peak gain is ω_p, then $r > 1/\omega_p C$ is needed. A straight-line analysis indicates that this is equivalent to $r > (R/\omega_0 C)^{1/2}$, where ω_0 is the open-loop unity-gain frequency.

ACTIVE FILTERS

The ability of the simple RC integrator and differentiator active feedback circuits to give filtering characteristics and to provide these characteristics accurately with small-sized capacitors shows that active filters can have advantages over passive filters. The subject of active filters is large and specialized. A fairly detailed description of active low-pass and high-pass filters is given in appendix 6 and further reading is given there for more complex filters. The band-pass filter is discussed briefly there also.

Two other common filter characteristics are the all-pass filter, which produces a constant-amplitude transfer function but with a frequency-dependent phase-shift, and the notch filter, which provided complete rejection at one frequency. Active filters showing these characteristics are included in the collection of feedback circuits in appendix 7 and the notch filter is also mentioned in chapter 4.

NON-LINEAR FEEDBACK CIRCUITS

The current summing method of analysis used for the inverting configuration of the operational amplifier is convenient for the analysis of non-linear circuits. Consider the circuit of figure 2.18(a). The feedback impedance is now non-linear, $\mathbf{Z}(V)$. Since the summing point is a virtual earth, the input current is V_1'/R. The amplifier forces this current through the feedback impedance $\mathbf{Z}(V)$. The output voltage is thus $V_2' = -\mathbf{Z}(V)V_1'/R$ and the transfer function

$$\mathbf{A}'(V) \equiv \frac{V_2'}{V_1'} = \frac{1}{R}\mathbf{Z}(V_2')$$
(2.18)

has the same shape as the V–I characteristics of the non-linear impedance.

Similarly if the non-linear impedance is the input impedance, as in figure 2.18(b), then

$$\mathbf{A}'(V) \equiv \frac{V_2'}{V_1'} = \frac{-R}{\mathbf{Z}(V_1')}$$

Examples of non-linear circuits are shown in figure 2.19. The circuit shown in figure 2.19(a) has two Zener diodes in series opposition. At voltages below the breakdown voltages, the impedance is large and the amplifier is approximately open-loop. Above the breakdown voltage, the output voltage cannot rise, so that saturation occurs. In this way an amplifier can be given controlled saturation levels.

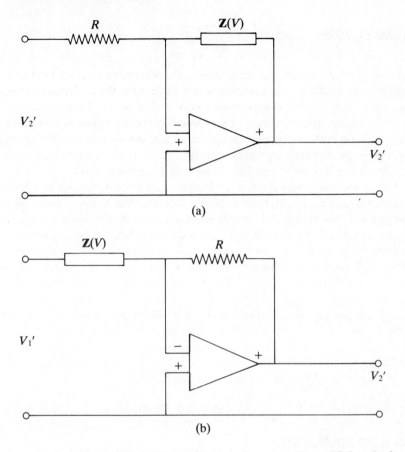

Fig. 2.18 Inverting feedback circuits with a non-linear impedance $\mathbf{Z}(V)$ as the feedback (a) or input (b) impedance.

The circuit shown in figure 2.19(b) has a diode as its feedback element. A diode has the characteristic

$$I = I_{00}[\exp(eV/kT) - 1] \qquad (2.19)$$

but the second term can usually be neglected so that

$$I = I_{00}\exp(eV/kT) \qquad (2.20)$$

In the circuit shown, the current summing method of analysis gives

$$\frac{V_1'}{R} = -I_{00}\exp\left(\frac{eV_2'}{kT}\right)$$

or

$$V_2' = \frac{kT}{e} \ln \left(\frac{-V_1'}{I_{00}R} \right) \tag{2.21}$$

which represents a logarithmic amplifier for $V_1' \leq 0$. If the resistor R and the diode are exchanged, an exponential amplifier is produced. Analog multiplication of two voltages can thus be achieved by computing their logarithms as above, adding the voltages representing the logarithms, and then taking the antilogarithm with the exponential amplifier.

In the circuit of figure 2.19(c) the two antiparallel diodes give a logarithmic response for each polarity of signal. If an a.c. signal is applied to this circuit, symmetrically about zero, the output waveform is similar to the input but has rounded peaks. The amplifier has a 'soft' saturation. Such a circuit is useful as an a.c. bridge detector (see chapter 7) since it has an effective automatic gain control. For large off-balance signals, a distorted signal is produced; but as the balance condition is approached, the effective gain increases and is near the open-loop gain when the bridge is balanced and a null signal is achieved.

The basic non-linear integrated circuit element is the multiplier, which produces an output $V_2 = V_{11} \times V_{12}/10$ for input signals V_{11} and V_{12}. This is described further in chapter 6. The symbol is shown in figure 2.20(a). If the multiplier is connected in the feedback loop of an operational amplifier, division can be performed as shown in figure 2.20(b).

ANALOG COMPUTATION

It has been shown that negative feedback circuits can be made which will accurately carry out a particular operation on a voltage signal. The original use of operational amplifiers was to carry out such operations on voltages proportional to particular variables in order to calculate the results of a particular mathematical equation. Now digital computers are more accurate, more convenient, and often faster. However, such analog computation is still valuable for calculations on variables which have to be done simultaneously with change in the quantity. For example, an immediate display may be needed of the logarithm of a variable, or the power. In these cases it would be slow and unnecessarily complicated to digitize the variable and perform the computation using a digital computer just for the purpose of the display.

So far we have seen circuits that can perform the following functions: addition $(V_2 = V_{11} + V_{12})$, inversion $(V_2 = V_1 \times (-1))$, subtraction $(V_2 = V_{11} \times (-1) + V_{12})$, amplification $(V_2 = aV_1)$, integration $(V_2 = \int V_1 \, dt)$, differentiation $(V_2 = dV_1/dt)$, logarithm $(V_2 = \log V_1)$, antilogarithm

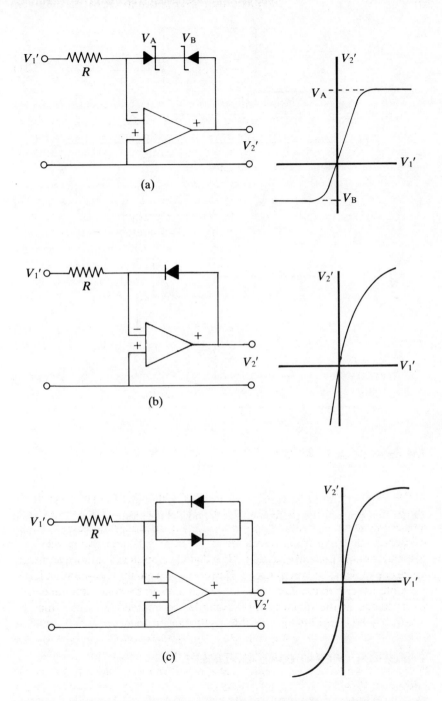

Fig. 2.19 The circuits and non-linear characteristics of feedback circuits with sharp saturation (a), a logarithmic response (b) and soft saturation (c).

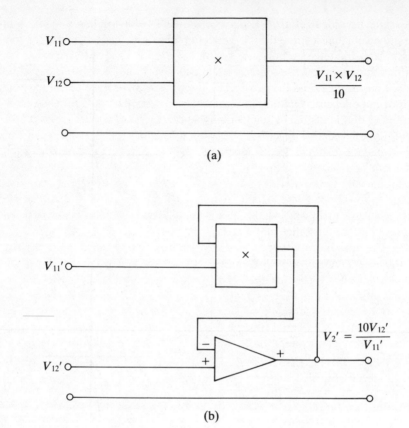

Fig. 2.20 The basic analog multiplier (a) and its use in a feedback circuit as a divider (b).

$(V_2 = \exp V_1)$, multiplication $(V_2 = V_{11} \times V_{12})$, and division $(V_2 = V_{11}/V_{12})$. Other functions can be performed easily and include: comparator $(V_2 = V_{21}$ if $V_1 > V_{ref}$, $V_2 = V_{22}$ if $V_1 < V_{ref})$, Schmitt trigger or comparator with hysteresis, absolute value $(V_2 = |V_1|)$, and true root-mean-square (TRMS) $(V_2 = (1/T) \int_0^T V_1^2 dt)$. Circuits for these are given in appendix 7, where many feedback circuits are collected together, and some are described also in chapter 3.

PRACTICAL OPERATIONAL AMPLIFIERS

A real operational amplifier will show non-ideal effects. The wide variety of devices available differ in that each has been made with one or more of the possible non-ideal effects reduced. Non-ideal behavior has already been assumed in that a limited high-frequency response, limited low-frequency gain, and limited output voltage have been used in the description. The common general-purpose integrated circuit operational amplifiers have high input impedances and those with FET input transistors have extremely high input impedances. The output impedance is more limited and it is recommended that loads, including feedback impedances, of less than about 1 kΩ should be avoided. Capacitive loads should be kept small as these will have a low impedance at high frequencies and this often results in instability. So that the stray capacitance across the feedback resistance is not significant at any frequency up to the unity-gain frequency, the feedback resistance should be kept below about 1 MΩ. These guidelines should enable most circuits to be made satisfactorily and, with care and suitable choice of device, component values outside this range may be used.

The output properties of the amplifier are often specified as limits to the voltage and current as well as by an output impedance. However, another important limit is the *slew rate*. Whereas the open-loop gain is specified for small-amplitude signals, the *full-power response* is normally limited at a much lower frequency. At high frequencies the maximum voltage swing is limited. The slew rate is specified by a maximum rate of change of V_{out} in volts per microsecond. This limitation is usually due to the charging of the internal compensation capacitor. When the amplifier is slew-rate-limited, the output signal, for a sine-wave input, becomes triangular and is reduced in amplitude. An apparent phase-shift is also introduced. If a very high output current is required, unity voltage gain, low output impedance amplifiers can be added in cascade with the operational amplifier output. In use this 'booster' amplifier should be within the feedback loop.

The input deficiencies of an operational amplifier can be described in terms of three d.c. (z.f.) equivalent generators, as shown in figure 2.21. The *input offset voltage generator* E_{os} represents the unbalance of the two input amplifier stages at the two input terminals. To obtain a zero output voltage, a differential input voltage of $-E_{os}$ would have to be applied. Since the amplifier has a differential input, only the differential offset voltage generator need be specified. It will normally be temperature-dependent. Facilities are often provided to cancel E_{os} and this will be described near the end of this section. The input transistors each require a bias current in order to operate and these can be represented as current generators I_{B-} and I_{B+}, the *input bias currents* for the inverting and non-inverting inputs. In integrated circuit amplifiers these transistors are made at the same time so that $I_{B-} \simeq I_{B+}$. If the amplifier is used in a circuit so that the two inputs are under very similar conditions, then the effects of these two currents may be made partially to cancel. The difference between these, $I_{B+} - I_{B-}$, is called the *input offset current* I_{os} and is about one-tenth of either of the individual currents.

The offset and bias sources have temperature variations as well as very

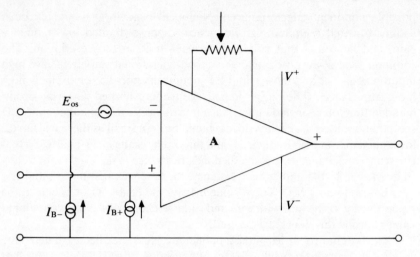

Fig. 2.21   A real operational amplifier represented by an equivalent circuit of an ideal amplifier together with input voltage and current sources.

slow time variations (*drift*). The same sources also have higher-frequency variations, but in this case they are usually considered separately as noise sources and we will discuss them in chapter 4.

To see how the offset voltage and bias currents can affect feedback circuits, consider the circuits of figure 2.22. In the inverting amplifier circuit of figure 2.22(a) the Thévenin equivalent source impedance must be included. In this case the source internal impedance has been added in series with the input resistance to give a combined impedance R_1 and the source potential has been made zero. The current generator I_{B+} has no effect since it is shorted out. The output voltage due to I_{B-} is $-R_2 I_{B-}$ and that due to E_{os} is $E_{os}(R_1 + R_2)/R_1$. The latter can be understood since such an output is needed to produce a voltage at the summing point to oppose E_{os}. Using the principle of super-position the combined effect of both sources will give an output voltage

$$V_2' = -R_2 I_{B-} + E_{os}\left(\frac{R_1 + R_2}{R_1}\right)$$

which indicates a non-zero output voltage for zero input signal. The relative polarities for E_{os}, I_{B-}, and I_{B+} will depend on the particular device. In many cases the output offset voltage given above may be reduced by suitable choice of components. The major problem is that the offset signal sources are often very temperature-dependent, so that compensation under all conditions is not easy.

In figure 2.22(b) the circuit of figure 2.22(a) has been extended by

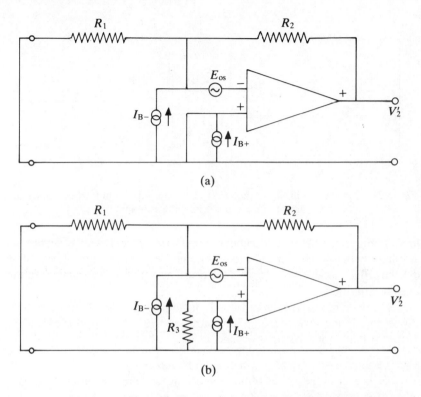

(a)

(b)

Fig. 2.22 Circuits to illustrate the effect of the non-ideal input offset voltage and input bias current sources on the inverting amplifier configuration (a). In (b) a resistance R_3 has been added to reduce the output offset voltage.

including a resistance R_3 in the non-inverting input connection. In this case the approximate analysis gives

$$V_2' = E_{os}\left(\frac{R_1 + R_2}{R_1}\right) + R_3 I_{B+}\left(\frac{R_1 + R_2}{R_1}\right) - R_2 I_{B-}$$

The current sources I_{B+} and I_{B-} are usually of the same sign, approximate magnitude, and temperature dependence, and hence can be compensated if $R_3 = R_1 R_2/(R_1 + R_2)$, which is the value of R_1 and R_2 in parallel. The output signal due to the offset voltage could also be cancelled by suitable choice of R_3 but, because the current and voltage offset sources have different temperature dependences, it is better to use a separate nulling method for the offset voltage, as described later.

In the integrator circuit shown in figure 2.23, the output voltage for zero input voltage, input earthed, is $V_2' = E_{os} - \int I_{B-}\, dt$, so that there is a permanent offset output voltage and the bias current flowing into the inverting

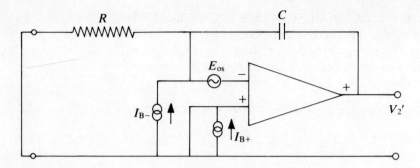

Fig. 2.23 A circuit to illustrate the effect of the non-ideal input offset voltage and input bias current sources on the integrator circuit.

input is integrated to produce a linear ramp. To integrate low-level signals, an amplifier with low bias current is therefore needed and the capacitor must be discharged at suitable times so that the charging does not eventually result in output saturation.

The need to analyze the full circuit, including all internal impedances, is shown in the non-inverting amplifier shown in figure 2.24. In this circuit the output voltage, for zero input voltage, is

$$V_2' = (R_S I_{B+} + E_{os})\left(\frac{R_1 + R_2}{R_1}\right) - R_2 I_{B-}$$

The total output offset voltage can be nulled by injection of a suitable voltage at the input. However, the manufacturers usually add the facility of an external bias circuit which injects a voltage inside the circuit to give zero output voltage for zero input voltage. This is shown in figure 2.25(a). A

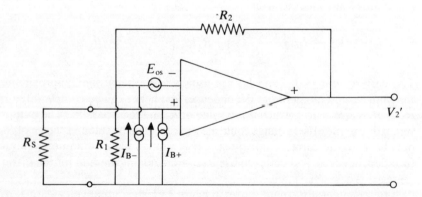

Fig. 2.24 A circuit to illustrate the effect of the non-ideal input offset voltage and input bias current sources on the non-inverting amplifier circuit.

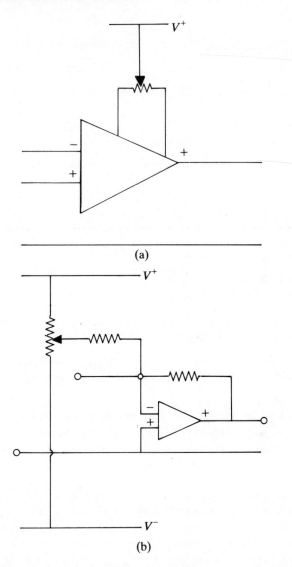

Fig. 2.25 An output offset voltage may be reduced by using the internal offset adjustment (a) or by injecting a suitable current into the summing point (b).

potentiometer is connected across the 'null' or 'bias' terminals and the top is connected to one or other of the power supplies V^+ or V^-.

It is possible to null the total output voltage under a given condition by the injection of an external current into the summing point using a circuit such as that shown in figure 2.25(b). To obtain the best temperature stability, it is best to null the offset currents and voltages independently.

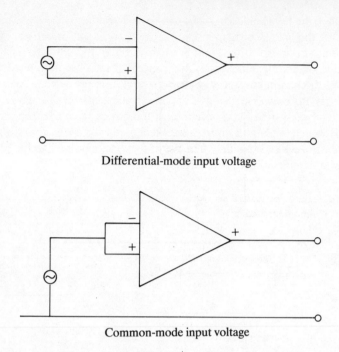

Differential-mode input voltage

Common-mode input voltage

Fig. 2.26   A differential amplifier is designed to respond to a differential input signal but to produce little output for a common-mode input signal.

The lack of balance of the input circuit is also characterized by the *common-mode rejection ratio* (CMRR). This is a measure of the ratio of the common-mode input voltage to the differential-mode input voltage required to produce the same output voltage (figure 2.26). The CMRR of an open-loop operational amplifier is usually about 100 dB at low frequencies but decreases at high frequencies.

If an amplifier with a large CMRR is required, then the whole operational amplifier circuit must have well balanced inputs and it is usually better to use an instrumentation amplifier. This is a fixed-gain amplifier designed to have a large CMRR and input impedance, but it is not meant to be used with negative feedback.

CONTROL CIRCUITS

Control circuits, control systems, servo-systems or stabilizing systems are systems that include a negative feedback loop to insure that a variable is kept at the required value although the system may be exposed to many influences.

Examples are the float valve in a water cistern, thermostats, servo-assisted car brakes, and the pen position on a potentiometric chart recorder. These systems may be purely mechanical or hydraulic, mixed electrical and mechanical, or purely electrical. The general principles that have been discussed in this chapter for purely electronic circuits apply and can be used to analyze these more diverse systems. The electronic feedback circuits provide a good reference system for comparison of the others since the components are usually nearly ideal and the powerful techniques of linear circuit theory make analysis easy and familiar. The use of feedback and null techniques in experimental circuits is discussed further in chapter 8.

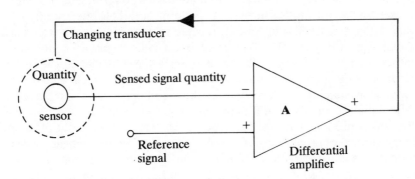

Fig. 2.27 A generalized circuit for a control system.

Consider the generalized feedback system shown in figure 2.27. The quantity to be controlled, or stabilized, is sensed in magnitude by some sensor or transducer (chapter 8). A signal is derived from this and compared with a reference signal by a high-gain differential amplifier. The output of the amplifier is used to change the magnitude of the controlled quantity. The negative feedback system strives to keep the differential input signal zero. The power to operate the system comes from the amplifier power supply since the signals to the amplifier are of small power but the changing transducer needs large power.

In the water cistern example, the floating ball is the sensor of the water-level variable quantity. The reference signal corresponds to the ball position at which the water flow is cut off. The amplification comes from the lever arm ratio of the ball and valve, while the necessary power is provided by the hydrostatic uplift on the ball. The water inlet valve is the changing transducer.

In a thermostat, the quantity is the temperature sensed by some thermometer and the difference signal between the thermometer output and some reference signal is amplified and used to drive a heater or a control valve for a heat source. Both of these examples are a bit unusual in that the control or changing transducer cannot provide a negative effect or change (such as a leakage of water or a supply of 'cold') but only a reduction in the amount of water or heat supplied. In these cases a continual bias is needed in the form of water loss or heat loss from the system. This is normally present.

The value of a control system is considerable. In a non-feedback system the components are adjusted to give the required result and then left. Aging of the components, changes in ambient temperature, etc., may result in a change of the value of the quantity. This would require manual readjustment, which is in effect an involved and time-consuming feedback circuit.

The control circuit automatically produces a null. Since external power is supplied, the sensor or transducer need not have a power output and can be chosen for precision rather than output performance. If the reference signal is varied, the system will automatically readjust to the new value. The reference signal is again only a lower-power signal so that it may be just a potentiometer rather than some heavy control valve. Since the amplifier is within the feedback loop, its performance is not critical in such qualities as gain magnitude, gain stability or distortion. It must just have high gain, a good differential circuit, and suffficient output power. Similarly the changing transducer need not have very ideal properties since it is within the feedback loop. The sensor usually needs to be of good quality and to be linear, since its output is compared with a reference signal. A non-linear output would require a knowledge of the non-linearity so that a suitable reference signal can be supplied. This last problem can be overcome if the reference signal is derived from an identical sensor with the same non-linearity. The experimental quantity in the experimental system then follows the same quantity which is varied independently in some reference system. Only the matching of the transducers is important in the quality of the control.

The principles of control systems can also be applied to more diverse systems where there is feedback. Examples are population dynamics in biology and national economics.

The systems that use negative feedback are so diverse that examples cannot be given to cover all possible combinations. Usually the analogous electrical circuit can be identified or the general feedback loop recognized.

The purely electronic circuits described earlier in this chapter can be considered as voltage control servo-systems in which the amplifier strives to keep the differential input voltage zero. However, usually the other approaches used in the chapter make the circuit analysis easier.

One electrical circuit that is best considered as a control circuit is the *active guard*. The simplest version is shown in figure 2.28. The amplifier output is used to keep the potential of a screen round the input lead at the same potential as that lead. In this way the input lead experiences a field-free environment and any leakage current through resistive or capacitive stray impedances to earth are reduced. The resistive and capacitive input impedances are therefore increased.

Control systems should have large negative feedback and even in mixed mechanical and electrical systems this can be checked simply. However, the feedback may easily change from negative to positive at one or more frequencies by some slight extra phase-shift. This results in oscillation or instability and will be discussed in chapter 3. In systems that are not purely electrical there is likelihood of non-ideal components which make the system analysis and operation difficult. Elements may exhibit non-linearity, backlash or hysteresis. The initial design should aim to reduce these possibilities.

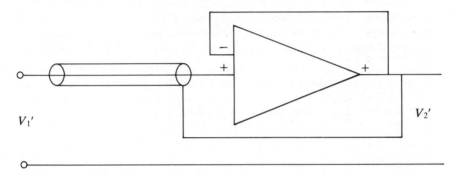

Fig. 2.28 An active guard to reduce the input capacitance and input leakage currents.

Control systems can be obtained commercially. They are usually power controllers designed for temperature stabilization with a thermocouple or some other thermometer input. They are normally made in two sections, the signal circuit containing the signal amplifier and reference circuit and a power amplifier or power control output stage. In the simplest form they provide an *on/off* output in which a mechanical or electronic relay switches the power circuit on or off. Although this highly non-linear circuit is adequate for many applications, a better device is *proportional* so that the power output is proportional to the departure of the input signal from the reference value. This results in smoother control. The range of the variable over which the system is linear is naturally limited and is smaller if the gain is larger. Normally the proportional band can be controlled.

Because the controller may be used in a wide variety of situations and there may be delays in the thermal system between the heater output and the thermometer input, the gain–frequency and phase–frequency response of the whole system needs to be variable to make the system stable under most circumstances. The stabilization is done with adjustable filters which add in variable signals corresponding to the integral and the differential of the differential input signal. Such controllers are called *proportional–integral–differential* (PID) *controllers*. The integral signal will be large and assert control if there is a persistent offset or difference between the quantity and the reference signal. It thus corrects for long-term changes. The proportional signal will be large if there is a rapid change in the quantity. The control signal will therefore be able to predict that there will be a large error signal and take early corrective action.

FURTHER READING

G. B. Clayton, *Operational Amplifiers*, Butterworth (1979).

J. G. Graeme, *Designing with Operational Amplifiers*, McGraw-Hill (1977).

J. G. Graeme, G. E. Tobey and L. P. Huelsman (eds), *Operational Amplifiers*, McGraw-Hill (1971).

R. W. Henry, *Electronic Systems and Instrumentation*, Wiley (1978).

D. H. Horrocks, *Feedback Circuits and Operational Amplifiers*, Van Nostrand Reinhold (1983).

T. E. Shepherd, *Operational Amplifiers*, Longman (1981).

Y. J. Wong and W. E. Ott, *Function Circuits: Design and Applications*, McGraw-Hill (1976).

3 POSITIVE FEEDBACK AND STABILITY

INTRODUCTION

The basic feedback circuit of figure 2.1 can represent both positive and negative feedback. Although the signal fed back through the network β is applied to the inverting input, the feedback will be positive if the network β includes inversion so that the loop gain is positive and greater than unity. In equation (2.4) for the gain of the closed-loop feedback amplifier,

$$\mathbf{A}' = \frac{\mathbf{A}}{1 + \mathbf{A}\beta}$$

the possibility of infinite closed-loop gain, oscillation, and instability was noticed for the condition $(-\mathbf{A}\beta) = 1$. The full analysis should consider $\mathbf{A}$ and β as complex quantities, but initially we will consider the phase-shifts only approximately, corresponding to inversion, π or $(2n + 1)\pi$, or non-inversion, 0 or $2n\pi$.

Consider the simple positive feedback circuit shown in figure 3.1(a), in which all the output signal is fed back to the non-inverting input terminal. The outcome will depend on the initial condition. If the initial output signal was positive, it would be amplified to increase the output signal and hence the feedback signal, and so on. The signal will increase positively and exponentially at a rate determined by the open-loop gain and the open-loop bandwidth of the amplifier. The increase in the signal continues until the amplifier saturates at its maximum output voltage V_{sat}^{+}. Similarly, if the initial voltage within the feedback loop was negative, the final result would be saturation at the maximum negative voltage V_{sat}^{-}. It should be noted that positive feedback results in the system moving *away from* the equilibrium condition for negative feedback in which there is no net input signal ($V_{+} = V_{-}$).

This positive feedback circuit is firmly locked into one or other of its two

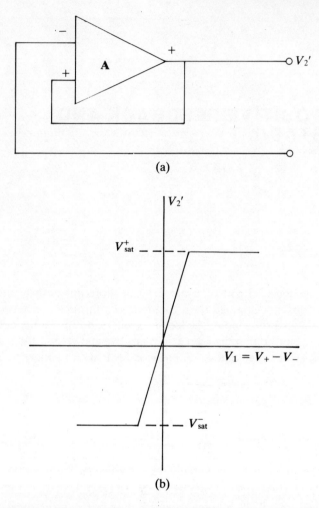

Fig. 3.1 An operational amplifier with positive feedback (a) and a transfer character-istic as shown in (b) will rapidly reach one of two stable states with $V_2' = V_{sat}^+$ or V_{sat}^-.

stable positions, since in these conditions the amplifier, with high gain, experiences a large input signal of a sign that reinforces its state. In an ideal amplifier, each of these two states is equally probable, and the state that results depends only on the noise signal in the initial state when the loop is closed. This circuit is a *bistable circuit* or a *bistable multivibrator*; it will retain its state and can hence be considered as a *memory element* or *latch*. It should be remembered that the + and − signs on the amplifier terminals only represent the relative polarities between the terminals and not the absolute voltages or voltages relative to the circuit earth.

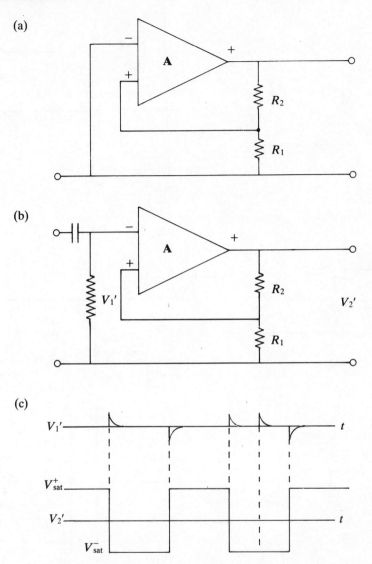

Fig. 3.2 An operational amplifier with positive feedback (a) has two stable states and can be triggered to change between states by the application of a suitable pulse as shown in (b) and (c).

The amount of positive feedback can be reduced by decreasing the loop gain with a potential divider for β as shown in figure 3.2(a). There will still be positive feedback provided $|A|R_1/(R_1 + R_2) > 1$, and the circuit will have similar behavior to the previous one except that the circuit is held less firmly in each of its saturated stable states. Because of this, the circuit can be more

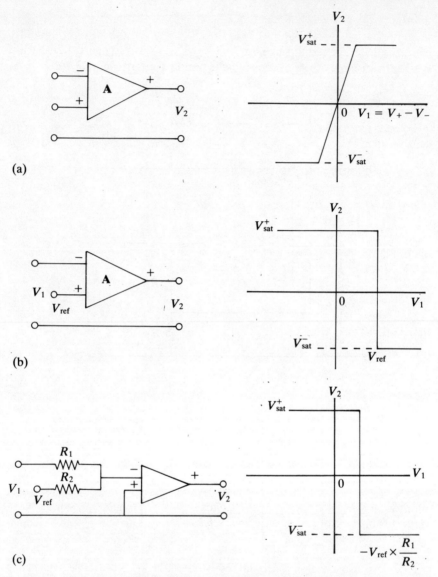

Fig. 3.3 The comparator has the symbol and characteristic shown in (a). The modifications (b) and (c) show how the device may be used so that the output transition occurs for a non-zero input voltage.

easily persuaded to change between its two stable states by the application of a voltage greater than $|V_{sat}^{\pm} R_1/(R_1 + R_2)|$, of the appropriate sign, to the inverting input.

When this voltage is applied, the amplifier experiences a net input voltage $V_1 = (V_+ - V_-)$ of the opposite sign to that previously existing so that there is positive feedback to the other stable state. The input signal need only be applied for a short time, just long enough to initiate the transition. Small control pulses applied through a CR network as shown in figure 3.2(b) can switch the bistable device as shown in the timing diagram (figure 3.2(c)).

COMPARATORS

The *comparator* is a bistable device without external positive feedback. It is a high-gain amplifier with well defined saturation levels so that the output is always at one of two states depending on the sign of the net input signal $V_1 = V_+ - V_-$, as shown in figure 3.3(a). The comparator will detect the sign of a signal if one input is earthed, or will give a binary digital output corresponding to the two conditions $V_+ > V_-$ and $V_+ < V_-$. The transition can be made to take place at a voltage V_{ref} rather than 0 V, as shown in figures 3.3(b) or (c). This functional unit is therefore valuable in converting analog signals into digital signals.

As described above, the comparator is a high-gain differential amplifier used open-loop. In practice the circuit is optimized for its comparator function with a rapid change of state between well defined voltage levels. However, in this open-loop condition it can be difficult to use since even small input signals (about 1 mV) will change its output state. Normally care has to be taken with the detailed circuit layout. Its high sensitivity often results in unwanted transitions if small spurious signals (noise) appear at its input.

The introduction of a small amount of positive feedback to a comparator results in a characteristic with hysteresis, as shown in figure 3.4. This is the same circuit that was described at the beginning of the chapter. The output still has one of two values but the transition takes place only when the input signal is greater than $|V_{sat}R_1/(R_1 + R_2)|$ rather than zero since the circuit provides a reference voltage that changes sign depending on the state of the output. This type of circuit is called a *Schmitt trigger*.

SATURATING OSCILLATORS

The bistable circuit that has been described so far in this chapter can be modified so that it will make transitions automatically after fixed periods of time controlled by an RC charging circuit. Consider the circuit of figure 3.5. The capacitor C will charge up towards $V_{sat}^\pm$ through R. When the voltage across the capacitor, V_C, reaches the positive feedback voltage $V_{sat}^\pm R_1/(R_1 + R_2)$, the amplifier experiences a net input voltage of the opposite sign

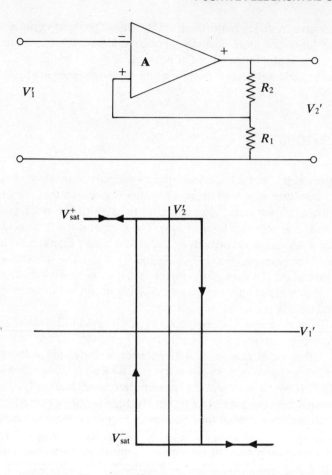

Fig. 3.4 The addition of positive feedback to a comparator produces a transition with hysteresis, as in a Schmitt trigger.

and makes a transition. The process repeats for the other polarity of the output to give a symmetrical square wave if the positive and negative saturation values $V_{\text{sat}}^{\pm}$ are equal. Small synchronizing pulses can be applied to the inputs to add to the signals already present. These pulses can initiate a transition and hence reduce the period and synchronize the transitions to some external source.

This type of oscillator is described by various terms. It is a *square-wave oscillator*, a *saturating oscillator*, a *relaxation oscillator*, or an *astable multivibrator*.

The capacitance charging process can be inhibited for one sign of the output voltage by the addition of a diode, as shown in figure 3.6. For positive output voltages, the diode will conduct, and hence it will prevent the capaci-

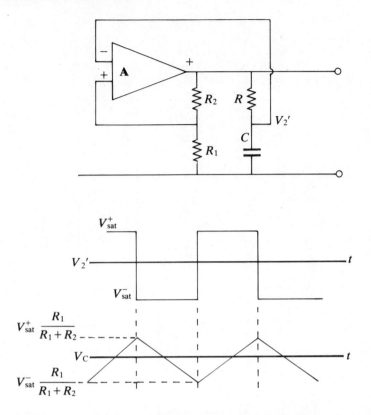

Fig. 3.5 A differential amplifier with positive feedback and a feedback signal derived from an RC relaxation circuit acts as an astable multivibrator.

tance voltage rising so that no transition will take place automatically. If, however, some trigger pulse causes a negative state to appear, the capacitor will charge and there will be a transition after a period when the capacitor voltage reaches the positive feedback voltage.

This circuit thus produces a single pulse of known length after a suitable trigger pulse has been applied. It is called a *monostable multivibrator*.

These circuits involve a feedback circuit in which there is positive feedback over a wide bandwidth and hence there is a rapid transition. They also involve a large amount of positive feedback (loop gain) so that the amplifier is driven firmly into saturation.

An integrated circuit that is widely used for timing purposes is the 555 (appendix 1). This comprises a comparator that senses the voltage across a capacitor that charges through an external resistor. There are also control circuits. The saturating oscillator reaches its most versatile form in the

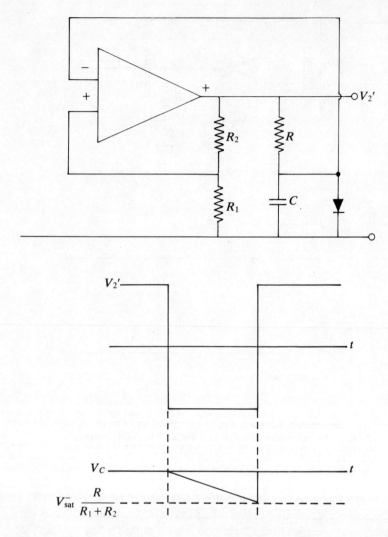

Fig. 3.6 The astable multivibrator may be changed into a monostable multivibrator if a diode is connected across the capacitor.

function generator. The same basic principles as described for the astable multivibrator are used but each function is optimized. In the circuit shown in figure 3.7 a d.c. (z.f.) voltage source V_{VCO} is fed to an integrator with a time constant RC to produce an accurate (negative-going) linear ramp. When the output voltage reaches a fixed value, $-V_{ref}$, the comparator output switches. The comparator output changes the sign of both the voltage source V_{VCO} and the comparator reference voltage V_{ref} for the next half of the cycle.

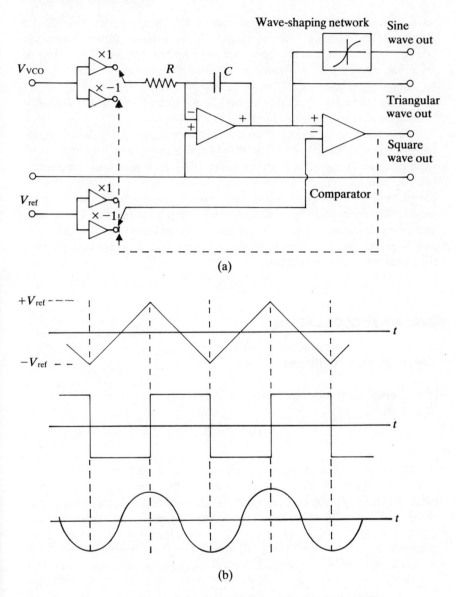

Fig. 3.7 The function generator circuit (a) with the output waveforms (b).

The output of the integrator is a triangular wave and the output of the comparator is a square wave. Both signals have a constant phase relation and constant amplitudes. The triangular wave can be fed to a non-linear circuit which amplifies the high-amplitude parts of the waveform less than the other parts to round the signal into a sine wave. Thus three waveforms of fixed amplitude and relative phase are available. Asymmetrical waveforms are possible if the voltage to the integrator has a different value for each half of the cycle. The period, or frequency, of the oscillation can be varied coarsely by changing the value of RC or, continuously, by varying the voltage V_{VCO}. This voltage can be supplied from outside the circuit, so that the oscillator becomes a *voltage-controlled oscillator* (VCO) (see chapter 6).

The function generator thus has the advantages that it is a voltage-controlled oscillator, often with a 1000:1 tunable range, it can operate over a wide range of frequencies from 1 mHz to 10 MHz, it produces three waveforms of constant amplitude, and the switching techniques used enable it to be connected easily to logic circuits for extra control. Amplitude and frequency modulation are easy. Its main disadvantage is that, although the square wave and triangular wave have accurate shapes, the sine wave has some distortion and often shows extra spikes at the voltage maxima and minima derived from the switching of the comparator.

SINE-WAVE OSCILLATORS

The oscillation conditions

In the general feedback equation (2.4),

$$\mathbf{A}' = \frac{\mathbf{A}}{1 + \mathbf{A}\beta} \tag{3.1}$$

the closed loop gain $\mathbf{A}'$ goes to infinity if the loop gain $(-\mathbf{A}\beta) = 1$ or $\mathbf{A}\beta = -1$. This condition can be restated in different ways: the loop gain has a magnitude of unity and a phase of zero, or alternatively, if a signal at any point in the loop is considered it will pass round the loop and reappear with the same amplitude and phase. The situation is best considered for the case where the condition is only reached at one frequency. The phase condition can be met when the phase-shift at that frequency is 0 or an integral multiple of 2π and the amplitude condition is met when the gain of the amplifier equals the attenuation of the feedback network. For the feedback circuit, this is the condition for a constant-amplitude output signal at that frequency. If the loop gain is increased slightly in magnitude, the amplitude increases exponentially with time, and if the loop gain decreases, the amplitude dies away exponentially. Changing the loop gain is therefore analogous to a change in the resistive term in a driven LCR tuned circuit. The infinite gain arises since zero input signal is needed for a constant output signal. Power from the d.c. supply to the amplifier is converted into the a.c. signal.

It should be noted that the two conditions, in amplitude and phase, on the loop gain are those necessary for sustained oscillation at constant amplitude. A separate condition or circuit element is required to specify what value that amplitude should be. Often this amplitude-defining condition is not considered in detail in oscillator design but the loop gain is adjusted to give oscillation at a suitable level and the existing non-linearity of the circuit keeps the amplitude constant. A good design will specifically incorporate some amplitude-defining element. This will be described later. Thus the three oscillation conditions are the two linear conditions:

(1) the loop-gain phase must be 0 or $2n\pi$;
(2) the loop-gain magnitude must be 1;

and the non-linear condition:

(3) there must be some system to define the amplitude of oscillation.

Phase-shift oscillators

If the oscillation condition is satisfied at only one frequency, and the circuit non-linearity is small, then the output will be a sine wave and the circuit will be a sine-wave oscillator. These circuits have the oscillation condition determined by a filter network in the feedback loop. Most of these networks will have RC or LC components and are hence called RC oscillators or LC oscillators. For historical reasons, many specific configurations have their own names, but the basic principles remain the same. Usually the specific advantages of each configuration depend on the amplifier properties, such as input and output impedances, gain, and non-linearity, since the amplifier is often a single active device that is far from ideal.

Consider the *phase-shift oscillator* shown in figure 3.8. The feedback loop

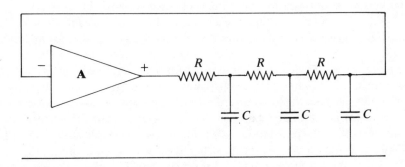

Fig. 3.8 A phase-shift sine-wave oscillator.

consists of an inverting amplifier with a frequency-independent gain $\mathbf{A}$ and no phase-shift (other than the inversion). The feedback network β consists of three equal stages of low-pass RC filter. Each stage of RC filter can, by itself, produce between 0 and $\pi/2$ phase-shift depending on the value of ωRC. The three stages might therefore be expected to produce a phase-shift of up to $3\pi/2$ and hence provide, together with the amplifier inversion, sufficient phase-shift to produce the oscillation condition. In fact the analysis is not quite so simple since there is mutual loading between the RC stages so that the required phase-shift occurs for $\omega RC = \sqrt{6}$ for the whole network if there is no loading at its ends. At this frequency the attenuation through the network is 29 so that $|\mathbf{A}| = 29$ is needed for the amplitude part of the oscillation condition.

Amplitude stabilization

The amplitude of oscillation needs to be specified. If the circuit were constructed of ideal linear components, the oscillation amplitude could be set at any level, but similarly it could change between levels with only slight disturbance. In practice such a circuit will only oscillate with a stable amplitude if the loop gain is accurately unity. In the above example, if the amplifier gain $\mathbf{A}$ is made slightly larger than the required value of 29, then the amplitude of oscillation rises until the amplifier saturates to some extent and gives out a sine wave with a square top. This distortion reduces the effective gain of the circuit to the required value. If the gain increases, there is more distortion, although the approximate signal size remains the same. There is thus a compromise between amplitude stability and distortion. The astable multivibrator introduced earlier has considerable distortion, is a highly non-linear amplifier, and has good amplitude control. It has large positive feedback over a very wide band of frequencies.

The amplitude stabilization can be achieved in a more controlled manner by using a more suitable non-linear element. An example is an inverting amplifier with more gradual saturation, such as that shown in figure 3.9.

For low-amplitude signals the amplifier is linear with a gain $\mathbf{A}' = R_2/R_1$, which is adjusted to be just greater than that needed to satisfy the amplitude oscillation condition. At higher amplitudes the diodes conduct and hence the amplifier gradually becomes non-linear with reduced effective gain. With a non-linear circuit the 'gain' needs careful consideration since there is a difference between the 'instantaneous gain' V_2/V_1 and the 'average gain' over the cycle (or many other definitions). The output of the amplifier is therefore a sine wave with the peaks rounded off. In this case the amplifier non-linearity stabilizes the amplitude but the distortion is not very pronounced.

The amplitude stabilization can be achieved without distortion if another feedback loop is incorporated to adjust the amplifier loop gain in order to

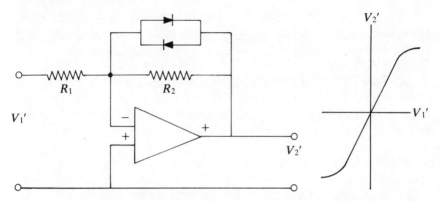

Fig. 3.9 Diodes across the feedback resistance R_2 of an inverting amplifier produce a soft limiting characteristic, as shown. This controlled non-linearity enables the amplifier in an oscillator circuit to stabilize the amplitude of oscillation with little distortion.

keep the output amplitude constant. A typical circuit is shown schematically in figure 3.10. The oscillator consists of a positive feedback loop with loop gain $(-A\beta)$. The loop gain is kept at a magnitude of unity by using a linear amplifier with a voltage-controlled gain. The control voltage is derived from some amplitude detector (true root-mean-square (TRMS) detector circuit, a.c. to d.c. converter or signal rectifier (chapter 2)) followed by a low-pass filter to smooth out any residual a.c. components. Thus a voltage proportional to the a.c. amplitude averaged over many cycles is obtained. This circuit is useful since the level of oscillation can be adjusted by changing the reference voltage in the negative feedback loop. There is no distortion of the waveform because the time-averaged signal is controlled rather than the instantaneous signal.

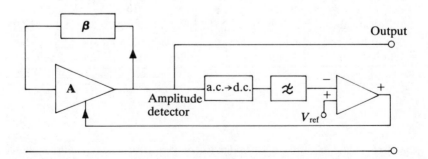

Fig. 3.10 An oscillator circuit that shows schematically how the amplitude may be stabilized by using negative feedback to change the loop gain.

Simple amplitude stabilization circuits involving negative feedback acting on the time-averaged signal can be made using the properties of specific resistors that have a large change of resistance with temperature or the power dissipated in them.

Consider the *Wien bridge oscillator* shown in figure 3.11(a). The bridge consists of one arm with *RC* in series and *RC* in parallel and another arm with resistors R_1 and R_2. The null signal is amplified and fed back to drive the bridge. The amplifier open-loop gain is large so that when the output signal is

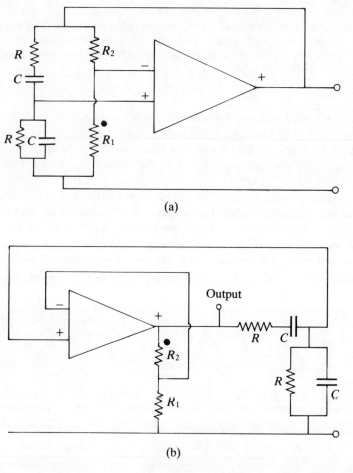

(a)

(b)

Fig. 3.11 Variants of the Wien bridge sine-wave oscillator circuit with amplitude stabilization using the self-heating of a temperature-sensitive resistor. In (a) R_1 has a positive temperature coefficient while in (b) R_2 has a negative temperature coefficient.

finite the differential input signal is nearly a null. The phase to the inverting input will be the phase at the output. The phase of the signal to the non-inverting input will be the same, in order to produce a null, only at the frequency where the two RC arms have the same phase angle or ratio of reactance to resistance. For this circuit this occurs when $\omega RC = 1$. This is the phase condition. The oscillation amplitude condition is given by the amplitude condition for the null. At the frequency given by $\omega RC = 1$ the RC arms have impedance ratio 2:1 so that $R_2 = 2R_1$ is needed.

The amplitude stabilization condition can easily be achieved by using for the resistance R_1 a resistor with a positive temperature coefficient such as a metal filament. The values of R_1 and R_2 are chosen so that at low amplitudes $2R_1 \lesssim R_2$ and oscillation starts and the amplitude grows. As the signal increases, the power dissipated in R_1 increases, its temperature rises, and hence its resistance rises. This results in more signal fed back to the inverting input of the amplifier and hence less net positive feedback. At some amplitude, $R_2 = 2R_1$ and the oscillation signal stabilizes. The negative feedback relies on the specific properties of the resistor, R_1, its temperature coefficient of resistance, its power dissipation, its thermal capacity, and its thermal insulation. The last two properties can be combined into a thermal time constant, which produces the averaging time constant or response time of the negative feedback circuit. So that the feedback responds to the average signal amplitude, the thermal time constant should be many half-periods.

The Wien bridge circuit can be redrawn as shown in figure 3.11(b). It can be seen that it is just another form of the phase-shift oscillator with the RC components providing the phase-shift of 0. The resistors R_1, R_2 act with the amplifier to give a non-inverting amplifier of gain $(R_1 + R_2)/R_1$. In figure 3.11(b) the temperature-varying resistor is shown as R_2 which needs to have a negative temperature coefficient. A thermistor is usually used.

The operation of oscillators with a tuned circuit in the feedback network, LC oscillators, such as that shown in figure 3.12, follow the same basic principles. Many variations are possible; the LC circuit may be connected for

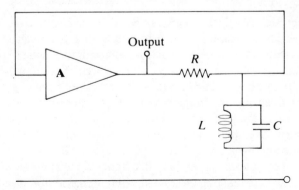

Fig. 3.12 A schematic circuit for an LC sine-wave oscillator.

series or parallel resonance or the signal may be connected between the amplifier and feedback network with a mutual inductance. The physical size and limitations of real components usually determine that RC oscillators are used below about 1 MHz and LC oscillators above this frequency.

The stability of the oscillator frequency is determined by the constancy of the component values and the rate of change of the phase–frequency variation. For an LC circuit the latter is governed by the Q of the tuned circuit. Compact, stable, high-Q tuned circuits can be made easily using the electromechanical resonance of piezoelectric crystals such as quartz. A piezoelectric material suffers a strain if an electric field is applied; conversely charges appear on its surfaces if a strain is applied. If a capacitor is made with a piezoelectric material as the dielectric, it will show a rapid change in impedance with frequency at frequencies where the crystal has a mechanical resonance. The electrical signal produces stresses that excite the mechanical resonance and the strains associated with this produce electrical signals back into the electrical circuit. These impedance variations can be approximated to either series or parallel electrical tuned circuit responses over a narrow range of frequencies and hence the piezoelectric crystal can act as the frequency-determining element in an oscillator.

STABILITY OF FEEDBACK CIRCUITS

The characteristics of circuits with negative feedback and with positive feedback are very different, with null signals and stability for negative feedback, and oscillation and instability for positive feedback. The same basic feedback circuit is involved, but the phase of the loop gain is either π for stability or 0 for oscillation. We have considered these two extreme cases in some detail and have simplified the analysis to phase-shifts of π and 0 because then the general, complex number, feedback equation (equation (3.1)) becomes straightforward.

In practice the distinction between positive and negative feedback is not as definite as the discussion so far may have indicated. In a given circuit a small extra phase-shift at one frequency may be sufficient to change a stable circuit into an oscillator. This unwelcome result may occur in a number of ways: in the design, because the value of the loop gain has not been considered at all frequencies other than the frequency of primary interest; at the construction stage, because of stray impedances or the non-ideal properties of the components which have not been allowed for in the calculation. Possibly replacement of one component by another nominally the same may cause oscillation. Although not complete, this section will describe some methods of analysis of the full feedback equation, indicate the requirements for instability, and hence suggest ways of stabilizing an oscillating feedback circuit.

The behavior of a feedback circuit is controlled by the loop gain $(-\mathbf{A}\boldsymbol{\beta})$. If a system is being designed from first principles using known components, the full linear differential equation for the output voltage can be written down. If the system is linear, the differential equation will be linear and can be solved to obtain the system response or gain–frequency variation. Using a suitably programmed computer this can be fairly straightforward. However, to determine whether the equation has a stable or unstable solution, there are simple criteria just involving the relative magnitudes of the coefficients of the terms in the differential equation. One such method is the Routh–Hurwitz criterion, and for this type of analysis the reader is advised to consult a book on control theory.

For the reader of this book, the differential equation governing the circuit operation is unlikely to be the main design consideration. Usually the circuit will have been assembled from functional building blocks. The voltage transfer function, or gain and phase variation with frequency, will be known for each section of the feedback loop, so that the value of $(-\mathbf{A}\boldsymbol{\beta})$ can be determined for each frequency. Allowance must be made for any loading between sections. Using the complex notation, and making suitable approximations, this calculation is not difficult in a design using well characterized components. If the system already exists, or contains components with unknown behavior, the transfer function of the whole, or parts, will have to be determined experimentally. This can be difficult and the calculation of the total loop gain from the parts involves multiplying the amplitudes of the individual transfer functions and adding the phases at each frequency.

The final aim is to plot the locus of the loop gain $(-\mathbf{A}\boldsymbol{\beta})$ in the complex plane. This is the *Nyquist plot* and is shown in figure 3.13 for an example at frequencies ω_1, ω_2, ω_3, and ω_4.

In the earlier, approximate, analysis the loop gain was considered to be real, so that only the real axis of this plot was used. Along the real axis the large negative feedback stable region, the positive feedback region $(|\mathbf{A}\boldsymbol{\beta}| < 1)$, and the critical oscillation point $(|\mathbf{A}\boldsymbol{\beta}| = 1)$ can easily be identified. For the full complex analysis the plane can be divided into three regions. For the negative real half of the plane, the feedback reduces the gain, $|\mathbf{A}'| < |\mathbf{A}|$, and the real or in-phase part of the loop gain is negative. For frequencies that have these values of loop gain, the system will be stable. For parts of the positive real half of the plane outside a circle of radius unity centred on the point $(1, \mathrm{j}0)$, there is no inherent stability although the feedback reduces the gain, $|\mathbf{A}'| < |\mathbf{A}|$. This is because the in-phase component of the feedback is positive; the gain is only reduced because of the presence of the out-of-phase or orthogonal component of the feedback signal. For frequencies where the loop gain is within the circle with unity radius, the feedback increases the gain, $|\mathbf{A}'| > |\mathbf{A}|$, since $|1 + \mathbf{A}\boldsymbol{\beta}| < 1$. At the point $(1, \mathrm{j}0)$ the gain becomes infinite and oscillation occurs.

The plot of the loop gain of the system in the complex plane for all

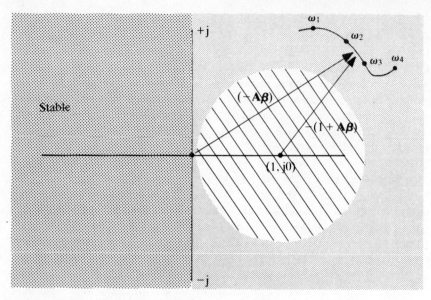

Fig. 3.13   The complex plane of the loop gain ($-A\beta$).

frequencies will enable the behavior of the system to be established. The full analysis, however, indicates that the condition for oscillation, the *Nyquist criterion*, is not that the locus passes through the point $(1, j0)$ but that the locus should 'enclose' the point $(1, j0)$. The point is enclosed if it is to the right of the curve progressing from $\omega = 0$ to $\omega = \infty$.

In figures 3.14(a) and (b) are shown examples for stable and unstable systems. The curve shown in figure 3.14(c) illustrates *conditional stability*. Although stable, this system cannot be guaranteed to be always stable. If the system gain reduces, such as due to some aging of the amplifier, power supply voltage reduction, or during the period when the system is turned on, the loop gain will reduce and oscillations will start. Once a system has started to oscillate it may be driven into some non-linear regime and not be able to recover.

The Nyquist plot and stability criterion are useful to show whether a circuit will be stable and to indicate how near instability it is. In general the circuit should be designed with the locus well away from the oscillation condition in both amplitude and phase at all frequencies. However, the theoretical or experimental determination of the loop gain at all frequencies, and its plotting, can take some time.

A simpler, and more easily visualized, presentation of the system response is provided by the *Bode plot*, which is the log–log plot of the amplitude of the loop gain against frequency and the linear–log plot of the phase against frequency. An example is shown in figure 3.15.

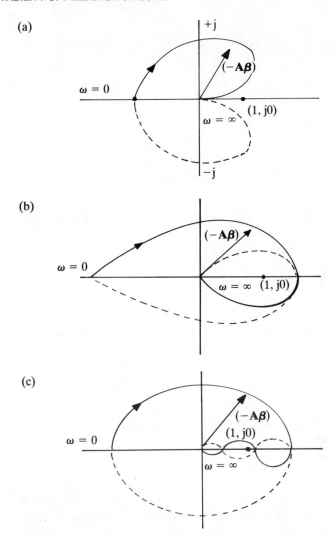

Fig. 3.14 Loci of the loop gain of typical feedback circuits showing a stable circuit (a), an unstable circuit (b), and a conditionally stable circuit (c). The broken curves are reflections of the locus in the real axis.

The Nyquist analysis shown in figure 3.14 suggests that the system will be unstable if the loop gain is greater than unity when the phase is 0. Here the loop gain reaches the phase needed for oscillation when the gain is A_1, less than unity. Similarly when the gain is unity the phase-shift is ϕ_1 and is insufficient to cause oscillation. The *gain margin A_1* and *phase margin ϕ_1* should be made large, and these values are a measure of the degree of stability.

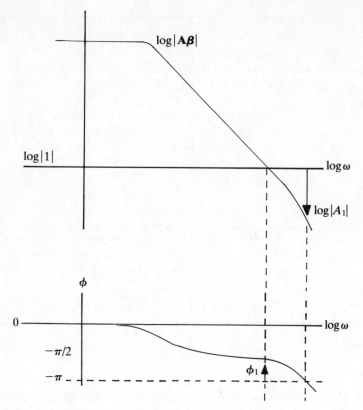

Fig. 3.15 The Bode plot of the loop gain showing the gain margin A_1 and the phase margin ϕ_1.

The usefulness of the Bode plot results from the simplicity with which $\log|\mathbf{A}|$ versus $\log\omega$ and $\log|\boldsymbol{\beta}|$ versus $\log\omega$ plots can be drawn, especially if the linearized approximation can be used. The $\log|\mathbf{A}\boldsymbol{\beta}|$ versus $\log\omega$ plot need not be separately computed and drawn since $\log|\mathbf{A}\boldsymbol{\beta}|$ is given, at each frequency, by the distance between the $\log|\mathbf{A}|$ and $\log|\boldsymbol{\beta}|$ curves if they are plotted on the same axes.

For many circuits there is a further simplification since the phase–frequency plot can be deduced from the slope of the $\log|\text{gain}|$ versus $\log\omega$ curve. This will happen for all circuits in which $j\omega$ occurs always as a product. If the linearized expression includes $(j\omega)^n$, then the phase-shift is given by j^n and is $n\pi/2$, while the slope of the $\log|\text{gain}|$ versus $\log\omega$ curve is n.

Formally this is given by

$$\phi = \frac{d(\log|\mathbf{A}|)}{d(\log\omega)}\frac{(-\pi/2)}{6} \qquad \text{dB/octave} \qquad (3.2)$$

A slope of 1 corresponds to 6 dB/octave or 20 dB/decade. The circuits for which this applies are called *minimum phase-shift networks*. For other circuits the phase-shift is less. Circuits and systems for which this equation does not work are those including a time delay (transmission, line, etc.), multiple-path circuits (bridge circuits and T filters, etc.), or rotations (Hall-effect devices, rotating machines, etc.).

For minimum phase-shift networks the *Bode criterion* for stability becomes easy to apply. $\text{Log}|\mathbf{A}|$ and $-\log|\boldsymbol{\beta}| = \log|1/\boldsymbol{\beta}|$ are plotted against $\log \omega$ on the same axes using the linearized approximation, as shown in figure 3.16. Their crossing point corresponds to $\log|\mathbf{A}\boldsymbol{\beta}| = \log|1| = 0$. The phase-shift at this frequency will be less than π, and hence the system will be stable if

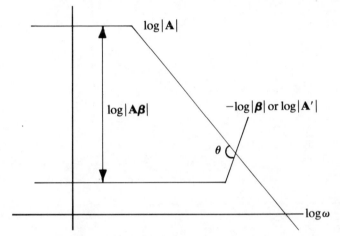

Fig. 3.16 The Bode plot of the loop gain can be deduced from the plots of $\log |\mathbf{A}|$ versus $\log \omega$ and $\log|\boldsymbol{\beta}|$ versus $\log \omega$.

the angle of closure θ between the curves corresponds to less than 12 dB/octave or 40 dB/decade. Since $\mathbf{A}' \simeq 1/\boldsymbol{\beta}$ for large negative feedback, $\log|\mathbf{A}'|$ may be plotted instead of $-\log|\boldsymbol{\beta}|$.

Note that there is a slight difficulty in defining the signs in our operational amplifier feedback circuit since the amplifier gain A may be inverting or non-inverting.

Consider the differentiator circuit shown in figure 3.17(a). The closed-loop gain $\mathbf{A}_1' = -j\omega RC$ and the Bode plot is shown. The curves for $\mathbf{A}$ and $\mathbf{A}_1'$ intersect with slopes of -1 and $+1$ corresponding to a closure rate of 2, 12 dB/octave or 20 dB/decade, $\phi = 0$. Thus the circuit is likely to be unstable. Stabilization can be achieved by adding a small resistance r in series with the capacitor C, as shown in figure 3.17(b). The Bode plot of $\mathbf{A}_2'$ is also shown. At low frequencies r can be neglected and $\mathbf{A}_2' = -j\omega RC$. Above a frequency given by $j\omega rC = 1$ the capacitance can be neglected and the amplifier

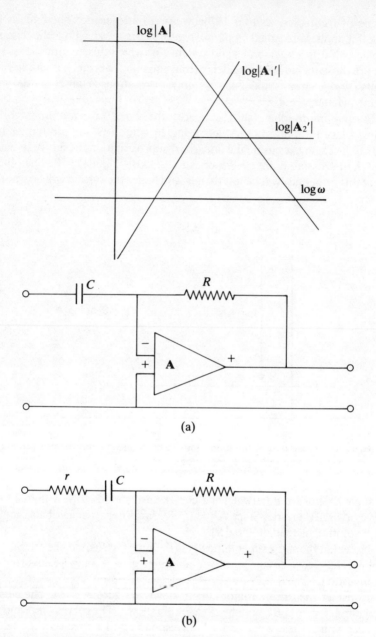

Fig. 3.17 The Bode plot of circuit (a) with gain $\mathbf{A_1'}$ shows that it is likely to be unstable. The addition of a resistance r to form circuit (b) produces a gain $\mathbf{A_2'}$ that is stable.

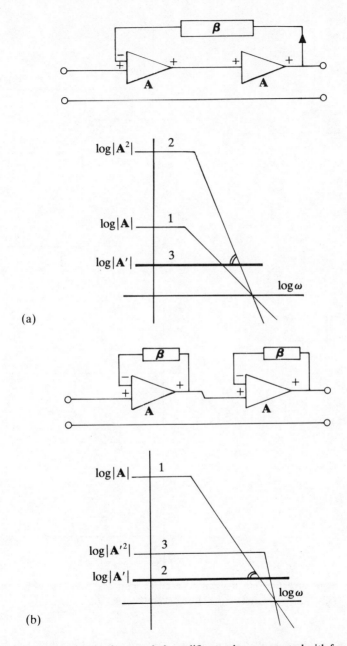

Fig. 3.18 The circuit of a cascaded amplifier can be constructed with feedback round the whole circuit as in (a) or round each constituent amplifier as in (b). The Bode plots show that the former is unstable but the latter is stable.

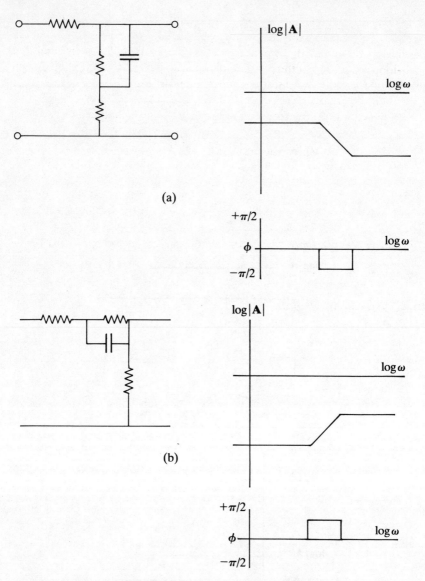

Fig. 3.19 Phase-correction circuits can be used to modify the loop-gain near the frequency where $|\mathbf{A}\boldsymbol{\beta}| = 1$ to produce a stable circuit.

becomes a simple inverting amplifier with a gain $-R/r$. Provided that the $|\mathbf{A}_2'|$ curve intersects the open-loop curve $|\mathbf{A}|$ in this inverting amplifier region when the angle of intersection corresponds to 6 dB/octave, the circuit will be stable. Often the non-zero output impedance of the preceding stage is sufficient to provide r and stabilize the circuit.

Another example is shown in the feedback supplied to a cascaded amplifier. A higher gain–bandwidth product may be obtained if several amplifiers are cascaded. In general one might think that the greater the open-loop gain the better the amplifier. However, this may result in instability. Consider the cascading of two identical amplifiers shown in figure 3.18.

In figure 3.18(a) the feedback network β is shown connected round the two amplifiers in cascade, open-loop. Each amplifier has an open-loop gain $\mathbf{A}$ (shown in curve 1) so that the two have gain $\mathbf{A}^2$ (curve 2). When resistive feedback β is applied, the characteristic curve 3 is produced, and this will result in instability. However, if each amplifier has its own feedback network and they are cascaded closed-loop as shown in figure 3.18(b), then the feedback is given by curve 2 and is stable. The final response is shown in curve 3.

Circuits involving non-linear elements and backlash require additional techniques.

Phase-correction circuits

Sometimes the phase of the feedback circuit β needs to be adjusted over a small range of frequencies about the frequency at which the loop gain becomes unity. This can be accomplished by *phase-correction circuits* such as those shown in figure 3.19.

FURTHER READING

J. Schwarzenbach and K. F. Gill, *System Modelling and Control*, Edward Arnold (1978).

4 NOISE AND INTERFERENCE

INTRODUCTION

In general, if a quantity is measured to a sufficiently high resolution, it will be found to vary with time about some average value, as shown in figure 4.1. This random fluctuation relative to the mean is called *noise* by analogy with sound. In a measuring system, random errors of measurement produce a distribution of results that is spread about the 'real' or average value. These 'errors' are due to a large number of independent effects in the measuring system which make it less than perfect. Other unwanted signals that are also referred to as noise are those introduced into the system from outside sources to cause *interference*, and these are not usually random.

An understanding of noise signals is important, since the presence of these unwanted signals is the ultimate limit on the precision to which signals can be measured and the smallest size of signal that can be detected. In many cases, therefore, the quality of the experiment is determined by the size of the noise signal. Even if ideal measuring instruments are used, the quantity being investigated will be found to fluctuate about some mean value because of some inherent uncertainty derived from the laws of nature.

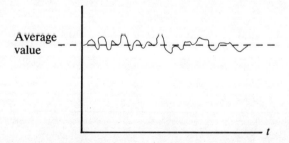

Fig. 4.1 The fluctuation with time of a measured quality about the average value.

Random noise signals fluctuate about a mean value and hence have the effect of spreading the distribution of measurements about the mean. Interference signals, however, may be of constant form, amplitude, and phase, so that they can add to the real signal. If this happens, the result will be a systematic error in the signal and the data. Although such effects are more important than the random noise effect, a detailed description of how to detect and correct them is not possible since it would be specific to each particular apparatus and experiment. To detect such effects, there should be many checks and calibration steps throughout an experiment.

Since the mean noise value is zero, the measure of the random noise is the power, intensity or root-mean-square (r.m.s.) value. Although the signal is described in most systems in terms of an amplitude, a voltage or a current, the quantity that matters when considering noise, low-level signals or very sensitive input devices is the power. The measure of the resolution of a measurement is the (signal power)/(noise power) or the *signal-to-noise ratio* (S/N). This can be expressed as a simple ratio but is more often expressed in *decibels* (see appendix 1). The decibel is a logarithmic measure of *power* ratio which is used in many different contexts. It is defined as

$$1\,dB = 10\log_{10}\left(\frac{P_1}{P_2}\right) \tag{4.1}$$

where P_1 and P_2 are the two powers. Thus the signal-to-noise ratio expressed in decibels is $10\log_{10}(S/N)\,dB$. If the powers are measured at the same place in the circuit, that is the impedance involved is the same, the decibels can be used as an amplitude ratio. Thus

$$10\log_{10}(P_1/P_2) = 20\log_{10}(V_1/V_2) \qquad etc. \tag{4.2}$$

The use of decibels by some people is very casual, and this impedance condition is not always valid, so that care should be taken in interpreting results. Also the decibel is sometimes used as a measure of the power P_1 in equation (4.1), but the value of P_2 that is used is not clearly stated. The convention used, or the value of P_2 assumed, should always be made explicit.

The essential feature of random noise (rather than interference) is that it is a random, incoherent fluctuation. This means that there is no relationship between one noise signal and another, or between two time periods of a single noise signal. If one considers two independent noise sources v_{n1} and v_{n2} in series, the resultant is $v_{n1} + v_{n2}$. The intensity is

$$\overline{(v_{n1} + v_{n2})^2} = \overline{v_{n1}^2} + \overline{2v_{n1}v_{n2}} + \overline{v_{n2}^2} = \overline{v_{n1}^2} + \overline{v_{n2}^2} \tag{4.3}$$

where the bar represents a time average. The cross-term averages to zero since v_{n1} and v_{n2} will fluctuate in sign as well as magnitude and there is equal probability of the positive products $(+)(+)$ and $(-)(-)$ occurring as the negative products $(+)(-)$ and $(-)(+)$. For random, independent, noise signals, therefore, the intensities add. For coherent signals, the amplitudes add. This is familiar in optical problems. Light from incoherent sources is added in intensity while that from coherent sources such as lasers add in amplitude to give interference effects. Although the cross-term averages to zero, it will have a non-zero value at any time. Its presence, therefore, increases the uncertainty in the noise measurement.

NOISE SOURCES

Unwanted signals, noise, come from a wide variety of sources. A detailed knowledge of the operation and behavior of all devices and systems, and hence the origin of their sources of noise, is not within the scope of this book and the reader is referred to more specialist texts. For discussion here, noise sources will be divided into three categories:

(1) Intrinsic, random noise sources, which exist because of fundamental laws of nature and are inherent in the circuit.
(2) Random noise sources that are in excess of those in (1). These are due to deficiencies in the particular devices used. This noise can, in principle, be reduced by the use of better devices, but this may not be possible in practice.
(3) Interference or pick-up, which can in principle be removed without affecting the signal itself.

INTRINSIC NOISE SOURCES

Thermal noise

Thermal, Nyquist, Johnson or *kT noise* occurs in resistors and other dissipative devices in thermal equilibrium at some temperature T. It is a consequence of the laws of thermodynamics and the thermal agitation of the system. If we consider a resistance R at an absolute temperature T, then a noise voltage v_n will appear between the terminals with intensity

$$\overline{v_n^2} = 4kTR\Delta f \tag{4.4}$$

where the bar represents a time average, k is the Boltzmann constant, and Δf is the bandwidth over which the measurement is made.

The spectrum of this noise is 'white', since the intensity per unit bandwidth, the spectral density, is independent of frequency (figure 4.2). Typical values are 0.127 μV (r.m.s.) for 1 kΩ over 1 kHz bandwidth at 293 K or normal room temperature.

This is the result from classical thermodynamics, and it is valid for frequencies given by $hf \ll kT$ (h is Planck's constant) or below about 600 GHz at normal room temperature.

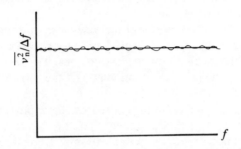

Fig. 4.2   The spectral density of 'white' noise is independent of frequency.

The noise arises from the thermal agitation or Brownian motion of the carriers and the atoms in the resistor. Each degree of freedom has energy $kT/2$ and the carriers' velocity fluctuates to give a fluctuating unbalance of charge between the terminals of the resistor, and hence a potential difference.

The dissipative part of any system provides a link between the system and its thermal surroundings. The link can work in both directions so that all dissipative systems experience these thermal fluctuations. Since all systems exhibit some dissipation and are at some non-zero temperature, this type of noise is always present and is often the ultimate limit to a measurement, electrical or mechanical. Reactive components will not contribute to this thermal noise except through any dissipative elements in their equivalent circuit, that is any lossy physical processes taking place. The reactive components will affect the spectrum, and this will be discussed later when considering equivalent circuits.

Shot noise

Electric current is composed of the flow of a series of charged carriers each with a fixed charge e, the electronic charge. In most currents there are many charges moving with a very slow average or drift velocity so that the net effect does not show evidence of the discreteness of the charge. However, if the individual carriers pass up a diode potential step or are emitted from a photocathode, each charge is independent and creates a current pulse in the system. These random current pulses result in an average current and fluctuations about this average. This form of noise is called *shot noise*. For a mean current I the noise intensity measured over a bandwidth Δf is given by

$$\overline{i_n^2} = 2eI\Delta f \qquad (4.5)$$

The spectrum is white up to a frequency equal to the reciprocal of the time taken for an individual current pulse. For a 1 μA current and 1 kHz bandwidth, the noise is 18 pA r.m.s.

Although the absolute noise level increases with current, the relative noise $(\overline{i_n^2})^{1/2}/I$ varies as $1/I^{1/2}$, and is hence largest for small currents in which the granularity of the current flow is most obvious. The shot noise can be reduced below the value given in equation (4.5) if the carriers interact with each other.

Shot noise and thermal noise thus arise from basic physical causes and cannot be eliminated. A given experiment therefore has to be designed to maximize the signal/noise ratio, for example by minimizing the value of R for a given size of signal. Thermal noise can be reduced by reducing the temperature T, but this is rarely of practical value unless the experiment has to be at a low temperature for other reasons. The main approach to improvement in S/N is to filter the combined signal and noise to reduce the bandwidth over which the noise appears while not reducing the signal intensity. This will be described near the end of this chapter.

REDUCIBLE NOISE SOURCES

These sources of noise are perhaps avoidable in the sense that one can at any time design, buy or use a good- or a bad-quality device. Some amplifiers or transistors generate less noise than others, although they may have the same operating properties in other respects. In general, this type of noise source becomes less important over the years since better devices are developed. The choice of a particular device for lowest noise performance cannot be generalized since each application and each year will require a different solution. The experimenter must be aware of the properties of all available suitable devices and methods in order to make an informed decision. The manufacturers' data sheets and the current literature must be read. The way the noise in devices is described and characterized will be described later.

The most common forms of noise that can differ between otherwise identical devices is *excess noise*. This is often due to defects or impurities in the material of the device and reveals itself as a fluctuation in the ability of the current to flow. Thus it may be a fluctuation in the emissivity of a cathode or a resistance fluctuation caused by a fluctuation in either the number of carriers or the scattering process. The resistance fluctuations, $\overline{r_n^2}$, appear in the circuit as voltage fluctuations only when a current flows, so that

$$\overline{v_n^2} = \overline{r_n^2}\, I^2$$

In general these excess noise sources occur at low frequencies, below about 1 kHz in good devices but below 1 MHz in some. The intensity spectrum often varies as

$$\overline{v_n^2} \simeq (1/f)\, I^2 \Delta f$$

and is called $1/f$ *noise* or *flicker noise*. Another common spectrum for excess noise has the form

$$\overline{v_n^2} \simeq \frac{1/f_0}{1 + (f/f_0)^2}\, \Delta f$$

where f_0 is some characteristic frequency.

It should be noted that this type of low-frequency excess noise is not important only in low-frequency circuits since it can modulate high-frequency signals to produce noise sidebands (see chapter 6). Consider a current $I = I_0 \cos \omega_c t$ at a high frequency ω_c. When passing through a resistance $r_n = r_{n0} \cos \omega_m t$ fluctuating at a low frequency ω_m, a voltage is developed

$$v_n = I_0 r_{n0} \cos \omega_m t \cos \omega_c t$$

$$= \tfrac{1}{2} I_0 r_{n0} \{ \cos[(\omega_c + \omega_m)t] + \cos[(\omega_c - \omega_m)t] \}$$

which has high-frequency components.

A fluctuating resistance, and hence excess noise, might be expected from poor contacts in which there is a contact resistance. Excess noise sources occur in switch contacts that are dirty or have a thin oxide or semi-insulating layer between the metal parts. A chemical cleaning fluid and a thin layer of oil will remove the resistance and prevent it reappearing. Gold contacts are used since this metal does not tarnish easily. A 'dry' solder joint (see appendix 2) is one in which there is a resistance, usually at grain boundaries, within the solder or between the solder and a metal conductor. These joints are often noisy. Similarly, components that have a granular construction with multiple contact resistances, such as carbon resistors and cermet resistors, are liable to show a large excess noise.

As well as the choice of a best device for minimum noise among several with the same nominal properties, there may be several different types of devices that may be used to produce a given function. For example, the input stage of an amplifier may be made from a bipolar or a field-effect transistor to produce the same bandwidth and gain. The noise performance is usually best using a junction field-effect transistor if the source impedance is large, and is best using a bipolar transistor if the source impedance is less than about 1 kΩ. Similarly for a given device there is an optimum bias condition and circuit configuration in order to maximize S/N. Such information may be obtained for a particular device from the manufacturer's data or by measurement.

INTERFERENCE OR AVOIDABLE NOISE

Interference or *pick-up* are terms used to describe the unwanted signals entering the signal path of a circuit from sources outside the circuit or perhaps from another part of the circuit. In principle, these noise sources can either be eliminated at source or can be prevented from entering the signal path. Naturally such perfection cannot always be achieved, but the techniques that can be used will be discussed later in this chapter.

Interference sources rarely have such continuous spectra as the random intrinsic or excess noise sources. The interference signals are either at discrete frequencies from sine-wave or repetitive sources that have a large harmonic content or are at discrete times in the form of pulses, spikes or other transients. The sources of such interference are many and various, and more can be expected to arise as the use of electronics increases.

Interference sources internal to the circuit

Spurious signals can be generated from within a circuit. The excess noise in dry joints and poor contacts has already been mentioned. Pick-up between one section of a circuit and another will be discussed later, when the pick-up by a circuit from an outside circuit will be discussed, since the mechanism is the same.

If the circuit is designed to operate with d.c. (z.f.) signals, special precautions are needed. This is because z.f. is a unique frequency and many spurious signals can be generated at this frequency. For example, rectification (chapter 6) of a signal at any frequency will generate a signal at z.f. A large-amplitude a.c. signal may generate an unexpected d.c. signal if there is some unknown non-linearity in the circuit.

A major source of interference in z.f. circuits is the thermoelectric effect. If a circuit consists of two, or more, dissimilar metals or conductors and the junctions between the dissimilar materials are at different temperatures, then an e.m.f. is developed within the circuit (figure 4.3). The effect can be large, with values as much as 420 μV/°C between copper and silicon and 1000 μV/°C between copper and copper oxide, which is a common contaminant on the copper surface. Even between pieces of pure copper with different histories of strain and annealing, voltages of 0.2 μV/°C are possible.

The thermoelectric e.m.f.s can be reduced by using only one material, usually copper, in the whole circuit and if possible using the same piece of copper with no joints. It should be remembered that the measuring instruments are also within the circuit, so that these should have carefully designed input sections made of good clean copper. Contacts, where necessary, should be made between freshly cleaned copper, although thin layers of gold plating

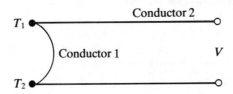

Fig. 4.3 In the thermoelectric effect, a voltage is produced if the two junctions between conductors 1 and 2 in a circuit are at different temperatures, T_1 and T_2.

can reduce the surface contamination. Copper can be cold-welded or crimped. Solders can be obtained which have a low thermoelectric voltage when used with copper. Where possible, joints should be close to each other so that they are at the same temperature.

Parts of a circuit can interact through the power supply, which is often common to all the stages. A high current drawn by one stage can reduce the power supply voltage to another stage by an amount equal to the voltage drop across the lead resistance and the internal resistance of the power supply. This is shown in figure 4.4(a). The supply voltage to a section of the circuit, section 2, which does not draw much current, is reduced by $I_1(R_{int} + R_{lead1})$ because of the large current I_1 drawn by a high-power section, section 1.

This effect can be eliminated by using separate power supplies for the sections or separate voltage-stabilizing circuits while keeping the same power supply. The effect can be reduced by making R_{int} as low as possible with a good voltage-stabilization circuit. If possible the feedback for the voltage stabilization should be taken from the power supply connections of the most voltage-sensitive circuit, since this is the voltage to be stabilized. To reduce high-frequency signals flowing between stages along the power supply, a low-pass (or high cut-off) filter can be introduced by placing large capacitors across the power supply very close to each circuit section. The capacitance and the lead and source impedance provides the filter. The effect of the

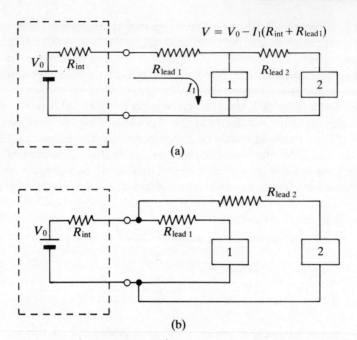

$$V = V_0 - I_1(R_{int} + R_{lead1})$$

(a)

(b)

Fig. 4.4 There may be interaction between circuits due to power supply lead resistance. In circuit (a) the power supply voltage to circuit 2 will be affected by the voltage drop across R_{lead1} due to the current flowing in circuit 1. This effect is reduced in (b) by keeping R_{int} small and using separate power supply connections.

voltage drop along the leads can be reduced by using low-resistance leads and by taking the currents along separate wires, as shown in figure 4.4(b).

The effect of power supply loading can result in interference between different sections of a circuit by direct injection of a spurious signal or in feedback since a large signal in a high-power output stage may reduce the supply voltage and hence affect the gain of a sensitive input stage.

A major source of interference within a circuit is a *parasitic oscillation*. In this effect an amplifier or other active subsection of a circuit exhibits some form of unexpected positive feedback and oscillates. The oscillation may be at a very low amplitude or be at a saturation level. In the latter case the effects are usually large, so that the problem can easily be identified. The parasitic oscillation can affect the circuit by introducing the oscillation signal into other parts of the circuit by the pick-up methods to be described later in this chapter. However, the most common effect is to alter the properties of the oscillating section of the circuit. The presence of the oscillations may simply stop the circuit performing its normal function, although on many simple tests no fault will be found. A low-level oscillation may just change the performance of the circuit, for example by reducing its gain.

The realization that a parasitic oscillation exists and its subsequent detection and correction are not simple. The oscillation may not be visible if the signal on its normal path through the circuit is investigated with an oscilloscope. It may be of very low amplitude or it may be filtered out subsequently. The oscillation may also cease when an oscilloscope or meter lead is applied to the circuit. The frequency of oscillation may be above the range of the oscilloscope or meter. The oscillation may be detectable by induction into a wire held near the circuit and fed to a sensitive meter or oscilloscope. Often a high-amplitude oscillation will dissipate considerable power in the oscillating part of the circuit and the transistor or integrated circuit will reach an unexpectedly high temperature. This can be sensed with a finger placed cautiously near the components (beware of high voltages). Since the feedback for the oscillation is often through stray impedances and the oscillation level is controlled by some non-linearity, both the frequency and the level of oscillation are very dependent on these stray impedances. A parasitic oscillation can often be detected by observing the behavior of the circuit while moving a finger cautiously near the circuit. The finger changes the stray capacitances to earth and between pairs of conductors and also introduces losses into stray capacitances and inductances. The level of oscillation is thus affected.

The source of the instability can be corrected by changing any intentional feedback to increase the stability margins and by screening or changing the layout of the circuit to reduce any feedback through stray impedances.

Since many circuits are sensitive to temperature changes, a high power dissipation in one part of a circuit can cause a temperature rise and hence can affect a sensitive part of the circuit. Care should be taken in the circuit layout to separate the high-power parts of the circuit (such as the output stages and the power supply and regulators) from the sensitive parts (such as the preamplifiers).

Interference sources external to the circuit

Interference may be obtained from all electrical sources external to the circuit. These include extragalactic radio waves, sun spots, fluctuations of the Earth's magnetic field, radio transmitters, the mains power supply, automobile ignition systems, and nearby machinery and circuits. All electrical and electromechanical systems should be considered as sources of interference and the precautions discussed later taken to reduce the effects.

As well as electromagnetic interference, other sources can affect a circuit. Some devices are light-sensitive, so that changes in light level can introduce signals into a circuit. Room lights normally have an intensity that depends to some extent on the instantaneous power dissipated and hence have a component at twice the mains (line) frequency, i.e. at 100 or 120 Hz.

Mechanical vibrations can affect the circuit operation. These effects are called *microphonics* and are caused by vibrations of wires in a magnetic field resulting in an induced e.m.f., by vibrations of conductors causing fluctuations in the stray capacitance between two conductors, and by strains in some dielectrics resulting in voltages developed across the dielectric. The response of a circuit to gentle tapping will test for the presence of microphonics. Circuits should be made small and rigid. The strain sensitivity of some coaxial cables can be reduced in special cables by the choice of the dielectric and the introduction of a conducting coating on the dielectric where it touches the conductors.

CHARACTERIZATION OF NOISE

The mechanisms of noise generation discussed earlier in the chapter for both device noise and interference suggest that the noise signals can be represented by equivalent noise sources, voltage or current generators or a fluctuating resistance (figure 4.5). Although one type of generator may represent the physical process most appropriately, the circuit theorems say that the others may be used to give an alternate equivalent circuit.

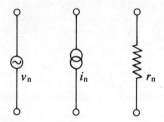

Fig. 4.5 Fluctuations in a circuit may be represented by equivalent noise sources including the voltage, current, and resistance sources, v_n, i_n, and r_n.

If a circuit contains several noise sources they can be reduced to a few equivalent noise sources, as is done in Thévenin's theorem, by adding the noise signal intensities if they are independent sources. Usually the noise of a real amplifier, as in figure 4.6(a), can therefore be reduced to a noise equivalent circuit consisting of a noise voltage generator and a noise current generator at the input of a noiseless amplifier, as shown in figure 4.6(b). The input terminals are usually chosen for the location of the equivalent noise generators since the most important real noise sources are here, where the signal is smallest. Some devices such as detectors may have their equivalent noise sources at the output terminals. If the equivalent noise voltage and

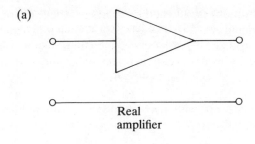

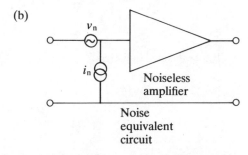

Fig. 4.6 The noise generated in a real amplifier (a) may be represented by the equivalent noise circuit shown in (b) consisting of a noiseless amplifier with a voltage source and a current source at the input.

current generators are, in part, derived from the same single physical noise source, such as a fluctuating resistance, then they will in part fluctuate together. The voltages derived from the sources will be partly correlated and the cross-term in equation (4.3) is not zero, so that the intensities no longer add. In this case some correlation coefficient has to be defined.

For some applications a full equivalent circuit is not known or is unnecessary so that alternative and simpler descriptions of the noise performance are given. Difficulties may also arise in giving a full, but simple, description since the noise spectrum may be very complicated.

The noise intensity at the output or input under specified conditions and bandwidth may be given. Since the signal-to-noise power ratio (S/N) is usually the important quantity, the *noise equivalent power* (NEP), which is the signal power needed to give $S/N = 1$, is sometimes given.

If a noise source has a white, frequency-independent, spectrum but arises from several sources, an equivalent noise voltage source can be specified, $(v_n)_{total}$, developed in series with the circuit Thévenin equivalent resistance R_S, as shown in figure 4.7(a). The noise voltage source includes the thermal noise of R_S, so that this is now noiseless and is present to describe the circuit operation for both the noise and any signal. This noise voltage source can be described simply in terms of an *equivalent noise resistance* R_n. This is the resistance that would be needed to produce this amount of noise at the circuit temperature T_c if it were all thermal noise. Thus from equation (4.4)

$$(\overline{v_n^2})_{total} = 4kT_c R_n \Delta f \tag{4.6}$$

If the noise spectrum is not white, a frequency-dependent noise resistance $R_n(f)$ can be introduced.

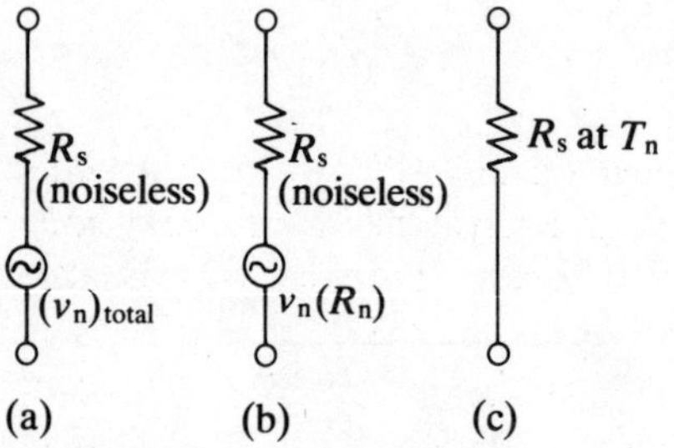

(a)　　　　　　(b)　　　　　(c)

Fig. 4.7 If white noise is generated in a circuit with an equivalent source resistance R_S, then it can be represented as (a) a noiseless resistance R_S in series with an equivalent noise voltage source $(v_n)_{total}$, (b) an equivalent noise resistance R_n or (c) an equivalent noise temperature T_n.

Although the equivalent noise resistance is a convenient simple description of the noise intensity, since it can be rapidly compared with the thermal noise from the actual resistances of the circuit, it is inconvenient because it is not a real resistance that can be used for the circuit analysis of the noise or the signal itself as in figure 4.7(b). This problem can be overcome by defining an *equivalent noise temperature* T_n. Equation (4.4) is again used, but the noise is assumed to be derived from the thermal noise in the real circuit resistance R_S at some temperature T_n so that

$$(\overline{v_n^2})_{total} = 4kT_n R_S \Delta f \tag{4.7}$$

as shown in figure 4.7(c).

In the same way the total white noise current can be described in terms of an equivalent shot noise current generator with an equivalent current I_{eq} flowing. Thus using equation (4.5)

$$(\overline{i_n^2})_{total} = 2eI_{eq} \Delta f \tag{4.8}$$

The *noise figure* NF is a quantity that is also used to describe the noise performance of a circuit. It is defined as the ratio of the signal-to-noise (power) ratios measured at the circuit input and output. Thus

$$NF = \frac{(S/N)_{in}}{(S/N)_{out}}$$

$$= \frac{S_{in}/S_{out}}{N_{in}/N_{out}} = \frac{1/G}{N_{in}/G(N_{in} + N_a)_{in}}$$

$$= 1 + \left(\frac{N_a}{N_{in}}\right)_{in} \geq 1 \qquad (4.9)$$

where G is the power gain and N_a is the noise added by the circuit assuming that it is added as an equivalent power at the input terminals. NF is greater than unity in a real circuit. The quantity is usually expressed in decibels, in which case it is greater than 0 dB.

It should be noted that the noise figure depends on the noise N_{in} being sent into the input terminals, so it is a quantity that depends not only on the circuit itself but also on how it is used. In general, therefore, the noise equivalent circuits are a better description. NF is usually used for microwave and transmission line systems, which always have a characteristic impedance associated with them. In these cases N_{in} is taken to be the thermal noise associated with the characteristic impedance and the noise figure becomes a convenient figure of merit.

NOISE EQUIVALENT CIRCUITS

Noise circuits are analyzed in a similar way to other circuits except that, usually, the noise intensities add rather than the voltages. Consider the addition of two noise voltage sources v_{n1} developed in R_1, and v_{n2} developed in R_2, as shown in figure 4.8(a). If v_{n1} and v_{n2} incorporate all the noise sources, then R_1 and R_2 are now noiseless. For signal analysis R_1 and R_2 are used and v_{n1} and v_{n2} are ideal voltage generators. The combined effect is a single noise voltage source

$$v_n = (\overline{v_{n1}^2} + \overline{v_{n2}^2})^{1/2}$$

in series with a resistance $R_1 + R_2$. If only thermal noise is involved, $\overline{v_n^2} = 4kT(R_1 + R_2)\Delta f$ as is expected since the noise is governed by thermodynamics and therefore does not depend on the way the resistances are actually made up.

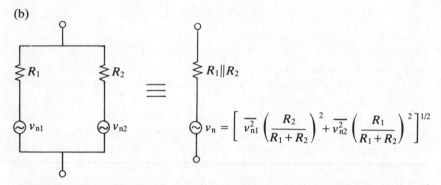

Fig. 4.8 Noise equivalent circuits obey conventional circuit analysis except that the source intensities, rather than amplitudes, add. The Thévenin noise equivalent circuits of a series (a) and a parallel (b) combination of noise sources is shown.

For a combination of parallel resistors, as shown in figure 4.8(b), a single equivalent noise voltage source

$$v_n = \left[\overline{v_{n1}^2}\left(\frac{R_2}{R_1+R_2}\right)^2 + \overline{v_{n2}^2}\left(\frac{R_1}{R_1+R_2}\right)^2 \right]^{1/2}$$

is developed in series with a resistance $R_1 \| R_2 = R_1 R_2/(R_1+R_2)$. This can be derived using the principle of superposition and considering the terminal voltage produced by each voltage source in turn. Again, the simple expected result is obtained if each noise source is the thermal noise source.

The Thévenin and Norton forms of the noise equivalent circuits can be used as shown in figure 4.9. In general $v_n = i_n R$ and if the noise is only thermal noise then

$$\overline{v_n^2} = 4kTR\Delta f$$

$$\overline{i_n^2} = \frac{4kT}{R}\Delta f$$

(4.10)

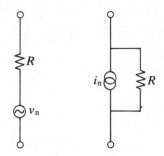

Fig. 4.9   Thévenin or Norton noise equivalent circuits may be used.

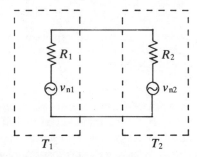

Fig. 4.10   The noise equivalent circuit of source v_{n1}, R_1 at temperature T_1 connected to a source v_{n2}, R_2 at temperature T_2.

Noise equivalent circuits can be more involved when parts of the system are at different temperatures, as shown in figure 4.10. The noise intensity in resistance R_1 at T_1 is $\overline{v_{n1}^2} = 4kT_1R_1\Delta f$ and that in R_2 at T_2 is $\overline{v_{n2}^2} = 4kT_2R_2\Delta f$. The noise voltage developed across R_2 by source v_{n1} is $v_{n1}R_2/(R_1 + R_2)$, so that the total power dissipated in R_2 from a thermal noise source R_1 is

$$P_{1\to 2} = 4kT_1R_1\Delta f\left(\frac{R_2}{R_1+R_2}\right)^2\frac{1}{R_2} = 4kT_1\frac{R_1R_2}{(R_1+R_2)^2}\Delta f$$

Similarly

$$P_{2\to 1} = 4kT_2R_2\Delta f\left(\frac{R_1}{R_1+R_2}\right)\frac{1}{R_1} = 4kT_2\frac{R_1R_2}{(R_1+R_2)^2}\Delta f$$

Thus there is a net electrical energy flow from the hotter to the cooler resistor proportional to the temperature difference. Electrical noise thus provides a mechanism for energy flow down a temperature gradient.

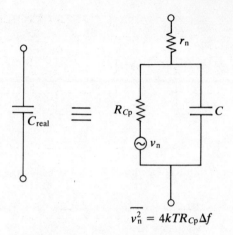

$$\overline{v_n^2} = 4kTR_{Cp}\Delta f$$

Fig. 4.11 The noise equivalent circuit of a real capacitance may include a contribution due to a parallel equivalent loss resistance R_{Cp} with its thermal noise source and a series fluctuating resistance, r_n.

Reactances can be included in noise equivalent circuits. A real component such as a capacitor should be included as its full equivalent circuit. With the reactive part, C, the lossy part is represented as either an equivalent series, R_{Cs}, or parallel, R_{Cp}, resistance. This lossy part will supply thermal noise to be included in any noise equivalent circuit (figure 4.11). There may also be some excess noise, which can be represented as a fluctuating resistance r_n either in series or in parallel and will generate a voltage $v_n = Ir_n$ when a current I flows. The full noise equivalent circuit is shown in figure 4.11.

Consider a noise equivalent circuit of a resistance R generating noise v_n with an ideal capacitor C in parallel with it, as shown in figure 4.12. The noise intensity measured across the circuit is calculated as in other circuits to be

$$4kTR\Delta f \left(\frac{1}{1 + j\omega RC} \right)^2$$

so that the ideal reactive elements filter noise signals and do not add to them.

Consider the simple noise equivalent circuit of an amplifier with independent noise sources v_n and i_n at the input, as shown in figure 4.13(a). It is connected to a source with Thévenin equivalent resistance R_S. From equation (4.9) the noise figure is

$$\mathrm{NF} = 1 + (N_a/N_{in})$$

$$= 1 + \frac{\overline{v_n^2} + R_S^2 \, \overline{i_n^2}}{4kTR_S \Delta f} \tag{4.11}$$

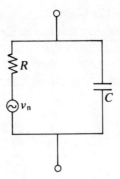

Fig. 4.12 The presence of a reactance in a circuit will not add noise but will modify the spectrum of the measured noise.

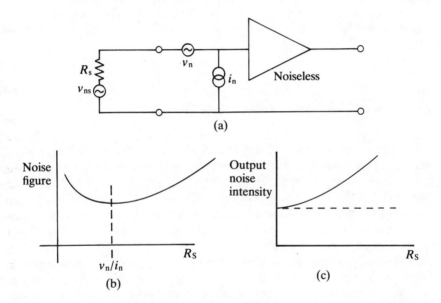

Fig. 4.13 For the simple noise equivalent circuit in (a) the noise figure shown in (b) has a minimum at $R_S = v_n/i_n$ but the output noise intensity shown in (c) increases monotonically as R_S increases.

This has a minimum value at $R_S = v_n/i_n$ as shown in figure 4.13(b). Although this value of R_S minimizes the noise figure, it does not necessarily maximize the important quantity S/N at the output. The noise at the output is

$$G(\overline{v_n^2} + R_S^2\,\overline{i_n^2} + 4kTR_S\Delta f) \qquad (4.12)$$

which increases with R_S as shown in figure 4.13(c) so that, if the signal power is independent of R_S, S/N at the output is largest for $R_S = 0$.

However the S/N at the output can be optimized for given values of R_S, v_n, and i_n by the use of an input transformer with turns ratio n, which will be considered ideal and noiseless. For a signal S generated with a source resistance R_s

$$(S/N)_{output} = \frac{n^2 S}{\overline{v_n^2} + R_S^2 n^4 \overline{i_n^2} + 4kTR_S n^2 \Delta f} \qquad (4.13)$$

since the incoming voltages are increased by n and the impedance R_S is transformed to $n^2 R_S$. This function will have a maximum for some value of n.

These calculations have assumed that the amplifier has an infinite input impedance, so that there is no loading. A finite impedance will load all noise sources similarly so that the basic results will hold. However, the noise of the input resistance then produces a significant contribution at the output and must be included in the noise equivalent circuit.

NOISE IN OPERATIONAL AMPLIFIER CIRCUITS

The operational amplifier is usually a differential amplifier. Its noise equivalent circuit consists of the same generators as the input offset voltage and current generators (chapter 2), but then they were z.f. (d.c.) generators whereas here they are a.c. generators with a specified spectrum. There are noise current generators i_{n-} and i_{n+} on the inverting and non-inverting inputs and a voltage generator e_n. Since this is a differential amplifier, the individual noise voltage generators on the two inputs may be combined to give the single generator e_n and this may be placed in series with either input or across the inputs as desired.

The principles of the noise equivalent circuit can be seen in the inverting amplifier circuit shown in figure 4.14(a). To determine the amplifier circuit noise, the signal source is assumed to have $R_s = 0$ and the signal amplitude is zero. The resistors R_1 and R_2 have thermal noise voltage sources $v_{n1}^2 = 4kTR_1 \Delta f$ and $v_{n2}^2 = 4kTR_2 \Delta f$. The current source i_{n+} is shorted out and does not contribute. The current source i_{n-} and the current v_{n1}/R_1 flow into the summing point and so contribute voltage intensities $\overline{i_{n-}^2} R_2^2$ and $\overline{v_{n1}^2} R_2^2/R_1^2$ at the output. The voltage source v_{n1} could alternately be considered as an input signal amplified by R_2/R_1.

The voltage source v_{n2} is in series in the feedback loop. With no other input signals, the output will follow the input plus this source, so that it appears directly at the output. The differential voltage source e_n can be

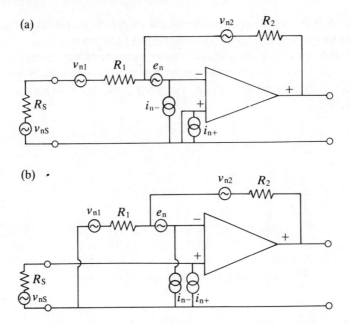

Fig. 4.14 Noise equivalent circuits for an operational amplifier in the inverting (a) and non-inverting (b) configurations.

considered to be in series with the non-inverting input. It is amplified by the amplifier, which is in the non-inverting negative feedback configuration for this signal with voltage gain $(R_1 + R_2)/R_1$. It should be noted that the amplification of this noise source, the *noise gain*, is different from the signal gain of the amplifier, $-R_2/R_1$. This distinction may be very significant for some circuit configurations, especially those involving capacitances since then the amplifier noise spectrum will differ from its gain response and hence the amplifier S/N will be frequency-dependent.

The output noise intensity is thus the sum of all these contributions:

$$\left(\frac{\overline{v_n^2}}{\Delta f}\right)_{\text{output}} = \overline{i_{n-}^2} R_2^2 + 4kTR_1 \left(\frac{R_2}{R_1}\right)^2 + 4kTR_2 + \overline{e_n^2}\left(\frac{R_1 + R_2}{R_1}\right)^2 \quad (4.14)$$

This noise, calculated at the output, can be referred back to the input by dividing by the closed-loop power gain. In this case the power gain is $(R_2/R_1)^2$, to give

$$\left(\frac{\overline{v_n^2}}{\Delta f}\right)_{\text{input}} = \overline{i_{n-}^2} R_1^2 + 4kTR_1 + 4kT\frac{R_1^2}{R_2} + \overline{e_n^2}\left(\frac{R_1 + R_2}{R_2}\right)^2 \quad (4.15)$$

The same principles may be used for more complex circuits.

Note that in the non-inverting feedback configuration shown in figure 4.14(b) the noise of the circuit obtained at the output is identical to equation (4.14) since the source is assumed in both to have zero resistance. A difference arises when the noise is referred back to the input since the power gain is now $[(R_1 + R_2)/R_1]^2$ so that

$$\left(\frac{\overline{v_n^2}}{\Delta f}\right)_{\text{input}} = \overline{i_{n-}^2}\left(\frac{R_1 R_2}{R_1 + R_2}\right) + 4kTR_1\left(\frac{R_2}{R_1 + R_2}\right)^2 + 4kTR_2\left(\frac{R_1}{R_1 + R_2}\right)^2 + \overline{e_n^2}$$

$$= \overline{i_{n-}^2}\left(\frac{R_1 R_2}{R_1 + R_2}\right)^2 + 4kT\left(\frac{R_1 R_2}{R_1 + R_2}\right) + \overline{e_n^2} \qquad (4.16)$$

If there is a source resistance R_S, with its own thermal noise, $\overline{v_{ns}^2} = 4kTR_S\Delta f$, then the inverting amplifier configuration equations (4.14) are modified by changing R_1 to $(R_1 + R_s)$. The power gain from the amplifier input terminals is still $(R_2/R_1)^2$ so that equation (4.15) becomes

$$\left(\frac{\overline{v_n^2}}{\Delta f}\right)_{\text{input}} = \overline{i_n^2}R_1^2 + 4kT\frac{R_1^2}{R_1 + R_S} + 4kT\frac{R_1^2}{R_2} + \overline{e_n^2}\left(\frac{R_1}{R_2}\right)^2\left(\frac{R_1 + R_S + R_2}{R_1 + R_S}\right)^2 \qquad (4.17)$$

In the non-inverting amplifier configuration, a source resistance produces extra terms at the output in equation (4.14)

$$4kTR_s\left(\frac{R_1 + R_2}{R_1}\right)^2 + \overline{i_{n+}^2}R_S^2\left(\frac{R_1 + R_2}{R_1}\right)^2$$

The power gain is still $[(R_1 + R_2)/R_1]^2$ so that equation (4.16) becomes

$$\left(\frac{\overline{v_n^2}}{\Delta f}\right)_{\text{input}} = \overline{i_{n-}^2}\left(\frac{R_1 R_2}{R_1 + R_2}\right)^2 + \overline{i_{n+}^2}R_S^2 + 4kT\left(\frac{R_1 R_2}{R_1 + R_2}\right) + 4kTR_s + \overline{e_n^2}$$

$$(4.18)$$

PREAMPLIFIERS

In an electronic system a signal will not be significantly degraded by noise, except interference, after it has been amplified to a high level such as 1 V. The circuit will therefore be designed so that a low-level signal is amplified as soon as possible. The noise in the first stage of amplification or the initial signal processing stage, such as a current-to-voltage converter, will have most effect on the signal, which is smallest at this point. This stage is usually called the *preamplifier* and must be designed for low noise.

The preamplifier can sometimes be made using standard feedback elements, such as integrated circuit operational amplifiers, but in general better noise performance can be achieved if the first stage of amplification is a discrete device. Such a device can be designed and made for its low-noise performance without the extra constraints imposed by the processing and layout required in the manufacture of an integrated circuit. This discrete amplifier stage may still be included within a feedback loop.

The detailed design of a low-noise preamplifier stage is beyond the scope of this book and specialist texts should be consulted. In general, the best designs can be found in the research literature or are given by device manufacturers. The design involves the choice of the best device, bias condition, and circuit configuration so that the noise performance is optimized consistent with adequate performance in other specifications such as gain, bandwidth, and input impedance. The choice of device is usually determined by the manufacturers' specifications, which give some form of noise equivalent circuit at one or more bias conditions. This device equivalent circuit then has to be incorporated into the full circuit including all the bias components and any feedback effects.

For a given type of device the total noise may be reduced by placing several devices in parallel so that the same input signal is applied to each device and the output signals are added. For bipolar and field-effect transistors, which have a current output, this can be achieved by passing all the output currents through the same load resistance. The signal voltage *amplitudes* add while the noise voltage *intensities* of the device add, so that for n devices the signal-to-noise ratio is improved by $\sqrt{n}$. However, the input leakage or offset current and input impedance are degraded by a factor n and the current noise of all the devices contribute.

For a given type of device the total noise may be reduced if the number of circuit resistors is kept as small as possible and the value of the series

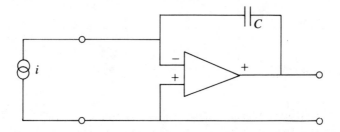

Fig. 4.15 The charge amplifier.

resistances is kept small or parallel resistances are kept large. In this way extra, thermal, noise will not be introduced. In some cases noiseless reactive capacitances can be used for the significant components. For example, the *charge amplifier* shown in figure 4.15 is used for current pulse signals from radiation detectors, which are reversed-biased diodes. The incoming light or ionizing radiation produces a pulse of current from a high-impedance source and the feedback capacitance converts this into an output voltage proportional to the charge. In this and other feedback circuits using capacitors to reduce the thermal noise, precautions have to be taken to remove the effects of z.f. (d.c.) offset and leakage currents.

INTERFERENCE REDUCTION

Interference or 'pick-up' arises when signals from one circuit or source are introduced in some way into the signal circuit of concern. The pick-up usually occurs via some stray impedance and naturally the size, type, and location of the offending impedance is not known. Similarly the source of the interference is often not known. This problem of attempting to eliminate an unwanted effect when most of the information is lacking is often approached by trial and error using a few standard tactics. However, the resolution of the problem can be accelerated if the sources of interference and the ways in which it can be introduced into the signal circuit are well understood.

Confusion and misunderstanding often arise because the problem is not well defined. This is particularly true in the description of a circuit. Consider the simple circuit shown in figure 4.16. The circuit consists of a source and two impedances Z_1 and Z_2 in series. For current continuity, a complete loop is needed and is drawn here. Ambiguity can arise if all parts of the circuit are not shown explicitly, but perhaps different earth points in the circuit are

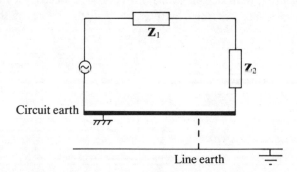

Fig. 4.16 A circuit may have separate circuit and line earths.

indicated with symbols to show that connections should be understood rather than explicitly joined together. For convenience the potential of one point in the circuit is used as a reference potential and all voltages are measured with respect to this point. This is the *circuit earth* (or *circuit ground*) and the choice is arbitrary. However, there is considerable conceptual and practical advantage in choosing for the circuit earth a potential that is an equipotential for both d.c. and a.c. signals and occurs in all parts of the circuit. This is drawn as a (heavy) horizontal line on the circuit diagram and the circuit is drawn with the components arranged roughly with the voltage axis vertical and the signal path from left to right. In the actual circuit, pick-up between different sections of the circuit can be reduced if this circuit equipotential conductor is of low resistance and inductance and physically extends to all sections of the circuit.

The circuit described so far is self-contained and will operate by itself. The circuit earth need have no fixed, constant or well defined relationship to any other 'earth' potential. The potential of the Earth itself, the building, the operator or the third (earth) pin of the mains power supply (line) is a convenient potential in that it is already available. Although a connection between the circuit earth and this *'Earth' earth, mains earth* or *line earth (ground)* is not necessary, a connection is often made with advantage since then there will be fewer potential differences in the total system and hence fewer currents flowing. The connection between these earths should be made in ways to be discussed later in order to prevent the introduction of more pick-up. The symbols used in figure 4.16 for the earths are not universal and other 'earths' may be defined. Separate equipotentials may be used for the signal in the circuit and the main structural components or chassis. Similarly separate conductors may be used for the signal and the power supply in a circuit. These will be joined at one point but are treated as separate 'earths' since the large currents flowing in the power supply circuit earth may cause it to depart from being an equipotential and hence the signal circuit may be affected.

The basic pick-up circuit is shown in figure 4.17. A voltage V_s is

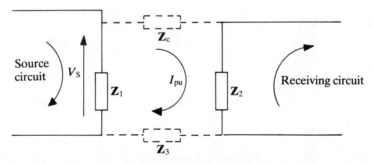

Fig. 4.17 Pick-up between circuits results when a current I_{pu} is driven by the source circuit through an impedance in the receiving circuit.

developed across an impedance $\mathbf{Z}_1$ in the circuit that provides the source of interference. This voltage acts as the driving potential for the pick-up current I_{pu}, which flows via some impedance $\mathbf{Z}_c$ (and perhaps also $\mathbf{Z}_3$) through an impedance $\mathbf{Z}_2$ in the receiving circuit. The requirements for interference are therefore a potential in the source circuit, some coupling circuit, and an impedance in the receiving circuit. Often the earth potentials are the same in all the circuits, so that $\mathbf{Z}_3$ is zero and the arrangement is simpler. Usually the coupling impedance $\mathbf{Z}_c$ is a stray impedance and often $\mathbf{Z}_2$ is also a stray.

Resistive coupling

Pick-up based on the coupling impedance $\mathbf{Z}_c$ being a resistance is not common since good insulation is normally easy to achieve. However at z.f. (d.c.) circuits using a high input resistance voltmeter or amplifier can experience leakage currents from parts of neighboring circuits at a different potential. The severity of the effect will depend on the ratio of the leakage and input resistances. The pick-up current can be intercepted with a passive earthed

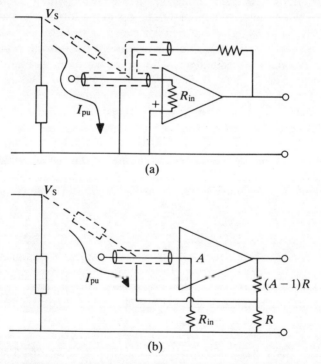

Fig. 4.18 The pick-up current may be intercepted by a passive guard, or screen, as in (a) or an active guard, as in (b), and therefore not flow through a receiving circuit impedance.

guard if the input is a virtual earth, as in figure 4.18(a), or with an active guard, as shown in figure 4.18(b).

Good-quality insulation using clean dry plastics, such as glass-fiber or resin or PTFE (Teflon), and good circuit layout will also reduce the pick-up current. Other forms of resistive pick-up will be discussed later in the section on earth loops.

Capacitive coupling

Capacitive coupling from a source circuit at V_S into a simple receiving circuit is shown in figure 4.19. The receiving circuit consists of a source with its internal impedance R_S and an amplifier with input impedance R_{in}. The coupling capacitance C_c is usually stray since there will always be a capacitance between any two conductors located near each other. The coupling circuit is a

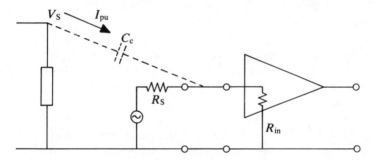

Fig. 4.19   Capacitive coupling causing pick-up.

high-pass CR filter consisting of C_c and the parallel combination of R_S and R_{in}. The effect is therefore most pronounced at high frequencies and in high-impedance circuits.

This type of pick-up can be reduced by decreasing the circuit impedance (R_S, R_{in}) or the coupling capacitance C_c. In practice C_c cannot easily be reduced by increasing the distances between the circuits and improving the layout because the capacitance varies as $\log d$, where d is the typical distance between the conductors. This can be seen in the usual equations for the capacitance between parallel wires or that between a conductor of circular cross-section and a surrounding coaxial conductor (as in a coaxial cable).

The principle and standard method of reducing this type of pick-up is by elimination of the capacitance C_c by the insertion of a low-resistance, and low-inductance, screen between the two conductors, as shown in figure 4.20(a). If this screen is an equipotential, the stray capacitances are now C_{c1} and C_{c2} so that the current from V_S goes harmlessly to earth, if the screen

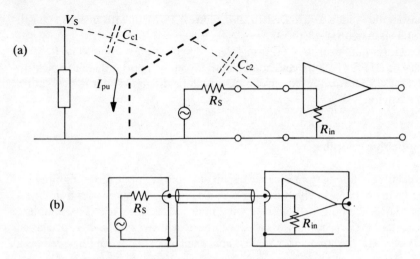

Fig. 4.20 Capacitive coupling can be reduced with a screen shown schematically in (a) and in practical form in (b).

series impedance is negligible. The presence of the screen increases the capacitance of the receiving circuit to earth (by an amount C_{c2}) and hence will reduce the high-frequency performance of the circuit. It is good practice in high-impedance circuits to screen each circuit, the receiving circuit and any likely interfering source circuits, and all conductors, as shown in figure 4.20(b). Metal boxes can be used for the circuit screens and coaxial cable for the connectors. Care should be taken over the details of the earth connections, and this will be expanded later in the discussion of earth loops.

Inductive coupling

A self-inductance coupling two circuits is very unlikely; however, mutual inductive coupling as shown in figure 4.21 is very common. A mutual inductance, or transformer, will exist between two circuits if the magnetic field of one couples into the other. This type of coupling is usually most important where there are coils or long parallel sets of wires or at the line frequency (50 or 60 Hz) at which there are significant currents and magnetic fields. Stray magnetic fields from a power supply transformer core can easily couple into another circuit.

The techniques for reducing inductive pick-up are shown in figure 4.22. A simple technique is by magnetic shielding, as shown in figure 4.22(a). A high-permeability material is placed between the circuits and any magnetic flux will be attracted into the screen and hence not couple the circuits. This solution has considerable practical difficulties and is hence only used in special

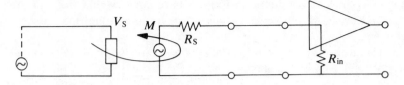

Fig. 4.21 Mutual inductive coupling causing pick-up.

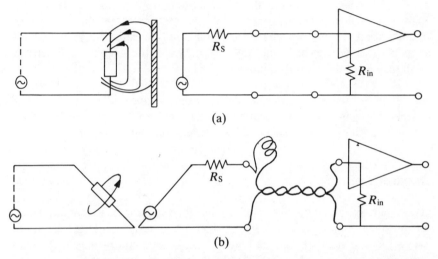

Fig. 4.22 Inductive coupling can be reduced with a magnetic screen shown schematically in (a). In (b) the coupling is reduced by arranging the conductors
to be orthogonal in the two circuits, twisting the conductors and introducing a canceling signal in a pick-up coil.

cases, either to shield a very sensitive part of a circuit (such as a coil) or to
screen a particularly bad interference source (such as a transformer). The
shielding materials are bulky, expensive, and difficult to form into a suitable
shielding enclosure. Some materials show a large decrease in permeability
after the strain necessary to form the enclosure.

The techniques shown in figure 4.22(b) are usually easier to apply.
Magnetic coupling can be reduced to zero by suitable orientation of the source
and receiving loops. This directional property not only eliminates the pick-up
but acts as a method of determining whether the pick-up is magnetic and also
its source. In order to reduce magnetic coupling, wires from different circuits
should not be arranged parallel over long distances. The layout of transformers should be determined experimentally before the components are
finally mounted. In high-quality circuits the transformers should have

magnetic shields. Toroidal transformers have cores wound from magnetic tape and hence have no gaps in their magnetic circuits and so produce less stray flux.

The size of the inductive coupling into a circuit will be approximately proportional to the loop area; all circuits should be compact, with the signal and return currents close and parallel. There will then be little net flux away from the circuit. The sign of the pick-up can be positive or negative, so that half of each circuit should be in one orientation and the other half with the loop in the reverse direction. These requirements can be met most easily by twisting the pair of wires together so that alternate sections are of opposite sign. For high-frequency signals, such wires are unsuitable since the series inductance and shunt capacitance are both high (see chapter 11). In this case coaxial cable can be used, since the current flow in the screen is symmetrical with respect to the central conductor.

If all these techniques fail to reduce the inductive pick-up, it can be cancelled by means of a *balancing inductor* or *'bucking coil'*. A coil is wound in the receiving circuit to act as a secondary coil to the pick-up. It is then oriented until its induced signal cancels the pick-up signal to give a null.

Wave effects

The capacitive and inductive coupling described so far refer to low-frequency or quasi-static pick-up conditions. At high frequencies and large distances, when the distance between the interference source and receiver is greater than about half a wavelength of the electromagnetic wave at the interference frequency, the interference energy should be considered as propagating as an electromagnetic wave and not as either an electrostatic or a magnetostatic field. These wave conditions are discussed more fully in chapter 11.

High-frequency interference problems come under the general terms *radiofrequency interference* (r.f.i.) or *electromagnetic interference* (e.m.i.). The mechanism of coupling is not always unambiguous. As well as the free-space wave propagation implied by the term 'radiofrequency', the signals can propagate as surface or transmission-line modes along the wires or other conductors of the circuit.

The sources of such interference are natural radio sources, such as sun spots and lightning, and man-made sources, such as radio transmitters and sparks and corona discharge in high-voltage equipment. Much equipment will produce, radiate or transmit along wires high-frequency signals. Sources within electronic equipment include switch contacts, fast switching signals in logic circuits (since these contain high-frequency Fourier components), switched-mode power supplies, c.r.o. timebases, and display raster signals.

The receiving circuit will pick up the interference if it acts as an antenna. At these frequencies a short length of wire, a coil or a loop will receive signals.

Even if the interfering signal is at a much higher frequency than the receiving circuit signal, there can be problems. The pick-up energy can upset some circuits; a non-linear element will rectify or demodulate the signal (see chapter 6) so that the lower-frequency envelope of the interference is injected into the receiving circuit.

The basic technique to reduce wave effects is screening. Electromagnetic waves are reflected by perfectly conducting sources. In real conductors the part of the wave that is not reflected is reduced in amplitude as it passes through the conductor because of the eddy currents produced. The electric and magnetic field amplitudes of the wave decrease with distance, z, into the conductor as

$$E = E_0 e^{-z/\delta} \qquad (4.19)$$

where the *skin depth*

$$\delta = (\rho/\pi\mu\mu_0 f)^{1/2} \qquad (4.20)$$

and ρ is the electrical resistivity and μ the magnetic permeability. For copper $\mu \simeq 1$ and $\rho \simeq 1.6 \times 10^{-8}\,\Omega\,\text{m}$, so that $\delta\,(\text{mm}) = 66.2/\sqrt{f}$; thus $\delta = 6.62\,\text{mm}$ at 100 Hz and 0.0662 mm at 1 MHz. A thickness of several skin depths is normally needed.

Copper is very expensive and heavy. A more economical screen can be made from tin-plated steel, which has a higher permeability. Although the resistivity is higher, the material is cheap and hence a greater thickness can be afforded. It can be soldered to make good joints. All joints should have low resistance along the whole length. Removable joints can be made using metal mesh or flexible conducting plastic gaskets. Holes can be left, although some penetration of the field will occur. The wave attenuates as it propagates through the hole as if it were propagating along a waveguide beyond cut-off. Thus holes should have a diameter much less than a wavelength.

Since high-frequency waves can propagate along wires in transmission-line modes or as surface waves, all leads into and out of a circuit susceptible to, or producing, r.f.i. must contain low-pass (or high cut-off) filters. Such filter units containing series inductors (lossy) and capacitors to ground are readily available for single leads and for installation on power supply leads. Care should be taken in installation since the details of the earth connections are important. High-frequency signals on single wires can be reduced by placing lossy ferrite beads on the wire to increase the high-frequency impedance and loss.

Unwanted signals and r.f.i. surface waves can be filtered from signal leads, and earth loops (see later) can be broken by sending signals over a section of their route, for example into or out of a screened enclosure, coded as binary pulses of light propagating inside a glass fiber. Optical fiber systems are available and consist of an input converter from the electrical signal to pulses of light and an output converter to change the light back to an electrical signal. Bandwidths of many megahertz are readily obtainable.

Earth loops

Earth (or *ground*) *loops* are frequently assumed to be the mechanism of pick-up, although this is often a statement of dogma or an expression of frustration and disbelief in the application of rational laws of nature rather than a result of experimental proof. The earth loop is a special form of the resistive or inductive pick-up processes discussed earlier.

An example of resistive interference was described near the beginning of the chapter and shown in figure 4.4. Resistive coupling can also take place between two circuits, or two parts of the same circuit, as shown in figure 4.23.

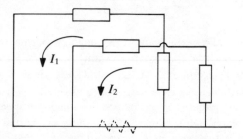

Fig. 4.23 Coupling between two circuits through a common impedance.

The two circuits are referenced to the same earth but are badly arranged so that the earth return currents I_1 and I_2 from the two circuits pass through a common physical part of the earth conductor. If the earth conductor were a perfect equipotential, no problems would arise. However, any non-zero resistance or inductance in the conductor allows a current flowing in one circuit to generate a voltage in the other circuit.

The basic earth loop circuit is shown in figure 4.24. The source and receiver are connected by a pair of wires. The circuit by itself will work, but often the source or receiver is 'earthed' or connected to some other reference point because of the requirements of the circuit components. For example, the source may be some device such as a transducer, which is physically and electrically connected to a building at the real earth potential. Similarly, the receiver may need to be connected to the real earth. The earth in question may not be the real earth but just another reference potential or equipotential in the system such as a chassis or equipment rack. Whatever the cause, the result is a low-impedance circuit loop. Currents flowing in the circuit earth lead will inject pick-up signals into the circuit if they pass through any stray resistance or inductance in this earth wire. The currents may be earth return currents from other circuits taking this path to give resistive pick-up as just described. However, the main earth loop problem is that large currents can be induced in the loop by transformer action. Note that two conditions are needed, an earth loop and a series impedance in the circuit earth.

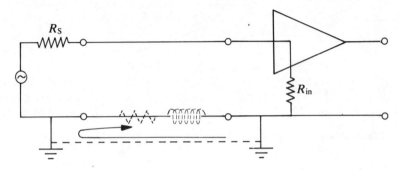

Fig. 4.24 The basic earth loop circuit.

Earth loops can be eliminated by insuring that only one earth connection is made. It was emphasized earlier that a self-contained complete circuit does not need connection to any other reference potential or earth. In general, no earth connections should be made unless the circuit will not work without them. Where possible, only sources and detectors that have no physical earth connections should be used. The circuit should have a high insulation from earth and the power supply should be isolated from earth either through a transformer or by the use of batteries. If the circuit needs a connection to earth to reduce capacitive pick-up by screening action, then the connection is usually best made at the point of the circuit where the signal is smallest.

Within a circuit, pick-up loops can exist easily since the separate sections are often powered from the same supply and hence there is a common earth connection. Also the signal is passed between sections along a coaxial pair of wires to provide another earth connection and hence a loop. The signal earth is normally cut at one point so that the signal wire still has a coaxial earthed shield round it to reduce capacitive pick-up, as shown in figure 4.25.

Earth loop correction

If the layout of the circuit and its earths cannot be improved to eliminate the earth loop, then the problem can be remedied by several techniques involving a special break in the circuit earth connection or a balancing of the circuit so

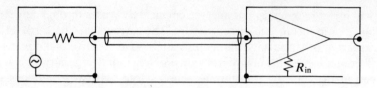

Fig. 4.25   A screen with no earth loop.

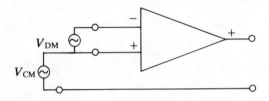

Fig. 4.26   A differential amplifier with differential-mode, V_{DM}, and common-mode, V_{CM}, signals.

that the signal becomes a differential-mode signal rather than a common-mode signal.

The distinction between these modes is shown in relation to a differential input amplifier in figure 4.26. The earth connection becomes less important if the signal is transmitted as a differential-mode voltage V_{DM} along a pair of wires separated from earth and with identical properties with respect to earth. In this balanced form, any pick-up will occur equally in each of the wires and hence produce no net differential-mode signal. The signal in each lead, with reference to the earth, is the common-mode voltage V_{CM}. If the signal level is high, such balancing is not so important and this amplifier converts a differential-mode voltage to a common-mode voltage.

Since the signal is V_{DM} and interference is probably mainly V_{CM}, the quality of the amplifier or similar circuit in reducing interference is given by the *common-mode rejection ratio* (CMRR), which is the ratio, V_{CM}/V_{DM}, of the voltages necessary to produce the same output amplitude. This ratio is frequency-dependent and is often expressed as an intensity or power ratio in decibels. In a symmetrical and well balanced system, the ratio should be very large and values of 100 dB are often achieved.

Breaking earth loops

The earth connection in a circuit can be broken although the signal is still transmitted. Two methods are shown in figure 4.27. An *opto-coupler* can be used to break the electrical circuit as shown in figure 4.27(a). The signal is

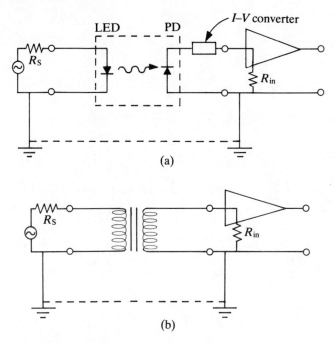

(a)

(b)

Fig. 4.27 Earth loops may be broken with an optical coupler as shown in (a) or a transformer shown in (b).

converted into a light intensity by means of a light-emitting diode (LED). The light is transmitted over a short distance and received by a photodiode (PD) or phototransistor. These devices can be obtained in compact packages, although the same principle is involved in long optical fiber links. Often the driver and receiving circuits are included in the package. Since special circuits are needed to make the signal transfer linear, opto-couplers are used mainly for digital signals. Since high-voltage isolation up to several kilovolts can also be achieved, opto-couplers are available to transmit signals between parts of a system separated by large z.f. (d.c.) voltages.

The transformer shown in figure 4.27(b) can also be used to break an earth loop. It is linear, but transformers usually have only a restricted frequency range. The several properties of the transformer were described in chapter 1. Here its value is that it has a very high rejection of a common-mode signal. That is, a voltage (relative to earth) applied simultaneously to both ends of the primary winding will produce no signal in the secondary. This is because no current will flow, the core will not experience any change in magnetization, and hence no e.m.f. will be induced in the secondary.

In practice, transformers and opto-couplers do not produce ideal common-mode rejection because of capacitive coupling. A common-mode signal on the primary, derived perhaps from an earth loop, will couple to the

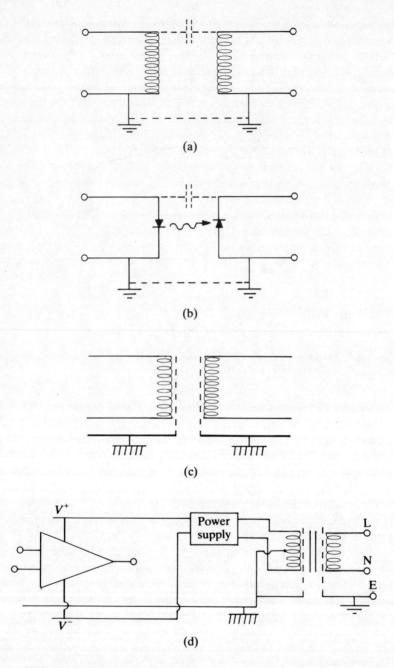

Fig. 4.28 Capacitive coupling shown in (a) and (b) can reduce the effectiveness of transformers and optical couplers in reducing pick-up. The primary and secondary electrostatic screens shown in (c) and (d) can reduce the common-mode signal transfer.

secondary through the stray capacitance shown in figures 4.28(a) and (b). This capacitance can be reduced by electrostatic screening, as discussed earlier. The opto-coupler screen must allow light to pass, and a transformer screen must be complete but must not be connected so as to form a complete circuit round the core or it will act as a secondary winding and currents will flow in it. The screen is connected to some good earth. However, since the presence of two distinct earths at separate potentials is the problem in an earth loop better common-mode isolation can be achieved with two screens connected to the earths of the primary and secondary circuits, as shown in figure 4.28(c).

The use of transformer isolation in the signal circuit is restricted by the limited bandwidth possible. The most common use of transformer coupling is to isolate the circuit earth from the mains (or line) power supply earth, as shown in figure 4.28(d). A circuit with a circuit earth isolated from the real earth potential can operate with any potential between these earths. Such a circuit isolated by transformer coupling or by the use of self-contained battery power supply is said to be 'floating'.

Balancing earth loops

If the basic cause of the earth loop cannot be eliminated, or the earth lead broken, improvements can be made by balancing the circuit so that only the difference between the effects of two earth loops affects the circuit.

A floating circuit is shown in figure 4.29. There will exist some leakage impedance Z_L to earth and some input lead series resistances R_1 and R_2. Any circulating earth loop currents, I_1 and I_2, will be different because the geometry and impedances in the loops will be different. Also the induced voltages in the leads will differ because the currents flow through different impedances R_1 and R_2. If both inputs are made equal then the same potential

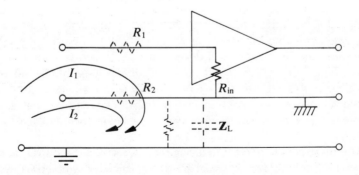

Fig. 4.29 An amplifier with unbalanced inputs.

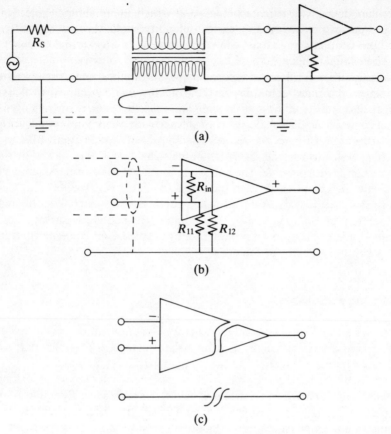

Fig. 4.30 A common-mode signal, such as that introduced by an earth loop, can be reduced by (a) a balancing transformer, (b) an instrumentation amplifier or (c) an isolation amplifier.

will be introduced into each lead to give no net input signal from the earth loops.

A simple technique to balance the input circuits is to use a *balancing transformer* or *balun*, as shown in figure 4.30(a). An earth loop current flowing in either input lead will develop a voltage across the transformer primary. The 1:1 transformer will induce an equal voltage into the other lead to give no net effect into the circuit. Above a few kilohertz the mutual inductance between the inner conductor and the screen of a coaxial cable dominates the series resistance and acts as a balun to reduce earth loop problems.

The principal method for reducing the effects of earth loops is to make the signal a differential-mode signal in a well balanced or symmetrical system. The signal is carried on a shielded pair of wires and the amplifier has a high input impedance with balanced inputs and a high common-mode rejection ratio, as shown in figure 4.30(b). Such an amplifier is called an *instrumentation amplifier*. It usually has a fixed gain and is not used with external feedback, since this would unbalance it.

The good properties of the instrumentation amplifier and a break in the earth connection are combined in the *isolation amplifier* shown in figure 4.30(c). Here opto- or transformer coupling is used between two stages of the amplifier and the power to the two halves is supplied through isolating transformers. Such amplifiers are expensive and of limited bandwidth and hence are only use for special applications.

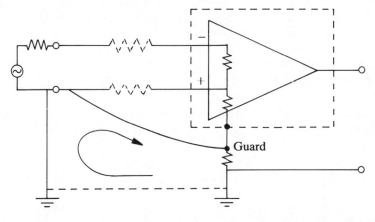

Fig. 4.31 The effect of an earth loop can be reduced with a guard circuit.

A *guard* is sometimes used to reduce the effects of an earth loop. An extra screen is placed round the circuit, as shown in figure 4.31. This increases the resistive and capacitive impedance to earth, but the main advantage is that a low-impedance lead can be connected to the earth of the source to provide an easy earth loop path and divert the current away from the input circuit itself. If such a connection cannot be made, the guard should be connected to the lower-potential input terminal.

FILTERING SIGNAL AND NOISE

The signal-to-noise ratio (S/N) can often be improved by filtering. The approach taken and the method used will depend on the relative distribution of the signal and noise in both frequency and time. If the signal and noise occur mainly at distinct and different frequencies, the signal can be passed by filters or the noise can be rejected by filters. Similarly, if the signal and noise occur mainly at distinct and different times, the signal can be passed or the noise rejected by switches.

Frequency-domain filtering

Filters can be used to separate signal and noise if the spectra are different. This is shown in figure 4.32. Intrinsic noise is usually white and excess noise has a large continuous low-frequency component whereas interference signals usually have a restricted spectrum perhaps at both a fundamental range and harmonics. In these cases the approach should be to design filters to pass the signals. For simpler spectra the low-pass, high-pass, and bandpass passive filters described in chapter 1 or the active filters described in chapter 2 and appendix 6 can be used.

A signal such as a square wave, with a narrow bandwidth at a fundamental frequency and also harmonics, requires a more complex comb filter. This can be achieved by a digital filter or modulation methods as described in chapters 6, 7, and 9.

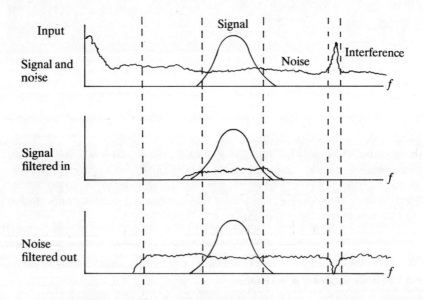

Fig. 4.32 The spectra of the signal and the noise in a circuit are usually different. Filtering can improve the signal-to-noise ratio by passing only the frequencies containing the signal or rejecting those frequencies containing a large amount of noise.

The spectrum of the signal should be carefully considered. Although the signal may be a good sine wave, a non-zero bandwidth will be needed since the signal amplitude has to be changed at some time. In general, a bandwidth of $1/\pi\tau$ Hz is needed if the time constant of the amplitude change is τ. This point is made more fully in chapter 6.

For sine and square waves with slowly changing amplitudes, the phase-sensitive detector (PSD) or switched capacitance filters described in chapter 9 are powerful techniques.

For a given signal spectrum and noise spectrum, there is an *optimal filter* characteristic or voltage transfer function which can be calculated from the spectra (see appendix 5). However, such sophistication is needed only in very specialized cases since simple calculations will usually give adequate results.

Interference signals often occur at discrete frequencies such as the line frequency (50 or 60 Hz) and harmonics of this frequency. The second harmonic (100 or 120 Hz) is present, for example, on power supplies after full-wave rectification. In these cases a good approach is to filter out the noise with a narrow-bandwidth rejection filter. Such a filter with perfect rejection at one frequency is called a *notch filter*. The rejection is complete because the circuit is basically a bridge with a frequency-sensitive null.

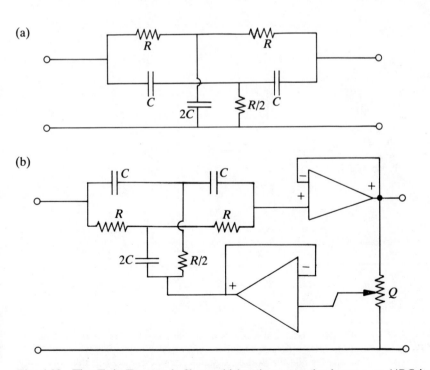

Fig. 4.33 The Twin-Tee notch filter, which rejects completely at $\omega_0 = 1/RC$ in passive symmetrical (a) and active (b) forms.

The most commonly used passive notch filter is the symmetrical Twin-Tee filter shown in figure 4.33(a). It is one of a class of filters with this two-path geometry and has total rejection at $\omega_0 RC = 1$ and $Q = 1/3$. Note that its performance is sensitive to the source and load impedances as well as the matching and accuracy of the components. An active notch can be made using a passive Twin-Tee filter in a feedback circuit, as shown in figure 4.33(b). The rejection frequency is the same but Q is considerably higher. At low and high frequencies the circuit approximates to a voltage follower since the voltages at the three terminals of the filter are the same. Near the rejection frequency, the attenuation is enhanced by the negative feedback.

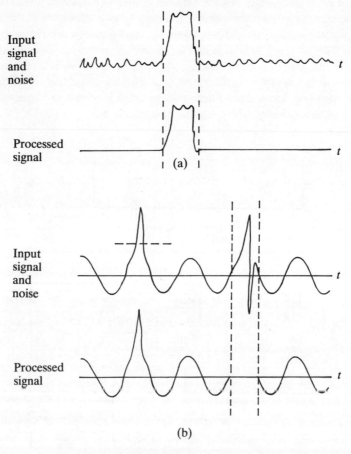

Fig. 4.34   If a signal only occurs at specific times while the noise occurs at all times, the signal-to-noise ratio can be enhanced by only allowing the whole signal to be received while the desired signal is present as in (a). If the noise only occurs at specific times, it may be reduced by clipping it or removing both signal and noise during the times that the noise is present as in (b).

Filter configurations that can be tuned or trimmed conveniently can be made. An easily tuned modification to the symmetrical Twin-Tee filter given here can be constructed by replacing the resistance $R/2$ by a potentiometer and placing the earth connection to the wiper of this potentiometer rather than to the junction of the components $R/2$ and $2C$.

Time-domain filtering

If the signal and noise occur mainly at different times, the signal-to-noise ratio can be improved by conditioning the combined signal differently at different times. If the signal occurs at only certain times whereas the noise is continuous, the circuit can be made continuous only during the *window* when the signal is present. The noise at other times is excluded. This is shown in figure 4.34(a) and is the principle of the boxcar integrator described in chapter 9.

Alternately interference noise has often been added to the signal as in figure 4.34(b). In this case the high amplitude of the signal plus noise can be clipped by a non-linear network or the signal and noise can be eliminated by some switching circuit for the period of the interfering signal if this can be identified. In this latter the signal is '*blanked*'.

The improvement in the signal-to-noise ratio by signal averaging is discussed in chapter 9.

FURTHER READING

A. Ambrozy, *Electronic Noise*, McGraw-Hill (1982).

K. G. Beauchamp and C. K. Yuen, *Data Acquisitions for Signal Analysis*, Allen and Unwin (1980).

M. J. Buckingham, *Noise in Electronic Devices and Systems*, Wiley (1983).

F. R. Connor, *Noise*, Edward Arnold (1982).

B. A. Gregory, *An Introduction to Electrical Instrumentation*, Macmillan (1981).

B. Jones, *Circuit Electronics for Scientists*, Addison-Wesley (1974).

H. W. Ott, *Noise Reduction Techniques in Electronic Systems*, Wiley (1976).

A. Van der Ziel, *Noise: Sources, Characterisation, Measurement*, Prentice-Hall (1970).

L. Wiechert, 'The avoidance of electrical interference in instruments', *J. Phys. E* **16** (1983) 1003–12.

5 DIGITAL CIRCUITS

INTRODUCTION

Most natural quantities, and hence experimental variables, can take any value within a restricted range. The electrical signals representing these quantities should reasonably be *analog signals*. Then, within the circuit the analog electrical signal, usually a voltage, is a continuous function of the experimental quantity and can take any value limited only by the current resolution or signal-to-noise ratio (figure 5.1). There can be considerable advantage, however, in representing the variable by a *digital signal*, in which the electrical variable can only take a few discrete values (figure 5.1). Each sequence or combination of these discrete values, or digital signals, will represent a particular value of the experimental quantity. With only a finite number of these signal pulses available to represent each value, there will be a limit to the resolution, or fineness, to which the value can be described. The theoretical limit to this resolution is the same for both analog and digital representations of a signal, as described by the information theory in chapter 6, but practical limitations usually favor the use of one or the other.

The most common form of digital system is the *binary logic* system, which has only two signal variable levels that are referred to as 0–1 or off–on or

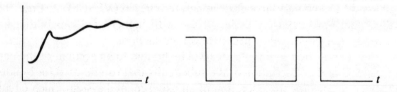

Fig. 5.1 Information may be presented as a continuous analog signal or as a sequence of discrete digital pulses.

false–true. If the signals are voltages and the voltage corresponding to 1 is higher than that corresponding to 0, then the notation is called *positive logic*. Similarly for *negative logic* there is a lower voltage level for the 1 than the 0. Positive logic is normally used and will be used for the examples here. The absolute voltage levels involved depend on the type or family of logic elements or circuits used and will be described later.

The advantage of the digital system is that, provided the signal-to-noise ratio is larger than unity, or alternately the noise is less than the difference between the levels of the two binary states, the noise can be removed by resetting the signal voltage levels to the appropriate designated values. The signal-to-noise ratio need not therefore be degraded as the signal is processed. A two-level system gives the greatest advantage in this respect.

Once the signal is in digital form it can be processed, manipulated, and stored using the powerful techniques of the digital computer. Many of the circuit techniques and components developed for number processing by computers can be used for signal processing. There is considerable advantage in converting an analog signal into digital form as early in the system as possible provided that sufficient signal resolution and bandwidth can be retained. Some digital instruments, such as digital voltmeters (DVM) (see chapter 8), can have superior performance over the equivalent analog instrument. Although digital circuits have advantages, there are inherent limitations in resolution, bandwidth, and speed of processing, so that analog techniques are needed for low-level, precise, and high-frequency circuits as well as for many feedback and control systems and for interfacing to transducers. Normally therefore the part of the system closest to the experimental variable will be in analog form, and the output of the system where the signal has to be converted into numerical data will be in digital form.

The design of large digital systems, such as computers, microprocessors or digital processing instruments, is a specialist occupation and beyond the scope of this book. Few people will be involved with such design but many will need to use these circuits and incorporate them into experimental systems. Since digital circuits are basically on–off switches with a few fundamental units repeated a large number of times, they can be easily made into large integrated circuits. These digital circuits are compact, cheap, and very powerful. Such circuits are classified roughly according to the number of components as medium-scale integrated circuits (MSI), large-scale integrated circuits (LSI), and very large-scale integrated circuits (VLSI). With time, they will become progressively easier to use with higher-level capabilities and functions that can be controlled by fewer instructions.

The description in this chapter will be limited to an account of the basic terms used and a description of the subcircuits that can be used for building ancillary circuits for the operation of an experimental system. Such circuits may be used for switching, counting, operating lights, relays and alarms, and in particular for making interface units between analog and digital circuits.

Coupling computers to the real, analog world is important. For many of the more complicated operations, a suitable integrated circuit usually exists and the introduction given here should enable its operation and its mode of use to be understood in conjunction with the manufacturers' description. In chapters 8, 9, and 10 the principles of operation of digital instruments and the interfaces between analog and digital systems will be described in more detail.

BASIC LOGIC

Binary signals operate according to simple classifiable rules and hence digital circuits are sometimes called *logic circuits*. In the binary system there are only two signal levels possible, corresponding to levels 0 and 1. All information, numbers, letters, voltage readings, instructions, etc., have to be expressed in some way in terms of 0s and 1s. There are many ways in which this can be done in order to provide a unique combination of 0s and 1s for each message. These methods are called *codes*, and usually standard agreed codes are used. These often have a simple mathematical relationship between the numerical message and the binary number.

Table 5.1 tabulates some common codes for numbers. The first sixteen numbers are shown. It should be noted that the numbers start at 0 so that 15 is the sixteenth number. This convention often causes confusion. In the first

Table 5.1 Some common codes for numbers.

Decimal	Binary	Octal	Hexa-decimal	Binary coded decimal			
	8421	(three bit)	(four bit)	Excess 3	5211	Gray	2421 p
0	0000	00	0	0011	0000	0000	0000 1
1	0001	01	1	0100	0001	0001	0001 0
2	0010	02	2	0101	0011	0011	0010 0
3	0011	03	3	0110	0101	0010	0011 1
4	0100	04	4	0111	0111	0110	0100 0
5	0101	05	5	1000	1000	0111	1011 0
6	0110	06	6	1001	1001	0101	1100 1
7	0111	07	7	1010	1011	0100	1101 0
8	1000	10	8	1011	1101	1100	1110 0
9	1001	11	9	1100	1111	1101	1111 1
10	1010	12	A				
11	1011	13	B				
12	1100	14	C				
13	1101	15	D				
14	1110	16	E				
15	1111	17	F				

column the usual digital numbers to the base 10 are shown. The numbers to the base 2, pure binary, are shown in the second column. The pure binary system has *binary digits* or *bits*, 0 or 1, starting from the right or *least significant bit* (1 s.b.) and increasing to the left or *most significant bit* (m.s.b.). The bits have significance according to the power of 2 represented by the position 3, 2, 1, 0 for four bits to give weighting of the bits in each position of 8, 4, 2, 1, as shown at the top of the column. Pure binary numbers will increase in number of bits indefinitely as the number becomes larger. This is inconvenient in the same way that large decimal numbers become inconvenient to handle as the number of digits increases. For use in a computer the problem is more than inconvenient since the computer involves a logical structure with capacity of a fixed number of bits for each operation, and it will not know how many bits are expected for each number. One solution is to use the scientific notation 3.46×10^6, etc. Another method is to use the binary coded decimal notation described shortly.

Although numbers to the base 2 and base 10 are either logical or familiar, some digital systems use other bases such as 8 (octal) or 16 (hexadecimal). These are shown in the next two columns. Letters A to F are used in the hexadecimal system to provide the lacking symbols above 9. In the octal system the symbols 8 and 9 are not used. It can be seen that octal numbers are equivalent to three-bit sequences and hexadecimal numbers are four-bit sequences.

To enable a person who is naturally used to the decimal system to interact with a digital system, the input and output signals will need to be in digital form. If the number and complexity of the operations is not large, it can be convenient to keep the decimal form present throughout the digital circuit between the decimal input and the decimal output. This is done using the *binary coded decimal* (BCD) notation. Each decimal digit is encoded in binary form. Thus $(82)_{10}$ becomes $(8)_{10}(2)_{10}$ and then $(1000)_2(0010)_2$ in BCD. Four-bit pure binary is used for each digit in this example. This method also simplifies some operations since four-bit units are used throughout, rather than the variable length units of pure binary. This system is inherently slightly inefficient since six of the sixteen possible combinations of a four-bit unit are not used for the numbers.

To encode the alphabet, punctuation marks, and common statements and commands such as 'carriage return', 'line feed', and 'bell' used on tele-types, an extension of this form is used. It is the American Standard Code for Information Interchange (ASCII) or ISO-7 code. It has eight bits of which seven are used to give 128 combinations. It is given in tables 10.1 and A1.1.

In most systems the information will be exchanged in standard groups of bits. In the BCD number system a standard group is of four bits. In the ASCII code it is eight bits. This group of bits may include a number and some identifying information such as its sign or exponent. Such a group is called a *byte*. Byte lengths are often eight, sixteen or thirty-two bits.

Although the form of BCD based on the pure binary number system is most common, there are many other possible ways of uniquely encoding the ten digits into a four-bit byte. Four examples are shown in table 5.1. The 'Excess 3' code is produced by adding binary 3 to the '8421' pure binary code. It has a more equal use of the symbols 0 and 1 and this can be shown to lead to fewer errors. However, its main advantage is that it exhibits complementarity. The pairs of digits that add up to 9 are complementary in 0 and 1. Thus 2 and 7 are 0101 and 1010. Thus subtraction of a digit from 9 can be performed just by changing all the 0s to 1s and all the 1s to 0s. Subtraction is not a simple operation using BCD and the use of this code can make it easier. Also the first (m.s.b.) bit is 0 for numbers up to 4 and 1 for numbers above. Thus if two digits are to be added, the presence of 1s in both m.s.b. locations indicates that there will be a digit to 'carry' into the next decimal column. The '5211 weighted' BCD code also has this property for the m.s.b. It is also a code to the base 5 since the next three bits repeat in sequence for 0 to 4 and 5 to 9.

The 'Gray' code is one of a series of codes used for counting or sequencing. In some operations such as counting passing objects or counting the angle of rotation of a shaft, the numbers will occur in a regular known sequence. In the '8421 weighted' code all the bits change in the transition from 7 to 8 but only one changes in the transition from 0 to 1. In some cases the former operation may take longer than the latter. The maximum speed is thus limited by one of the counts (here 7 to 8). The Gray code is arranged so that only one bit changes between each number increment and each count thus takes the same, minimum time.

The '2421 weighted' code is simply another weighted code. There has to be some convention as to which '2' is used first. In the example given here there is a fifth bit 'p'. This five-bit code is one of a series that can detect errors in transmission. The p bit is a parity bit, which is added so that the total number of 1s in the five bits is always odd. If the five-bit byte is now transmitted, the receiver can check if an error has been made in transmission (a 0 to 1 or a 1 to 0) by verifying the parity, or just counting the number of 1s. On detecting an error a request can be made for another transmission. This error-detecting scheme only works if the error rate is low so that a maximum of only one error is likely in every five bits. More parity bits can be added and with sufficient bits, each recording the parity of different combinations of the signal byte, the code can be made to be both error-detecting and error-correcting, in that the bits in error can be identified by the receiver.

GATES

The basic circuit element in a digital, or logic, circuit is the *gate*. This is a circuit unit with one or more binary input terminals and a binary output terminal. The principles can be illustrated using the two-input gates. The discussion will include one-input gates as special cases and the argument can be easily extrapolated to multi-input gates. Since the only input and output signals possible are those voltages corresponding to logic 0 and logic 1, the behavior of each gate can be described by the output signals produced for each possible combination of input signals. Such a table of all possibilities is called a *truth table*.

Consider the gate shown in figure 5.2(a) with inputs A, B and output X. There are four possible input combinations shown by the four rows. There are $2^4 = 16$ possible combinations of 0,1 for the X column and hence 16 possible two-input gates exist.

Some of the more common possibilities are shown in figure 5.2(b). The first two X columns have either 0 or 1 as the output signal. These are not interesting and indicate perhaps an unresponsive gate. The output $X = A$ is a one-input gate since the signal on input B is irrelevant. This is the *identity gate*, which is used usually as a buffer or unity amplifier. The gate $X = B$ is similar. The outputs $X = \bar{A}$ (NOT A) or $X = \bar{B}$ (NOT B) represent one-input gates in which the output is the opposite of the input. This is the *inversion gate* or *NOT gate*.

The *AND gate* gives an output (logic signal 1) if both A AND B have inputs (1), $X = A.B$. If this is combined with an inversion at the output so that there is no output (0) only if A AND B have inputs (1), the *NAND gate* (NOT AND) is obtained, $X = \overline{A.B}$.

The *OR gate* gives an output (1) if there is an input (1) at either A or B or both ($X = A + B$), and the *NOR gate* has an inversion of the output signal, $X = \overline{A + B}$. Another similar gate is the *EXCLUSIVE OR gate*, which gives an output (1) if either A or B has an input (1) but excludes the condition with inputs on *both* A and B.

The symbols for these gates used in the British and US standards are shown. In both a circle at any junction between an input or output lead and the body of the symbol indicates inversion of the signal.

Gates produce an output that depends directly on the input signals at that time. Although any real gate will have some finite speed of response, the output is ideally an instantaneous response to the inputs. A circuit with such a behavior is called *combinatorial*. This may be contrasted with a *sequential* circuit in which the output depends on the previous values of the inputs as well as the instantaneous values; it has some form of memory of the past.

COMBINATORIAL LOGIC

A combinatorial circuit has a direct response and can be analyzed with theorems to construct equivalent circuits rather like Thévenin's theorem for

(a)

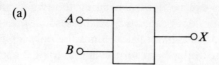

Inputs		Output X									
A	B		A	B	$\bar{A}$	$\bar{B}$	AND	NAND	EXCL. OR	OR	NOR
0	0	0	1	0	0	1	1	0	1	0	0	1
0	1	0	1	0	1	1	0	0	1	1	1	0
1	0	0	1	1	0	0	1	0	1	1	1	0
1	1	0	1	1	1	0	0	1	0	1	1	0

(b)

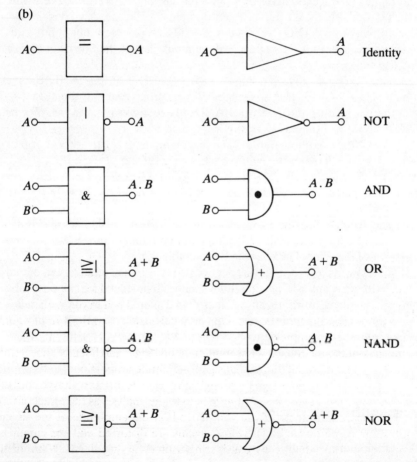

Fig. 5.2 The basic two-input gates.

linear circuits. It is possible to construct a circuit to give a particular truth table in many different ways and such circuits will be functionally equivalent. These possible circuits may include one with the least number of gates and others made from only certain types of basic gates. A circuit can be reduced to its simplest form, or its constituent gates can be changed, according to certain specific rules. This reduction can be done by several methods using Boolean algebra, Venn diagrams or Karnaugh maps. For a description of these techniques, detailed texts should be consulted. A few practical points are introduced here. In general, an optimal solution is rarely needed in research circuits unless maximum speed is required or there is a strong urge for elegance. However, some knowledge of the basic techniques is required in order to complete a circuit at all.

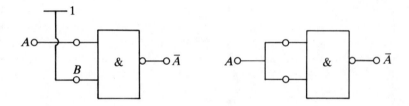

Fig. 5.3   Two methods of connecting a two-input NAND gate to act as a NOT gate.

Some gates are commonly made and easy to obtain. These are usually the identity, NOT, AND, OR, NAND, and NOR gates. Some gates can be made from others. For example, in figure 5.3 there are shown two ways of using a NAND gate to construct an inverting gate. The negation gates NOT, NAND, and NOR are more valuable for constructing other gates, and each gate can be constructed from suitable combinations of either NAND or NOR gates. A valuable pair of identities, called *De Morgan's relations*, allow transformations to be calculated. These are

$$\overline{A + B} = \bar{A} . \bar{B} \qquad (5.1)$$
$$\overline{A . B} = \bar{A} + \bar{B}$$

Other relationships exist. An obvious identity is

$$\bar{\bar{A}} = A \qquad (5.2)$$

If an inverting gate is placed on each input and output connection, the circuit operation changes from positive logic to negative logic and a simple calculation shows that in changing from positive to negative logic, or the reverse, the gate function changes, so that

$$\text{in positive logic} \quad \begin{aligned} \text{NOR} &\equiv \text{NAND} \\ \text{NAND} &\equiv \text{NOR} \\ \text{OR} &\equiv \text{AND} \\ \text{AND} &\equiv \text{OR} \end{aligned} \quad \text{in negative logic}$$

In principle, all combinatorial identities can be proved by a comparison of the truth tables. However, this method may not always be practicable in complicated circuits.

Combinatorial circuits are used largely as ancillary circuits to more complex systems. Specific uses are to change the format of information and to 'gate', route, and convert signals. An AND gate will act as an identity gate for

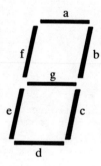

Fig. 5.4   A seven-segment display.

signal A if $B = 1$ but it will have output 0 if $B = 0$. It thus passes or blocks the signal and acts as a 'gate' controlled by the signal on B. Routing or multiplexing (see also chapter 8) allows logic signals to control the particular path that a signal is to take. For example, if an input signal is applied to the A inputs of two of the gates just described and the control signal is applied to one B input and the inverted control signal to the other, then the input signal can be routed to one or the other output. Analog signals can be similarly routed if the 'gates' are replaced by relays or electronic analog switches turned on or off by logic signals.

Signal conversion or *decoding* can be performed by combinatorial circuits. For example a signal in pure binary form can be decoded or encoded to BCD. Similar conversions are decimal to BCD, binary to octal, etc.

A common decoding operation is in the instructions to displays. Consider the familiar seven-segment display shown in figure 5.4. For each of the numerals, and other common symbols, that can be constructed from this display, certain of the segments need to be activated. An encoder will convert binary or BCD input signals into signals to the appropriate segments a,b,c,d,e,f or g. Thus a 7 requires the illumination of segments a, b, and c.

A multi-bit input signal is used to command one of several output terminals to go to 1 while the others remain at 0. This can be used to illuminate one lamp to display one of several outcomes. Analog-to-digital and digital-to-analog conversions are described in chapters 2 and 8.

Some arithmetic operations can be performed by gate circuits. The parity check process is an example. The addition of two single-bit binary numbers follows simple rules and is performed by a half-adder or full-adder circuit. The former simply adds two single bits of two binary numbers while the full-adder also adds in any 'carry' bit from the less significant column which had been added before. However, to remember the 'carry' between each separate addition requires a sequential logic circuit or memory.

LOGIC FAMILIES

The description of logic circuits in terms of gates and logic levels 0 and 1 is general. In practice the gates have to be made from some particular circuit elements, diodes, bipolar transistors or field-effect transistors. The set of gates derived from one particular method of circuit construction using certain components will have specific characteristics in such properties as impedance, speed, and power consumption. Such sets of gates made from one common construction process are called *logic families* and there are widely recognized standard characteristics, such as voltage levels corresponding to 0 and 1, for each such family wherever they are made.

The most basic logic element is the switch itself. A series combination of two switches is *on* if switch A AND switch B are *on*. Circuits of this type using mechanical or electrical switches or relays are simple, rugged, and reliable, but are bulky. They are used for small systems such as security interlocks, where such characteristics are desirable.

The resistance logic (RL) OR circuit is shown in figure 5.5(a). It is a simple passive adding circuit. The output X will be at earth potential unless A OR B is at the supply potential. The diode logic (DL) or diode–resistor logic (DRL) OR gate shown in figure 5.5(b) is an improvement on the simple circuit. These two families suffer from many problems, low input impedance and relatively high output impedance, so that there is mutual loading and one gate can drive few other gates. This is because the circuits are passive and there is no signal gain. The signal is 0 or V^+ at the input corresponding to a low-impedance connection to one or other of the power supply potentials. However, at the output of the gate the logic level 1 is no longer at V^+ since

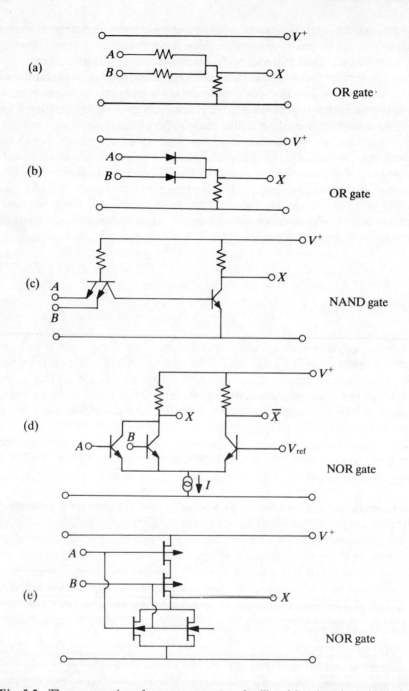

Fig. 5.5 The construction of some common gate families: (a) resistor logic (RL), (b) diode–resistor logic (DL), (c) transistor–transistor logic (TTL), (d) emitter-coupled logic (ECL), and (e) complementary MOS (CMOS) logic.

there will be a voltage dropped across the resistors in the RL gate or about 0.6 V dropped across the forward-biased diode in the DL gate. Thus the voltage values of the two logic levels are not fixed and will be indistinguishable after several gates have been cascaded. The isolation between the output and input is not good so that any voltage change applied to the output terminal from some other circuit will affect the input voltage. The DL gate has better reverse isolation than the RL gate. Such families are obviously not very useful but can have application in small circuits where their simplicity, ruggedness, and lack of moving parts are an advantage. In particular, the DL family is often used to form a diode-matrix memory or to form simple gates to link larger circuit subsections.

The RL and DL gates can be improved by the addition of an active, inverting, transistor output stage to give resistor–transistor logic (RTL) and diode–transistor logic (DTL). These gates then become inverting gates, which are more versatile as described earlier. The circuit loading, input and output impedances, logic level degradation, and isolation problems are all reduced. However, this solution is not often taken since the circuits are then fairly complex with bias components, so once active devices have been included it is normal to use even more complicated circuits which can be made into integrated circuits with nearly ideal properties. The following families are usually made in the form of integrated circuits.

A transistor–transistor logic (TTL) NAND gate is shown in figure 5.5(c). This is a simplified diagram and real circuits make the most use of the advantages of integrated circuit construction, for example the input transistor has two emitters. The TTL family is very frequently used because it is very versatile. The standard supply voltages are 0 and +5 V with logic level 0 threshold below 0.8 V and logic level 1 threshold above 2 V. The family has many variants, with each branch of the family optimized for one particular parameter, high speed or low power for example. More details are given in appendix 1.

The emitter-coupled logic (ECL) family shown in figure 5.5(d) is based on the long-tailed pair differential amplifier described in chapter 1. Since the transistors do not saturate, the gates are very fast. Each gate always draws a constant current from the power supply regardless of its state since the current is simply switched from one transistor to another. Thus the power supply can be simpler and, as varying currents do not flow in the power supply and earth circuits when the gate switches, there is less likelihood of pick-up from these sources. This family is used only where very high speeds are needed because it uses a very large current and power.

The complementary metal oxide–silicon (CMOS) family uses n-channel and p-channel MOS transistors together as shown in a NOR gate in figure 5.5(e). This logic family has many valuable features that make it ideal for the non-specialist to use, and it is recommended for nearly all research purposes. The basic form of CMOS gate is a series connection of complementary transistors between the power supply lines. The turn-on voltages of the devices are adjusted so that, when the input signal is applied to both gates together, one turns *on* and the other turns *off*. The common point, the output, is thus effectively connected to either the high or low power supply potentials.

The CMOS family takes little power since one or other of the devices in series is always off. Power is taken only in charging the circuit capacitances during a transition. The power needed is thus approximately proportional to the frequency of operation. The input impedance is very high and the output impedance is low. The power supply voltage can be anywhere between +3 V and +15 V. The transition voltage between logic 0 and logic 1 voltage levels is at half the supply voltage. A more detailed description of the CMOS family is given in appendix 1.

Very large and complex circuits can be easily made in integrated circuit form (MSI, LSI, and VLSI). These are well designed and constructed and

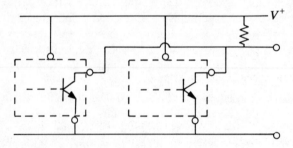

Fig. 5.6   Open collector gates with wired OR connection.

their cost increases little with the complexity, whereas the cost and effort of interconnecting many integrated circuits is large. Therefore the design of a circuit should be based around a few sophisticated integrated circuits, perhaps not using all their features, rather than an assembly of a large number of basic gates.

The output circuit of a logic gate is important. It must have a low output impedance in order to be able to drive several gates and also the capacitance of any connecting cable. The output performance can be improved by placing several gates or buffers in parallel.

One useful output circuit is the *open collector* or *wired OR* configuration shown in figure 5.6. The output is in the form of a current generator, in this case a bipolar transistor collector. To complete the circuit, an external load is required. Some gates are constructed in this way for extra flexibility. The wired OR function is achieved by connecting two, or more, gate outputs to the same load. In this connection the output is logic 0 if either output A OR output B passes current; that is, if either were logic 0 by itself. Most gates do not have wired OR facility so that if it is wanted a special buffer unit with open collectors will have to be added. A single transistor could also be used.

Another useful output configuration is the *three-state logic* output. The two normal output states are low-impedance connections to logic 0 or logic 1. The third state is activated by a logic signal, on a special three-state input, which disconnects the output terminal from the gate, as shown in figure 5.7. With this circuit signals *A* and *B* can be multiplexed onto a common signal line *X* by a control signal *C*. The ability to multiplex the outputs is valuable when

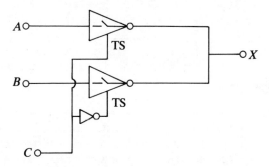

Fig. 5.7   Three-state (TS) output gates.

several outputs are connected to a common bus or signal line. Without this ability to disconnect the gates from the circuit, the low output impedance that is otherwise always present would short other signals on the bus.

SEQUENTIAL LOGIC

Many logic circuits are *sequential*, so that the output depends on the previous values of the input signals as well as the instantaneous values. For this function, some memory ability is needed. Sequential systems may be *asynchronous* (or *ripple-through*), in which the output follows a change in the input after the normal response time of the gates. On the other hand, *clocked* or *synchronous* systems have a timing or *clock* input, which controls all the changes within the system so that the state of the whole system changes simultaneously and is thus well known at all times. Before the clock pulse, the gate will not respond to the changes in the input signal.

A binary memory element is bistable in either one of its two possible output states. It is constructed using positive feedback as described in chapter 3 and is called a *flip-flop*. There are many forms but the basic memory element is the latch shown in figure 5.8. The data are applied to the data input and transmitted to the output, to appear as Q and its complement $\bar{Q}$, when the control input is of one polarity. A change to the other control input polarity causes the output to hold at that value of Q. The timing of the control input can therefore be arranged so that the latch stores the data only when the input signal has stabilized.

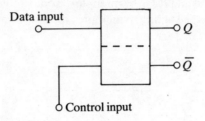

Fig. 5.8   The basic latch.

Control of input signals is very important since they may be noisy or contain unwanted signals. Once within a well constructed circuit few problems arise but external signals can be very varied. The *Schmitt trigger* described in chapter 3 shows hysteresis, as shown in figure 5.9. The amount of hysteresis is usually about 10% so that small amounts of noise superimposed on the signal will not cause a premature transition. The Schmitt trigger will also sharpen up a slowly varying input signal to make a steep pulse edge.

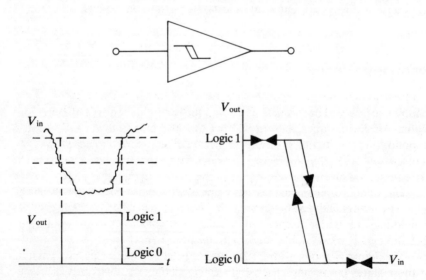

Fig. 5.9   The Schmitt trigger.

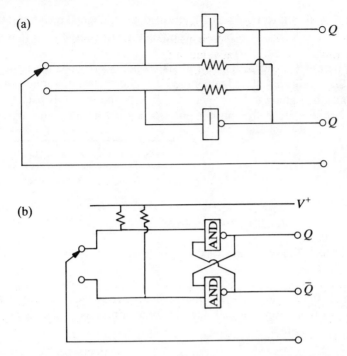

Fig. 5.10 Switch debouncing circuits using NOR gates (a) or NAND gates (b).

Mechanical switches, when used to provide an input signal to a logic circuit, can produce incorrect operation since the fast logic circuit will respond to any sparks, multiple switching or oscillation at the switch contacts. Debouncing circuits or input latches such as that shown in figure 5.10 are essential for positive operation. In figure 5.10(a) the two inverters are in series in a loop so that they have two possible stable states $Q = 0$ and $Q = 1$. The resistors are added to prevent the outputs being shorted to earth by the switch. The switch controls which of the two states the system is in. It will not respond to the switch fault condition which will be a switch open circuit. A malfunction with the switch accidentally going to the other control is extremely unlikely.

The standard simple latch is the *R–S latch* or *R–S flip-flop* shown in figure 5.11. The letters R and S stand for 'reset' and 'set'. It can be constructed from individual gates with feedback, but usually an integrated circuit is used. The $R–S$ flip-flop has two stable states with output $Q = 0$ or $Q = 1$; a complementary output is also provided. The memory element can be placed in either of these states by placing a signal (1) on *either* the 'set' input or the 'reset' input. The normal storage state is with $S = R = 0$. This memory unit must not be brought into the state with $S = R = 1$ since the final stored state on return to $S = R = 0$ will not be defined since it will depend on which state, $S = 0, R = 1$ or $S = 1, R = 0$, is reached on the return from $S = R = 1$ to $S = R = 0$.

The output Q reaches the stored state once S or R has an input. To prevent the disallowed state happening by accident, through noise on the other input, the signal can be brought rapidly and automatically back to 0 to give the stored state if the input 1 pulse is applied in differentiated form

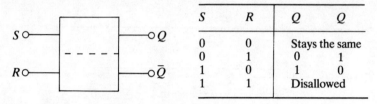

S	R	Q	Q
0	0	Stays the same	
0	1	0	1
1	0	1	0
1	1	Disallowed	

Fig. 5.11   The R–S flip-flop symbol and truth table.

through a CR filter. The front edge of the pulse then operates the flip-flop and the output is then stored after a few RC time constants as the signal has reduced to a low value.

SYNCHRONOUS LOGIC

The R–S latch has two inconveniences: the disallowed input condition can cause wrong operation and, since its operation is asynchronous, it responds to the instantaneous input values. Because of this, feedback from the output to the input may cause improper operation. These problems can be eliminated by clocked or synchronous logic gates. These gates have similar functions but only operate on the edge of a clock signal, that is when a clock signal applied to a special control input makes an upward (or downward) transition. Thus the input signal can be applied and altered but the transition at the clock input will allow the gate to operate only when all the input voltages have settled down. All gates in the circuit can be operated from the same clock signal so that all the gates in the whole circuit will operate together and oscillation is not possible.

Clocked gates use the master–slave principle. The gate is in two sections. The input section, the master, accepts the data and the output section, the slave, stores it. In the storage mode the sections are disconnected so that the output signal cannot cause oscillation even if it is fed back to the input.

The D-type flip-flop is shown in figure 5.12. It is derived from the R–S latch and can be used in two modes, direct and clocked. In the direct mode it

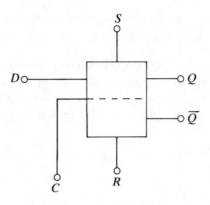

	Inputs				Outputs	
	Clock	Data	Reset	Set	Q	$\bar{Q}$
Clocked	⟋	0	0	0	0	1
	⟋	1	0	0	1	0
	⟍	–	0	0	No change	
Direct	–	–	0	0	Use clocked mode	
	–	–	1	0	0	1
	–	–	0	1	1	0
	–	–	1	1	Disallowed	

– Represents 'don't care' .

Fig. 5.12 The *D*-type flip-flop symbol and truth table.

acts like an *R–S* latch. The *R–S* inputs override the clock (*C*) and data (*D*) inputs. The data input goes through the master to an internal set (*S*) input and also through an inverter to give a complementary input to an internal reset (*R*) input. Thus the disallowed state ($R = S = 1$) is automatically prevented. On the positive-going edge of the clock pulse the data signal present at this time thus sets or resets the latch. There is no change in state on the negative clock transition. In this clocked state the external *R* and *S* inputs must be 0. The *D*-type flip-flop is the basis of the shift register, which will be described later.

The *J–K flip-flop* shown in figure 5.13 is the most versatile memory element. There are two modes, clocked and direct. In the clocked mode with $R = S = 0$ the four possible combinations of *J* and *K* govern the behavior of the output Q, $\bar{Q}$ on the next upward transition of the clock signal. The initial value of *Q* is Q_n and the final value Q_{n+1}. The truth table shows that, with $J = K = 0$, clocking makes no change, as the signal is stored. With $J = 1$, $K = 0$, the output *Q* is sent to 1, and with $J = 0$, $K = 1$, a 0 is stored in *Q*.

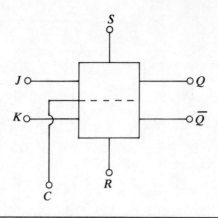

	Inputs					Outputs
	C	J	K	S	R	Q_{n+1}
Clocked	⟋	0	0	0	0	Q_n no change
	⟋	1	0	0	0	1
	⟋	0	1	0	0	0
	⟋	1	1	0	0	$\bar{Q}_n$ complement
	⟍	–	–	0	0	Q_n no change
Direct	–	–	–	0	0	Use clocked mode
	–	–	–	1	0	1
	–	–	–	0	1	0
	–	–	–	1	1	Disallowed

–   Represents 'don't care'.
n Represents present state.
$n+1$ Represents next state.

Fig. 5.13 The J–K flip-flop symbol and truth table.

With $J = K = 1$, clocking will complement the stored state. There is no change at the negative transition of the clock. In the direct mode the clock has no effect and the R and S inputs have their usual effects.

The master–slave clocked flip-flop can safely be used with feedback since there is no danger of oscillation. The simple feedback arrangements for the D-type and J–K flip-flops shown in figure 5.14 produce the *T-type flip-flop*. The T stands for toggle or clock. In operation a complete cycle of the C (or T) input is needed to change Q (or $\bar{Q}$) from one state to the next. Thus the output changes by one cycle for two cycles of the input. It is a binary divider as shown in the timing diagram in figure 5.14(c). It is also useful to produce a signal with equal on–off periods from an asymmetrical pulse (figure 5.14(d)).

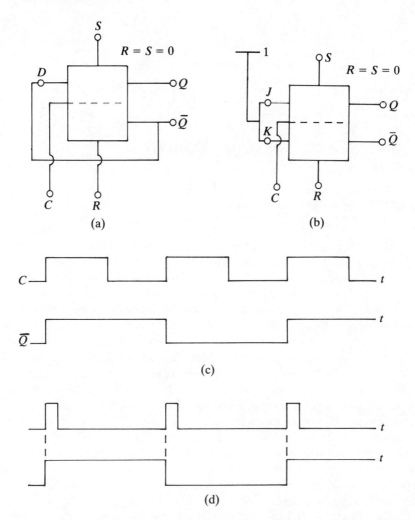

Fig. 5.14 The *D*-type and *J–K* flip-flops can be connected to produce a *T*-type flip-flop as in (a) and (b). This acts as a binary divider with waveforms as in (c) and can produce a waveform with equal on–off periods from a uniform stream of pulses as in (d).

Cascaded *T*-type flip-flops can be used to divide a number of pulses, and hence a frequency, by successive factors of 2 as shown in figure 5.15. The number of pulses will be counted and the total displayed with the most significant bit on the right. The unit will need to be set at the start of the count. Other counting methods can be used with feedback paths between the stages to give division by factors other than 2. However, integrated circuits with 'divide by *N*' functions are obtainable and *N* can be set by logic signals.

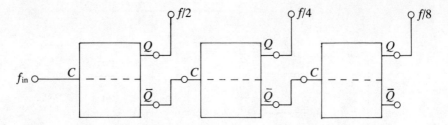

Fig. 5.15 Cascaded *T*-type flip-flops acting as a binary divider.

SHIFT REGISTERS

A *shift register* consists of a linear array of memory elements such as the *D*-type flip-flop and is shown in figure 5.16. The shift register is a useful building block and can be made in many ways. Some methods of construction use extremely small memory elements and are hence compact and can have many stages. A *static* shift register will hold the memory state even with no clock pulse operating, whereas a *dynamic* shift register stores the signal in the form of a charge on some capacitance. This charge will leak away slowly so that there is a minimum operating (clock) frequency necessary so that the charge is refreshed. The data in the register are in a linear array. A sequence of bits in time at one point is called a *serial* signal, while a sequence of bits appearing on a set of terminals at one time is a *parallel* signal. Naturally the serial signal is slower but takes less wire, space, and circuit complexity. The signals into and out of a shift register can be serial or parallel. The four-element shift register shown in figure 5.16 has serial input, serial output, and also parallel output. Parallel input requires extra gates to break the serial signal path while the parallel input is applied. Some shift registers can reverse the direction of transmission.

The shift register can perform many useful functions. It can convert between serial and parallel formats. If the clock is stopped, a static shift register acts as a store for a binary number. In a synchronous system the register acts as a delay unit, as the data take several clock pulses to pass through the register serially. The delay can be used to hold up a signal while another operation is performed on another related signal before they are brought together.

A signal within a register can be circulated continuously if the output is connected to the input to form a loop. For example an *N*-stage register containing only one 1 will act as a 'divide by *N*' counter since the 1 will appear at the output every *N* clock pulses. A very long shift register, connected in a loop, will act as a memory and the information can be recovered every time the signal cycles the loop.

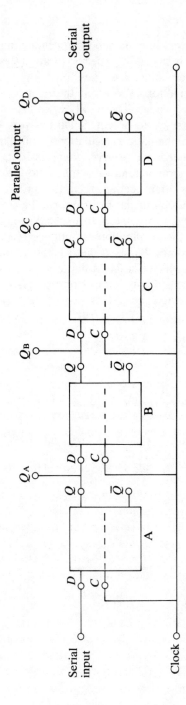

Fig. 5.16 A serial-in, serial-out and parallel-out shift register.

MEMORIES

In large systems a memory may be needed for many multi-bit bytes. In an array memory each bit is stored in a specific location described by a binary address. Memories come in many types, each optimized for a specific function. To store a signal for a short time during an operation, a *random-access memory* (RAM) is needed. These will vary in size and speed depending on the use to which they are to be put. Small but very fast RAMs will be needed for use during mathematical calculations, while large, but slower and cheaper, memories are needed to store programs and data. Data may need to be stored in permanent form on removable magnetic disk or tape store.

Information that is often needed, such as a program to calculate the logarithm or to operate a particular machine, can be stored on a *read-only memory* (ROM). This has a permanent store set by the manufacturers for the particular purpose and the information can only be read, not written, after manufacture. A compromise between these two extremes is the programmable ROM (PROM), which is a ROM that can have its memory contents changed but only by extracting it from its normal place and placing it in a special programming machine.

FURTHER READING

S. J. Cahill, *Digital and Microprocessor Engineering*, Ellis Horwood (1982).
P. M. Chirlian, *Analysis and Design of Integrated Electronic Circuits*, Harper and Row (1981).
J. R. Gibson, *Electronic Logic Circuits*, Edward Arnold (1983).
D. Lancaster, *CMOS Cookbook*, H. W. Sams (1977).
T. J. Stonham, *Digital Logic Techniques*, Van Nostrand Reinhold (1983).

6 NON-LINEARITY, MODULATION AND MIXING

INTRODUCTION

The linear circuits described in the first four chapters are very valuable for manipulating signals. The analysis of linear circuits is simple because the principle of superposition holds. That is, the effect of each signal applied separately can be added to give the resultant. If the problem has been solved for one amplitude, it has been solved for all amplitudes. If the problem has been solved for two waveforms, then it has been solved for the sum and difference waveforms also. This in turn leads to the use of the complex impedance and to Fourier analysis. Fourier analysis was mentioned in chapter 1 and is described in more detail in appendix 3. The principle is that sine waves can be considered as the basic functions for all waveforms, so that any wave can be built up from a summation of sine waves of suitable amplitude and phase. For a repetitive waveform, the summation is a series containing sine waves of z.f. (d.c.), the waveform repetition frequency, and multiples of this frequency. For a non-repetitive waveform, the summation is an integral over a band of frequencies. In a linear system, therefore, if the circuit can be solved for sine waves at all significant frequencies, it can be solved for any waveform. For a linear system, the input signal can be broken down into its constituent sine waves, the effect of the circuit on each calculated, and the output signal produced by recombining the sine waves.

In non-linear circuits, signal amplitudes no longer add linearly and circuit elements do not produce an output signal amplitude proportional to the input amplitude. Although a signal at any point can be broken down into its constituent sine waves, this is of little help to the analysis as the effect of the non-linear circuit on the signal will depend on the amplitude of the signal actually passing through. Therefore signals are distorted and the circuit is often difficult to analyze by considering a time-varying signal. Non-linear circuits are often best considered as manipulators of frequencies rather than

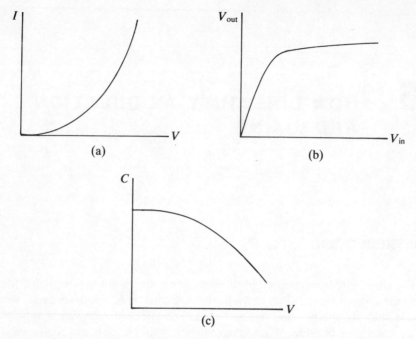

Fig. 6.1 Typical non-linear characteristics for (a) an impedance, (b) an amplifier, and
(c) a capacitor (varactor).

amplitudes. The introduction of a non-linear circuit element enables the
information at one frequency to be translated to another frequency.

Typical non-linear circuit elements are shown in figure 6.1 for a resistance (a), a voltage transfer function (b), and a capacitance (c). A full analysis
of the behavior of a signal in a non-linear element can be made if the actual
I–V, V_{out}–V_{in} or C–V relationship is known. The full analysis for a specific
non-linearity can be very lengthy since the output signal amplitude has to be
calculated for the input signal amplitude existing at each instant of time.
Usually, however, approximations can be made so that the non-linearity is of
a simple analytical form.

To show the basic principles, consider the non-linear characteristic
shown in figure 6.2(a). If a sine wave is applied about the bias point, the shape
of the output signal can be found graphically by considering how the
amplitude of the input signal at each instant of time is transferred to the
equivalent time point of the output signal. The waveforms are shown in figure
6.2(b) where it can be seen that distortion occurs. The output signal still has
the same periodicity as the input signal but it has extra Fourier components or
harmonics and these can be calculated. The spectra of the input and output

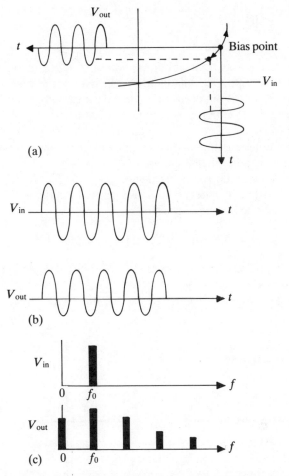

Fig. 6.2 The operation of a typical non-linear circuit showing (a) the time variation of the signal on the characteristic, (b) the input and output waveforms, and (c) the spectrum of the input and output waveforms for a sine-wave input signal.

signals are shown in figure 6.2(c). The exact amount of distortion and the exact relative amplitudes of the Fourier components will depend on the amplitude of the input signal as well as the shape of the non-linearity. There is therefore not a linear relationship. The general principles are illustrated in the output spectrum. For a single input frequency, f_0, there are components at f_0 and all its harmonics as well as at $f = 0$. A non-linear element will therefore exhibit *harmonic generation* ($f_{out} = nf_{in}$, n integral) and *rectification* ($f_{out} = 0$, $f_{in} \neq 0$). For any particular application, the device and its bias point will be chosen to emphasize the required output component.

RECTIFICATION

Rectification, or the conversion of an a.c. signal into a d.c. (z.f.) signal, is performed on signals to transfer information from one form to another, or on power signals to supply circuits that need such a form of power. The signal rectification, or detection, needs to be precise with a well established relationship between the output and input. The precision signal rectifier was considered in chapter 2 and will be considered later in this chapter in the discussion of demodulators and detectors. Power rectification requires high power efficiency rather than accuracy.

The most common rectifying device is the simple diode, which has a characteristic with a high degree of non-linearity for large-amplitude signals. Although the diode has the characteristic

$$I = I_{00}[\exp(eV/kT) - 1] \simeq I_{00}\exp(eV/kT)$$

since the exponential is large compared with unity, simple approximations can often be made.

For large-amplitude signals, the exponential characteristic of the diode

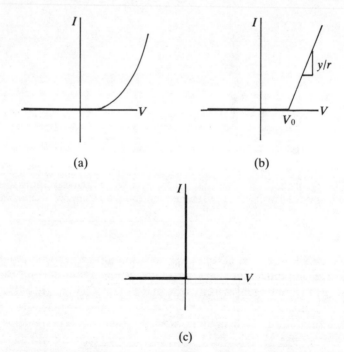

(a)   (b)

(c)

Fig. 6.3   The characteristics of the p-n junction diode showing the exact characteristic (a) and two levels of approximation for large-signal analysis, (b) and (c).

shown in figure 6.3(a) can be approximated to that of a voltage-controlled switch as shown in figures 6.3(b) and (c). In the approximation of (b) the diode is 'off' for voltages below $+V_0$ and appears to have a small series resistance r for large voltages. The value of V_0 is typically 0.6 V for silicon p–n junction diodes and less than this for germanium junction diodes and Schottky diodes. The value V_0 is determined by I_{00}. A more drastic approximation is shown in figure 6.3(c), which can be used for signals much bigger than V_0.

A rectifier is normally followed by a low-pass filter to remove any a.c. component remaining. This is usually an RC filter since inductors to form an LC or LR filter are expensive. With a large C and a small R the power loss can be made small. In power circuits the filter series resistance is the output resistance of the transformer and diode rectifier stage. The load resistance has to be included if the total filtering ability of the circuit is calculated. Active regulators are often used since then smaller values of capacitance can be used.

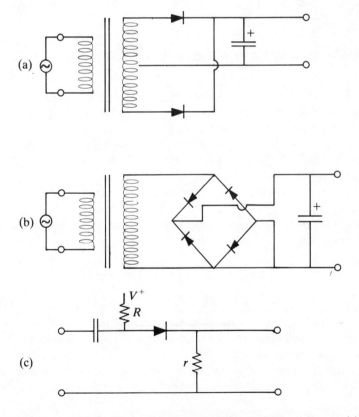

Fig. 6.4 Full-wave power rectifier circuits using a centre-tapped transformer (a) and a bridge rectifier (b). Figure (c) shows a signal rectifier circuit.

In these the output terminal voltage is kept constant by a feedback circuit which alters the voltage drop across a transistor in series with the load.

Typical power rectifier circuits are shown in figures 6.4(a) and (b). The bridge rectifier is usually preferred since the two extra diodes are cheaper than the more complex transformer used in the full-wave rectifier circuit. This needs a centre tap on the secondary and only half of the secondary is used at any one time.

A simple passive signal rectification circuit is shown in figure 6.4(c). If the bias circuit R, V^+ is ignored at first, the a.c. signal from the low output impedance source imposes a voltage across the diode and the small resistance r in series. The voltage is dropped mainly across the diode. The output signal is the voltage developed across r by the current flowing. The response of the circuit thus corresponds to the $I = V$ characteristic of the diode. The bias circuit allows a constant direct current to pass through the diode so that the input voltage is impressed across the most non-linear part of the non-linear characteristic as in figure 6.2(a).

HARMONIC GENERATION AND FREQUENCY MIXING

A major use of non-linear circuit elements is in the generation of the harmonics of an input signal and the sum and difference frequencies of two simultaneous input signals. Although any non-linear element may be used, and normally one with a large non-linearity is chosen, the description here is for an element with a small non-linearity since the important features can then be seen more easily.

Consider a resistive component with a characteristic that can be expressed as a power series in the voltage. If a voltage is applied and the current flowing is taken as the output signal, then an expansion of the conductance is most convenient:

$$G(V) = G_0 + G_1 V + G_2 V^2 + \dots \tag{6.1}$$

Note that G_1, G_2, etc., do not have the dimensions of conductance. If this device is used in a circuit such as that shown in figure 6.5, the output voltage $V_{out} = RI$ is proportional to the output current, and the resistance R can be neglected in the non-linear analysis if it is less than the resistance of the non-linear element $(1/G)$. For other systems an expansion in another variable may be more appropriate. For example, for an amplifier the gain may be used with

$$A(V) = A_0 + A_1 V + A_2 V^2 + A_3 V^3 + \dots$$

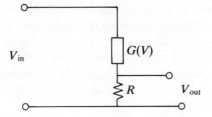

Fig. 6.5 A circuit to demonstrate the action of a non-linear conductance $G(V)$.

If the device is biased then the expansion may be in the voltage $(V - V_{bias})$ relative to the bias point.

Consider an input signal consisting of a single-frequency sine wave $V_{in} = V_0 \cos \omega t$. Then

$$V_{out} = RI_{out} = RG(V)V_{in}$$
$$= R[G_0 V_0 \cos \omega t + G_1 V_0^2 \cos^2 \omega t + G_2 V_0^3 \cos^3 \omega t + \ldots]$$
$$= R[G_0 V_0 \cos \omega t + \tfrac{1}{2} G_1 V_0^2 (1 + \cos 2\omega t)$$
$$+ \tfrac{1}{4} G_2 V_0^3 (\cos 3\omega t + 3 \cos \omega t) + \ldots]$$
$$= R[\tfrac{1}{2} G_1 V_0^2 + \ldots + G_0 V_0 \cos \omega t + \tfrac{3}{4} G_2 V_0^3 \cos \omega t + \ldots$$
$$+ \tfrac{1}{2} G_1 V_0^2 \cos 2\omega t + \ldots + \tfrac{1}{4} G_2 V_0^3 \cos 3\omega t + \ldots] \quad (6.2)$$

The input and output spectra are shown in figure 6.6. The output signal has components at zero frequency (rectification), at the input frequency (the linear component), and at harmonics or multiples of the input frequency. The relative strength of each component will depend on the relative magnitude of the relevant coefficient in the power expansion.

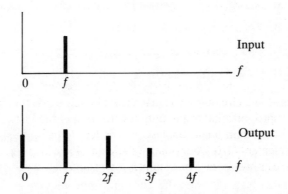

Fig. 6.6 The input and output spectra for a sine wave applied to an arbitrary non-linear conductance.

Notice that one of the d.c. output terms is derived from the coefficient, G_1, of V^2 and also that its amplitude is proportional to the input intensity or power. This coefficient is thus very valuable and devices called square-law detectors are often optimized to enhance G_1. In the balanced mixer (which will be described later) the output signals from the odd coefficients G_0, G_2, etc., are reduced to leave G_1 as the dominant coefficient since the higher even coefficients are usually small.

For harmonic generation the appropriate coefficient is made large and a band-pass filter is included in the output circuit to pass the required frequency. This may take the form of a parallel tuned circuit to replace the resistance R in the circuit shown in figure 6.5.

Consider the behavior of this non-linear element when two sine waves are applied simultaneously at frequencies ω_1 and ω_2 and amplitudes V_{01} and V_{02}:

$$
\begin{aligned}
V_{in} &= V_{01} \cos \omega_1 t + V_{02} \cos \omega_2 t \\
V_{out} &= RI = RG(V) V_{in} \\
&= R[G_0(V_{01} \cos \omega_1 t + V_{02} \cos \omega_2 t) \\
&\quad + G_1(V_{01} \cos \omega_1 t + V_{02} \cos \omega_2 t)^2 + \ldots] \\
&= R[G_0(V_{01} \cos \omega_1 t + V_{02} \cos \omega_2 t) \\
&\quad + G_1(V_{01}^2 \cos^2 \omega_1 t + 2V_{01} V_{02} \cos \omega_1 t \cos \omega_2 t + V_{02}^2 \cos^2 \omega_2 t) + \ldots] \\
&= R\{G_0 V_{01} \cos \omega_1 t + G_0 V_{02} \cos \omega_2 t + \tfrac{1}{2} G_1 V_{01}^2 (1 + \cos 2\omega_1 t) \\
&\quad + G_1 V_{01} V_{02}[\cos(\omega_1 - \omega_2)t + \cos(\omega_1 + \omega_2)t] \\
&\quad + \tfrac{1}{2} G_1 V_{02}^2 (1 + \cos 2\omega_2 t) + \ldots\} \tag{6.3}
\end{aligned}
$$

$$
\begin{aligned}
&= R[\tfrac{1}{2} G_1 (V_{01}^2 + V_{02}^2) + \ldots \\
&\quad + G_0(V_{01} \cos \omega_1 t + V_{02} \cos \omega_2 t) + \ldots \\
&\quad + \tfrac{1}{2} G_1 (V_{01}^2 \cos 2\omega_1 t + V_{02}^2 \cos 2\omega_2 t) + \ldots \\
&\quad + G_1 V_{01} V_{02} \cos(\omega_1 - \omega_2)t + \ldots \\
&\quad + G_1 V_{01} V_{02} \cos(\omega_1 + \omega_2)t + \ldots] \tag{6.4}
\end{aligned}
$$

This spectrum is illustrated in figure 6.7. The output signal again contains a linear term and terms at zero frequency (rectification) and at harmonics with the same strengths as if each signal were applied separately. However now there are extra terms at the difference and sum frequencies ($\omega_1 - \omega_2$) and ($\omega_1 + \omega_2$). These components derive from the 'cross-term' in the square-law part of the expression where the product of the signal amplitudes is

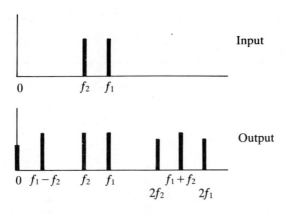

Fig. 6.7 The input and output spectra for two equal sine waves applied to an arbitrary non-linear conductance.

calculated. This therefore involves multiplication. A full expansion to higher terms shows the generation of other components such as those at frequencies $(2\omega_1 + \omega_2)$, $(2\omega_1 - \omega_2)$, $(\omega_1 + 2\omega_2)$, $(\omega_1 - 2\omega_2)$, etc. The generation of sum and difference frequencies is called *mixing*.

MODULATION

To convey information, such as a signal $a\cos\omega_m t$, some quantity that can be transmitted from the source to the receiver must be changed in this manner. For example a current or voltage could vary in this way; $V = V_0 a\cos\omega_m t$. The transmitted signal may be a radio wave corresponding to a field $\cos(\omega_c t + \phi)$ at a high frequency ω_c. In this case the amplitude, frequency or phase could be varied at ω_m to give signals $V_0(1 + a\cos\omega_m t)\cos(\omega_c t + \phi)$, $V_0\cos[(\omega_c + b\cos\omega_m t)t + \phi]$, $V_0\cos(\omega_c t + c\cos\omega_m t)$. These represent the *modulation* at ω_m of the *carrier wave* at ω_c and correspond to *amplitude modulation* (AM), *frequency modulation* (FM), and *phase modulation* (PM). The waveforms and spectra of typical signals are shown in figure 6.8. The exact form and detail of the spectrum of FM depends on the value of b/ω_c but consists of signals at f_c and $f_c \pm nf_m$ where n takes all positive integral values. The waveform and spectrum of PM is similar to that of FM. Further details about FM and PM can be found in the further reading at the end of this chapter. If the signal is in binary digital form, the modulated wave switches between two fixed states and the modulation method is called amplitude shift keying (ASK), frequency shift keying (FSK), and pulse shift keying (PSK).

The carrier may be a pulse train. In this case the pulse amplitude, pulse

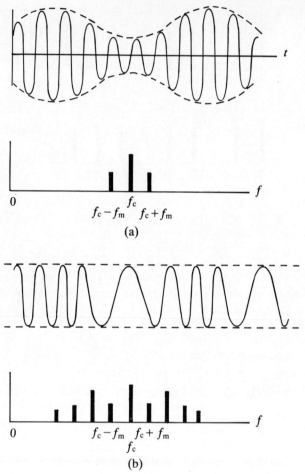

Fig. 6.8 Schematic waveforms and spectra for (a) amplitude modulation and (b) frequency or phase modulation.

width or pulse position will be modulated to give *pulse amplitude modulation* (PAM), *pulse width modulation* (PWM), and *pulse position modulation* (PPM) as shown in figure 6.9.

The analogy of PAM is AM and of PPM is PM. The spectra are rather complex and will not be discussed here.

Another form of pulse modulation is *pulse code modulation* (PCM) in which the signal amplitude is sampled at regular intervals and the voltage at each sampling time is converted into a binary number, which is conveyed as a series of binary signals or pulses. The details of this digitizing procedure are described in chapters 8 and 9 and appendix 5.

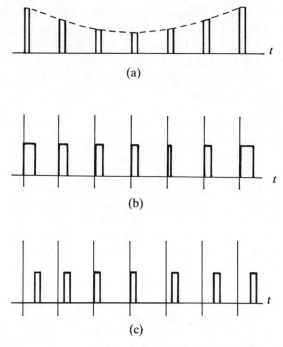

(a)

(b)

(c)

Fig. 6.9 Schematic waveforms for (a) pulse amplitude modulation (PAM), (b) pulse width modulation (PWM), and (c) pulse position modulation (PPM).

AMPLITUDE MODULATION

A carrier wave at frequency ω_c, carrying information at ω_m by amplitude modulation, has a waveform

$$V = V_0(1 + a\cos\omega_m t)\cos\omega_c t$$
$$= V_0[\cos\omega_c t + \tfrac{1}{2}a\cos(\omega_c - \omega_m)t + \tfrac{1}{2}a\cos(\omega_c + \omega_n)t] \tag{6.5}$$

Normally $\omega_m \ll \omega_c$ and the modulation and demodulation operations are mathematically easier if $a < 1$. The spectrum, shown in figure 6.8(a), thus consists of a component at the carrier frequency ω_c and two equal components spaced at ω_m on each side of ω_c. The operation of amplitude modulation, or multiplication by a carrier sine wave, produces a translation of the signal at ω_m (and $-\omega_m$!) along the frequency axis by an amount ω_c. This is described in more detail in appendix 3.

The information in the signal is contained in a and ω_m and is hence located in these latter two spectral components rather than in the signal at ω_c.

These two symmetrical components are called *sidebands*. Since no information exists in the carrier spectral component at ω_c, transmitter power can be saved with no loss of information if it is not transmitted. In this case the receiver can, in principle, reconstruct the value of ω_c in order to determine the value of ω_m from the sidebands by averaging the two sideband frequencies $(\omega_c \equiv \frac{1}{2}(\omega_c - \omega_m) + (\omega_c + \omega_m))$. This is called *double sideband suppressed carrier* (DSBSC).

Alternately the bandwidth, or the section of frequency space that is necessary to transmit the information, can be reduced by only transmitting one of the two symmetrical sidebands. If the carrier and only one sideband are transmitted, the receiver can determine ω_m by subtraction $(\omega_m \equiv (\omega_c + \omega_m) - \omega_c)$ to give *single sideband* (SSB). Economy in both transmitter power and bandwidth can be made by transmitting only the one sideband. If the carrier is not transmitted, the receiver can only determine ω_m if it knows the value of ω_c that is being used. This can be done by having oscillators at identical frequencies in both transmitter and receiver. In practice this is not difficult to achieve to a sufficient accuracy. This is economical in power and is called *single sideband suppressed carrier* (SSBSC).

Normally the information to be carried is contained in a range of frequencies, each of which has a different value of a. Thus an audiofrequency signal will have components between about 100 Hz and 15 kHz, with a peak in the amplitude distribution at about 1 kHz. To represent this spread of frequencies and amplitudes in the actual signal, or the *baseband signal*, a schematic spectrum is sometimes drawn as in figure 6.10(a) and extends up to

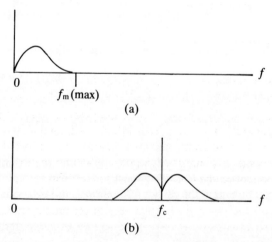

Fig. 6.10 A schematic representation of the sidebands generated in amplitude modulation. The spectrum in (a) represents the time-averaged spectrum of the baseband signal, which becomes the sidebands in the spectrum (b) when the baseband signal amplitude modulates a carrier at f_c.

some maximum frequency, $f_m(max)$. The spectrum of the signal when its amplitude modulates a carrier at ω_c is shown in figure 6.10(b) and corresponds to translation along the frequency axis. For full AM the necessary total bandwidth is $2f_m(max)$ although the redundancy described above shows that this apparent doubling of the necessary frequency space is not essential in order to transmit the information if suitable transmitters and receivers are used.

The filters used in the baseband and the carrier frequency parts of a circuit define the range of frequencies that can be passed. It is thus important to know the spectrum, and in particular the value of $f_m(max)$, of any signal to be transmitted. Sometimes the existing frequency components are not immediately obvious. Consider a system designed to measure the (z.f.) amplitude of some signal at ω_c. In this case the signal has no intentional modulation. The necessary system bandwidth is, however, non-zero and is governed by the time that can be allowed for the signal amplitude to reach its equilibrium value. If the bandwidth is $2\omega_m(max)$ then the amplitude will change exponentially with a time constant $\tau \simeq 1/\omega_m(max)$ toward its equilibrium value after the system is switched on or the value changed. This amplitude change is an effective modulation and some bandwidth is needed. In a system such as the phase-sensitive detector described later, the signal-to-noise ratio is enhanced by reducing the bandwidth of the system as much as possible to exclude noise. The amount of this reduction is limited by the bandwidth necessary to pass the signal and in practice this is determined by the time available to wait for the system to reach equilibrium after each change in the input signal amplitude.

Modulators and demodulators

Amplitude modulation has been described in equation (6.5) as a multiplication of a (high-frequency) carrier wave by a (low-frequency) modulation signal to produce sum and difference frequencies in addition to the carrier signal. The generation of sum and difference frequencies was shown in equation (6.4) to result from the simultaneous application of the two sine waves to a general non-linear component. It will be seen that the required spectral components come from the cross-product term in the V^2 term, so that this term should be optimized. In equation (6.4), if ω_1 and ω_2 are converted to ω_m and ω_c with $\omega_m \ll \omega_c$, it will be seen that the resultant Fourier components, shown in figure 6.7, are spaced so that the amplitude modulation components at $\omega_c - \omega_m$, ω_c, and $\omega_c + \omega_m$ can be separated from the others easily with filters. In general, therefore, amplitude modulation requires a multiplication process and can be achieved with any non-linear component with a square-law characteristic. Suitable filters are also necessary.

Demodulation or *detection*, which is the recovery of the information, $a\cos\omega_m t$, from the modulation signal, is also accomplished by the cross-product term in the square-law component of a non-linear device followed by a low-pass filter. Consider an input of an amplitude-modulated signal $V_{in} = V_0(1 + a\cos\omega_m t)\cos\omega_c t$ into the general non-linear component used before. The output is

$$V_{out} = RI = R(G_0 V_{in} + G_1 V_{in}^2 + \ldots) \tag{6.6}$$

$$= R[G_0 V_0(1 + a\cos\omega_m t)\cos\omega_c t + G_1 V_0^2(1 + a\cos\omega_m t)^2\cos^2\omega_c t + \ldots]$$

$$= R[G_0 V_0 a(\cos\omega_m t\cos\omega_c t) + G_0 V_0\cos\omega_c t$$

$$+ G_1 V_0^2\cos^2\omega_c t + 2G_1 V_0^2 a\cos\omega_m t\cos^2\omega_c t + G_1 V_0^2 a^2\cos^2\omega_m t\cos^2\omega_c t$$

$$+ \ldots]$$

$$= R[\tfrac{1}{2}G_1 V_0^2 + \tfrac{1}{4}G_1 V_0^2 a^2$$

$$+ G_1 V_0^2 a\cos\omega_m t$$

$$+ \tfrac{1}{4}G_1 V_0^2 a^2\cos 2\omega_m t$$

$$+ \tfrac{1}{2}G_0 V_0 a\cos(\omega_c - \omega_m)t + G_0 V_0\cos\omega_c t + \tfrac{1}{2}G_0 V_0 a\cos(\omega_c + \omega_m)t$$

$$+ \tfrac{1}{2}G_1 V_0^2 a\cos(2\omega_c - \omega_m)t + \tfrac{1}{2}G_1 V_0^2 a\cos(2\omega_c + \omega_m)t$$

$$+ \tfrac{1}{8}G_1 V_0^2 a^2\cos(2\omega_c - 2\omega_m)t + \tfrac{1}{8}G_1 V_0^2 a^2\cos(2\omega_c + 2\omega_m t)$$

$$+ \tfrac{1}{2}G_1 V_0^2\cos 2\omega_c t + \tfrac{1}{4}G_1 V_0^2 a^2\cos 2\omega_c t$$

$$+ \ldots] \tag{6.7}$$

Since $0 \ll \omega_m \ll \omega_c$, filters can easily eliminate the zero-frequency terms and the terms near and above ω_c. The term at the frequency $2\omega_m$ would cause distortion but can be made small if $a \ll 1$. In general it cannot be separated from the term at ω_m since ω_m represents a baseband signal component which might itself extend over a frequency range with a high component greater than twice the lowest component.

In practice, demodulation can be achieved efficiently. It is equivalent to rectification of a signal with a slowly varying (at ω_m) amplitude. Non-linear components are chosen with a large non-linearity.

In this section the non-linear element has been shown to be capable of performing operations on frequencies in an analogous way to the operations of operational amplifiers on voltages. With suitable non-linear elements and filters, a signal at ω_1 can be transformed to one at $n\omega_1$ where n is an integer (harmonic generation); a signal at ω_1 can be displaced along the frequency axis by an amount ω_2 to give a signal at $\omega_2 \pm \omega_1$ (amplitude modulation) or displaced in the other direction from $\omega_2 \pm \omega_1$ to ω_1 (detection) or converted to a z.f. signal (rectification). In general, a frequency $n\omega_1 \pm m\omega_2$ can be generated from ω_1 and ω_2, with n and m integers.

Practical modulators, demodulators, and mixers

Although amplitude modulation and demodulation and frequency mixing can be accomplished by a general non-linear element, the actual operation is performed by the square-law term. Thus, to increase efficiency and to reduce unwanted harmonics and frequency components, which have to be filtered or introduce distortion, circuits are used that make this term as large as possible compared with the other terms.

For signal manipulation, when high powers are not involved, there are integrated circuit *multipliers* which will accurately perform a multiplication. These normally take signals V_1 and V_2 and produce an output $V_1 \times V_2/10$ as shown schematically in figure 6.11. The scale factor is introduced because

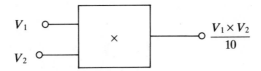

Fig. 6.11 A schematic analog multiplier.

most analog signals in circuits involving integrated circuits have values between $+10$ V and -10 V and hence the output will also need to be between these limits. From zero frequency (d.c.) up to about 1 MHz, a typical device may have a 1% full-scale accuracy and linearity with a high input impedance and low output impedance. The integrated circuit device can take either sign of the two inputs and is termed a 'four-quadrant' multiplier since it works all over the V_1–V_2 plane.

The multiplier is a very versatile circuit element. The range of operations that it can perform is shown in table 6.1. If the same signal is applied to both inputs, it acts as a square-law device so that it can perform analog squaring, intensity or power computation, rectification, demodulation, and second-harmonic generation. If separate signals are applied to the two inputs, it can calculate the product, act as a voltage-controlled attenuator, a modulator or mixer, an AM demodulator or a phase-sensitive detector.

These precision multipliers are constructed using two main techniques. In the more accurate, but slower, method a train of square or triangular pulses is produced at a constant rate. The pulse height is made proportional to V_1 and the pulse width to V_2. The time average of these pulses is produced by a low-pass filter and is proportional to V_1V_2. This is shown in figure 6.12(a). The

Table 6.1 The possible functions of an analog multiplier.

Input signals	$V_1 \times V_2$	Filter type	Filter output	Function
V_{01} V_{01}	V_{01}^2	–	V_{01}^2	Square Intensity Power
V_{01} V_{02}	$V_{01}V_{02}$	–	$V_{01}V_{02}$	Analog multiplier
$V_{01}\cos\omega t$ V_{02}	$V_{01}V_{02}\cos\omega t$	–	$V_{01}V_{02}\cos\omega t$	Voltage-controlled attenuator
$V_{01}\cos\omega t$ $V_{01}\cos\omega t$	$V_{01}^2\cos^2\omega t$	Low pass $\omega_0 \ll 2\omega$	$V_{01}^2/2$	Intensity, power True r.m.s.
$V_{01}\cos\omega t$ $V_{01}\cos\omega t$	$V_{01}^2\cos^2\omega t$	High pass $\omega_0 \ll 2\omega$	$\dfrac{V_{01}^2}{2}\cos 2\omega t$	Second-harmonic generator
$V_{01}\cos\omega t$ $V_{02} \propto I_1 = \dfrac{V_{01}}{|Z|}\cos(\omega t + \phi)$	$\dfrac{1}{|Z|}V_{01}^2\cos\omega t\cos(\omega t+\phi)$	Low pass $\omega_0 \ll 2\omega$	$\dfrac{V_{01}^2}{2|Z|}\cos\phi$	Power
$V_{01}\cos\omega t$ $V_{02}\cos(\omega t+\phi)$	$V_{01}V_{02}\cos\omega t\cos(\omega t+\phi)$	Low pass $\omega_0 \ll 2\omega$	$\dfrac{V_{01}V_{02}}{2}\cos\phi$	PSD
$V_{01}\cos\omega_1 t$ $V_{02}\cos\omega_2 t$	$V_{01}V_{02}\cos\omega_1 t\cos\omega_2 t$	–	$\dfrac{V_{01}V_{02}}{2}\left[\cos(\omega_1+\omega_2)t + \cos(\omega_1-\omega_2)t\right]$	Mixing
$V_{01}\cos\omega_c t$ $V_{02}(1+a\cos\omega_m t)$	$V_{01}V_{02}(1+a\cos\omega_m t)\cos\omega_c t$	–	$V_{01}V_{02}(1+a\cos\omega_m t)\cos\omega_c t$	Amplitude modulation
$V_{01}(1+a\cos\omega_m t)\cos\omega_c t$ $V_{01}(1+a\cos\omega_m t)\cos\omega_c t$	$V_{01}^2(1+a\cos\omega_m t)^2\cos^2\omega_c t$	Low pass $\omega_m < \omega_0 \ll \omega_c$ High pass $\omega_0 < \omega_m$	$V_{01}^2 a\cos\omega_m t$	Amplitude demodulation

more common method is the 'transconductance multiplier' method shown in figure 6.12(b) in which one input V_1 is applied to an amplifier that has a gain or transconductance proportional to V_2. The output signal is thus proportional to $V_1 V_2$. In the most common design, a voltage-controlled current source (current mirror) is used to alter the gain of a differential amplifier.

At frequencies above about 1 MHz these techniques cease to be very accurate. Simplified transconductance multiplier circuits are used and these are usually called mixers or modulators. At even higher frequencies, much simpler circuits have to be used and these are normally based on simple non-linear elements such as the diode. All these circuits are usually 'balanced' so that the symmetry of the circuit is used to cancel out either the odd- or the even-order terms in the expansion of the non-linearity.

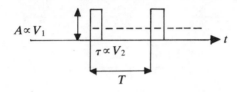

(a)

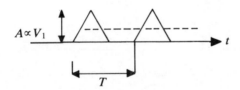

(b)

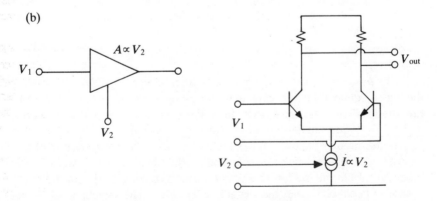

Fig. 6.12 Practical analog multipliers work by the generation of rectangular or triangular pulses as shown in (a) or by the use of a voltage-variable gain amplifier or transductance multiplier as shown in (b). The broken lines in (a) represent the output, which is the average of the input pulses.

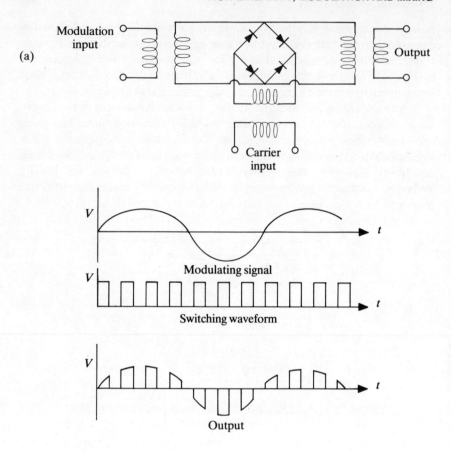

Fig. 6.13 Balanced multipliers for high-frequency use have a large-amplitude carrier signal which switches the modulating signal on and off as in (a) or between direct and inverting as in (b).

The modulators shown in figure 6.13 can best be analyzed by considering the high frequency carrier signal to have a large amplitude, so that it switches the diodes from having a very high impedance to having a negligible impedance to the smaller-amplitude modulating signal.

In the circuit of figure 6.13(a), the diodes have a high impedance for one half of the carrier waveform at ω_c and hence the signal at ω_m is passed. On the other half-cycle the diodes have a low impedance compared with the signal source impedance so that the signal is attenuated. The switching waveform can be written as the Fourier series of a positive-only square wave (see appendix 3)

$$\tfrac{1}{2} + (2/\pi)(\cos\omega_c t - \tfrac{1}{3}\cos 3\omega_c t + \dots) \tag{6.8}$$

(b)

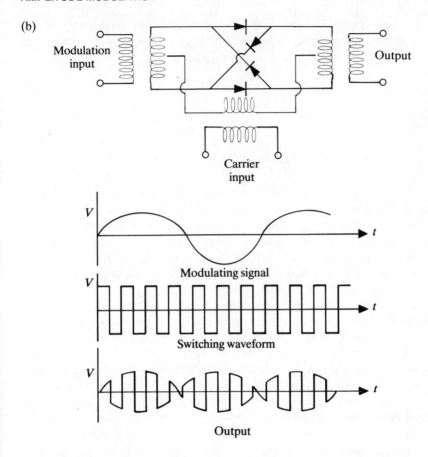

Fig. 6.13 Continued.

which multiplies the modulation signal $V_m \cos \omega_m t$ to give

$$V_{out} = V_m \cos \omega_m t [\tfrac{1}{2} + (2/\pi)(\cos \omega_c t - \tfrac{1}{3} \cos 3\omega_c t + \ldots)]$$
$$= (V_m/2) \cos \omega_m t + (V_m/\pi)[\cos(\omega_c + \omega_m)t + \cos(\omega_c - \omega_m)t] + \ldots \quad (6.9)$$

This contains no component at the carrier frequency even if a large signal is applied provided that the system is well matched. The modulation signal is multiplied by each Fourier component of the square wave so that all odd harmonics of ω_c will have sidebands.

The ring modulator shown in figure 6.13(b) is similar but produces full-wave modulation. The carrier signal switches the diodes so that the modulating signal is connected directly or in reverse to the output. The switching waveform is thus a symmetrical square wave

$$(4/\pi)[\cos\omega_c t - \tfrac{1}{3}\cos 3\omega_c t + \ldots] \tag{6.10}$$

to give

$$V_{\text{out}} = (2V_m/\pi)[\cos(\omega_c + \omega_m)t + \cos(\omega_c - \omega_m)t] + \ldots \tag{6.11}$$

For detection or demodulation of an amplitude-modulated signal, a square-law detector (table 6.1) or the square-law term of a general non-linear element can be used (figure 6.5). The simplest method however is to use a diode, or a balanced set of diodes, with a large-amplitude signal so that the diode acts as a voltage-controlled switch operated by the signal itself. A circuit such as those shown in figure 6.4 is suitable. This is the *linear* (although the diode is inherently non-linear) or *envelope* detector.

A typical detector is shown in figure 6.14. The large signal is applied across the diode and a resistance R, where $R_{\text{diode}}(\text{on}) \ll R \ll R_{\text{diode}}(\text{off})$, so that no voltage is developed across R for negative half-cycles and the full voltage appears for positive half-cycles. The signal is thus rectified and the mean value is obtained by passing it through a low-pass filter and a final high-pass filter removes the d.c. (z.f.) signal to leave just the modulation. In practice the low-pass filter is obtained by adding a capacitor C_1 in parallel with R and the high-pass filter is obtained by adding a capacitor C_2 in series with the load resistance R_L. Then, provided C_2 is small, the low-pass filter characteristic frequency is approximately $\omega_{01} \simeq 1/C_1 R_{\text{diode}}(\text{on})$ and the high-pass filter characteristic frequency is approximately $\omega_{02} \simeq 1/C_2 R_L$.

A full analysis can be done by analyzing the spectrum of the signal after rectification, $V_{\text{out}}(1)$. This consists of a half sine wave with amplitude modulation at ω_m. If the input signal is $V_0(1 + a\cos\omega_m t)\cos\omega_c t$ then the carrier sine-wave factor $\cos\omega_c t$ is replaced by the Fourier series of a half cosine wave to give

$$V_{\text{out}}(1) = V_0(1 + a\cos\omega_m t)\left(\frac{1}{\pi} + \tfrac{1}{2}\cos\omega_c t + \sum_{n=1}^{\infty}(-1)^{n+1}\frac{2\cos 2n\omega_c t}{\pi(4n^2 - 1)}\right) \tag{6.12}$$

which has components at all odd harmonics of ω_c. The filter characteristics can be introduced to give the final output signal

$$V_{\text{out}}(3) = \frac{V_0}{\pi}a\cos\omega_m t \tag{6.13}$$

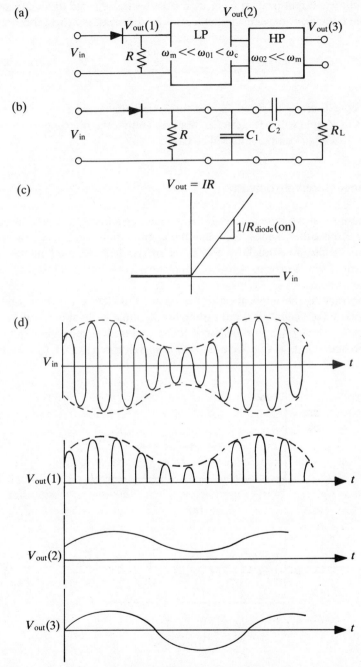

Fig. 6.14 A typical demodulator or detector circuit shown in functional form in (a), the circuit in (b), the diode large-signal approximation used in (c), and the waveforms in parts of circuit in (d).

If full-wave rectification were used with some balanced diode arrangement, then the Fourier series has only even components and (6.12) becomes

$$V_{out}(1) = V_0(1 + a\cos\omega_m t)\left(\frac{2}{\pi} - \sum_{n=1}^{\infty} \frac{4\cos 2n\omega_c t}{\pi(4n^2 - 1)}\right) \tag{6.14}$$

In this case there is no term ω_c and the lowest unwanted frequency components in $V_{out}(1)$ will be nearer $2\omega_c$ than ω_c, so that the filtering to separate ω_m from the other components will be easier.

The phase-sensitive detector

The phase-sensitive detector (PSD) is a signal-processing device that goes under various other names, including the combinations of: phase-sensitive/coherent/synchronous/tracking and detector/rectifier. Related names are homodyne, synchrodyne, product detector, correlation detector, and radiometer detector.

Contrary to the implication in the name, this device is rarely used to detect phase (see later). It is most often used to take a signal in a bandwidth $2\Delta f$ at a frequency f_0 and translate it to be centered at zero frequency, as shown in figure 6.15. A sine wave at $f = f_0$ is thus changed to a z.f. (d.c.) signal

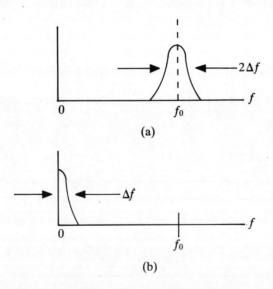

Fig. 6.15   The phase-sensitive detector (PSD) takes information at frequencies near f_0 (a) and converts it to information near zero frequency (b).

proportional to the input amplitude. A frequency $f = f_0 \pm f_m$ is translated to a sine wave at $+f_m$ and $-f_m$ (these differ in phase by π) with the efficiency decreasing for $f_m \gtrsim \Delta f$. The signals $f_0 \pm f_m$ correspond to sidebands of f_0. Thus the bandwidth Δf is needed to accommodate an amplitude modulation at frequencies f_m up to Δf and this amplitude modulation is changed to a signal at f_m with an amplitude proportional to the modulation amplitude. Alternately, a bandwidth Δf is needed for signals that change their amplitude over a time shorter than $1/\Delta f$.

The net result is that of a narrow band-pass filter plus an amplitude modulation detector (rectifier). As well as performing the useful function of detection, it has a major advantage in improving the signal-to-noise (S/N) ratio since noise occurs fairly evenly over the spectrum, whereas signals often occur over narrow bands centered at well defined frequencies (e.g. $2\Delta f$ at f_0).

There are two extra features that make the PSD more useful than a simple band-pass filter followed by a detector:

(a) The center frequency f_0 is determined by a separately supplied 'reference' signal and will follow it as it is varied in frequency or phase.
(b) Unlike a conventional band-pass filter the bandwidth can be adjusted easily and accurately in both width $(2\Delta f)$ and sharpness over a wide range since it is defined by a low-pass filter above 0 Hz. Thus filters with extremely large effective Q $(f_0/2\Delta f)$ can be simply constructed.

The analysis of the PSD can be made by studying the signal in the time domain or the frequency domain. We will consider the former first. The simplest form of PSD can be represented by the switch circuit shown in figure 6.16. The signal is either passed unchanged or is inverted with alternations at alternate half-cycles of the reference signal V_{ref} at f_0. The reference signal is usually applied as a sine wave and it is made into a squared wave internally. The signal then passes through a low-pass filter (width Δf). Figure 6.17 shows the waveforms of V_{in}, V_{ref}, and the output waveforms after the switching circuit $V_{out}(1)$ and finally $V_{out}(2)$, which is the dashed average value (or d.c. component).

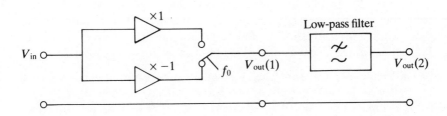

Fig. 6.16 The basic operation of the PSD.

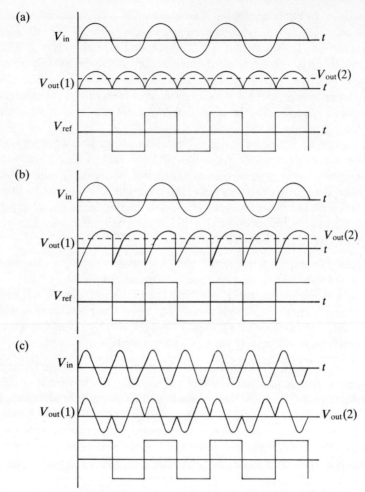

Fig. 6.17 The waveforms at the input and output of the PSD for (a) a sine wave at the
same frequency and in phase with the reference signal, (b) a constant
phase difference between the input and reference signals, and (c) an input
signal at twice the reference signal frequency and in phase with it.

Figure 6.17(a) shows the result of an input sine wave at the same
frequency and in phase with the reference. Figure 6.17(b) shows the effect of a
phase-shift and figure 6.17(c) the result for an input sine wave at $2f_0$.
Inspection should give the effect of the PSD on the following input signals:

(a) All values of phase-shift when V_{in} is at f_0. Note the output sign inversion if
$\pi > \phi > 2\pi$. Normally ϕ is adjusted to zero to give a maximum output.

(b) An input signal at $f_0 + f_m$ where $f_m \ll \Delta f_0$. This is best analyzed by
considering f_m as a slowly varying phase and using (a) above.

(c) Input signals at $f_0 \pm f_m$ where $f_m \gg \Delta f$.

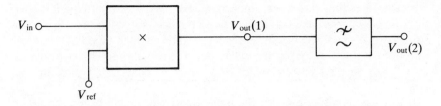

Fig. 6.18   The PSD considered as a multiplier followed by a low-pass filter.

(d) Input signals at $2f_0$, $3f_0$, etc., and all phases. Note that odd and even harmonics of f_0 behave differently and for odd harmonics the relative efficiency of detection decreases as $1/n$ for a harmonic nf_0.

(e) A square wave at f_0 for all phases. In this case there is no signal lost in the low-pass filter if $\phi = 0$ and hence this is in some ways the most efficient arrangement.

The PSD operation can also be described by considering it as a mixer.

Consider the circuit of figure 6.18 with an input $V_1 \cos(\omega_1 t + \phi)$ and a sine-wave reference $V_0 \cos \omega_0 t$. The multiplier output is

$$V_{out}(1) = V_1 V_0 \cos(\omega_1 t + \phi) \cos \omega_0 t$$
$$= \tfrac{1}{2} V_1 V_2 \{\cos[(\omega_0 + \omega_1) t + \phi] + \cos[(\omega_0 - \omega_1) t + \phi]\} \qquad (6.15)$$

If $\omega_0 \sim \omega_1 \gg 2\pi \Delta f$ then the first term is filtered out and

$$V_{out}(2) = \tfrac{1}{2} V_1 V_0 \cos[(\omega_0 - \omega_1) t + \phi] \qquad (6.16)$$

If the reference input V_0 and ϕ are constant then

$$V_{out}(2) \propto V_1$$

In the previous analysis a switch was used as the multiplier and the signal was multiplied by a square wave alternating between ± 1 at a frequency f_0. The switch multiplier is used rather than an analog multiplier because it is much easier to make with stable amplitude and accurate waveforms. In practice a transistor switch is used.

The use of a square wave instead of a sine wave for multiplication means, however, that the system is equivalent to the multiplication in the circuit of figure 6.18 by each of the Fourier components of the square wave. These are the odd harmonics with weight $1/n$ as we have seen before.

This does illustrate a very important point. With a switch-type PSD the filtering effect is not like that in figure 6.15 but like that in figure 6.19. Thus a square-wave signal will be efficiently detected by a switch-type PSD, but the output for a sine-wave input at f_0 will be degraded by the noise from the bands at $3f_0$, $5f_0$, etc., which is also detected unless a separate low-pass filter is added.

For use as a phase-meter the input frequency is also f_0 and the input amplitude must also be stabilized. The two circuits described so far give an output $\sim \cos \phi$ if a sine-wave input is used. If the input signal is a square wave, the switch-type circuit gives an output $\sim \phi$. The PSD has a theoretical advantage of a factor of 2 in signal-to-noise ratio compared with non-coherent

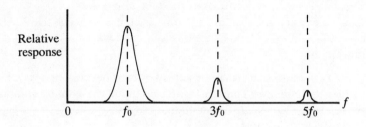

Fig. 6.19   The relative response of the switch-type PSD.

amplitude detectors. This is because the input and reference signals are adjusted to be in phase. Out-of-phase, orthogonal (noise) signals are thus not detected in the PSD. The total noise power at any frequency can be split up into two equal orthogonal components and only one of these will pass through the detector. In practice, the advantage is considerably more because of the higher Q, larger dynamic range, etc.

Figure 6.20 shows how the signal-to-noise (power) ratio is altered by a detector. The PSD has the 3 dB advantage mentioned above. For large input signal-to-noise ratio the linear detector has no loss in signal-to-noise between output and input, whereas the square-law detector degrades the signal because of the noise introduced at the signal frequency from other parts of the spectrum. The advantage of the PSD is emphasized at low S/N where the signal is less than the noise. Under these conditions the S/N is still not degraded since the reference signal provides the knowledge of which frequency components are signal and which are noise. The linear detector of large S/N has good performance because the large signal component at ω_c switches the diode at ω_c (see figure 6.14) in a similar way that the reference signal does in a PSD. The 3 dB loss arises because the detector cannot distinguish the in-phase and out-of-phase components.

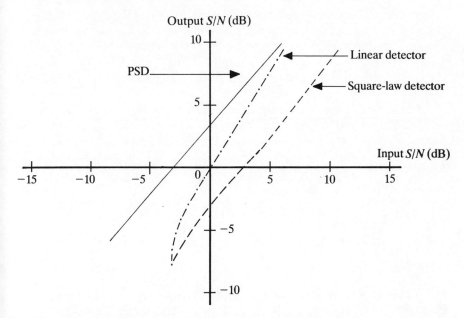

Fig. 6.20 The effect on the signal-to-noise ratio of different types of amplitude modulation detectors.

If the reference and input signals are both derived from the same source and a high-quality on–off switch is used as the detector, the PSD performance can be very high in dynamic range and detectable level. The limitations are usually in the stability of the d.c. part of the circuit after the detector and of any phase-shifting networks such as might be in the reference part of the circuit.

Chopper amplifier

An important application of modulation and detection methods is the *chopper amplifier*. This is a method of producing a high-quality d.c. (z.f.) amplifier. Conventional d.c. (z.f.) amplifiers have a poor performance since zero frequency is a unique frequency and many unwanted signals, or noise, appear at or near this frequency. Examples are thermoelectric e.m.f.s due to temperature differences in the circuits containing different conductors and low-frequency ($1/f$) noise. Also in a d.c. amplifier circuit there is no way of distinguishing between the bias and signal circuits, so that any small change in the bias point or device characteristics of the first stage are amplified and change the bias point of later stages as well as appearing as a signal.

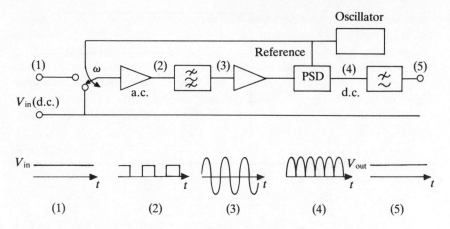

Fig. 6.21   The circuit diagram and typical signals of a chopper amplifier.

The chopper amplifier shown in figure 6.21 overcomes these problems by changing the z.f. signal to a high-frequency a.c. signal for amplification. The input signal modulates a carrier and after amplification the detection, and hence translation back to z.f., is carried out by a PSD. In practice the signal will not be true z.f. but have some bandwidth Δf extending above 0 Hz. The a.c. amplifier must therefore have a bandwidth $2\Delta f$ symmetrical about the carrier frequency and the final low-pass filter must have a bandwidth Δf. For the highest precision the modulation is carried out by a switch, or chopper, which periodically passes or blocks the signal into the amplifier. The carrier is thus a square wave with an amplitude equal to the input signal amplitude.

FREQUENCY MODULATION

Expressions for frequency modulation (FM) and phase modulation (PM) were given earlier as $V_0 \cos[(\omega_c + b \cos \omega_m t)t + \phi]$ and $V_0 \cos(\omega_c t + c \cos \omega_m t)$. These are very closely related since for a signal $V_0 \cos \Phi$, where the phase $\Phi = \omega t + \phi$, we can describe the frequency ω as $d\Phi/dt$. Thus modulation of the frequency corresponds to the modulation of the differential of the phase. Only FM will be considered here.

Frequency modulation has an advantage over amplitude modulation in that the same results can be achieved with a worse signal-to-noise ratio for the signal into the receiver. This will be considered in the section on information theory at the end of this chapter but it is basically because there are many sidebands in FM and these are well spread in frequency so that it is less likely that noise will occur in the correct amplitude and phase in all the sidebands simultaneously and hence be detected as a signal. Another advantage is that the signal amplitude and hence power is constant so that the modulator design is easier. The receiver and detector can easily improve an incoming signal by making the amplitude constant again. Interfering signals usually add or subtract from the signal to cause apparent amplitude modulation. In an FM detector this can easily be removed by making the signal amplitude constant but in an AM detector it is detected and appears as a noise signal.

If the carrier signal is a sine wave, frequency modulation is usually accomplished using a *voltage-variable capacitor*, *varactor* or *varicap*. This is a semiconductor diode used in reverse bias so that it has a high resistance. The charge distribution within the diode is such that it acts like a small capacitance. The magnitude of this capacitance varies with the applied voltage bias. A schematic circuit of an FM modulator is shown in figure 6.22. An oscillator is constructed with an amplifier and an LCR circuit tuned to the carrier frequency. Some amplitude control is incorporated so that the oscillation amplitude is small and not sufficient to affect the value of the capacitance, which is a varactor. A large modulating bias voltage at the modulating frequency ω_m is applied across the varactor to change the oscillation frequency. The resistance R_1 and the capacitance C_1 are both large so that the modulation bias circuit does not affect the tuned circuit and the bias signal is not lost through the inductance L_1, which has a low, low-frequency, impedance. Some non-linear network may have to be added in the modulating circuit so that the frequency change is proportional to the modulating voltage, since varactors do not all have a suitable C–V relationship.

The principle of one method of *FM demodulation* or *FM detection* is

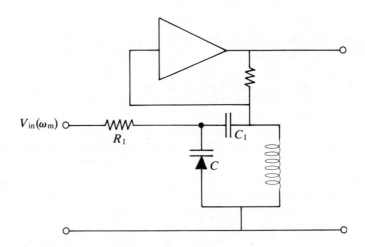

Fig. 6.22 A schematic circuit of a frequency modulator.

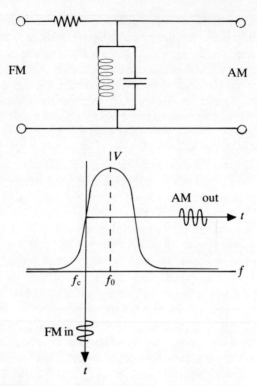

Fig. 6.23 A schematic circuit of an FM demodulator that converts the FM to AM, which is later itself demodulated.

shown in figure 6.23. The FM signal is applied to an *LC* band-pass circuit tuned to a frequency $f_0 \pm f_c$ such that a change in the input frequency produces a change in the amplitude of the output signal proportional to the frequency change. The FM is thus changed into AM, which is detected in the way described earlier. In practice a balanced circuit is used to make the conversion more linear. Other methods will be described in the next sections.

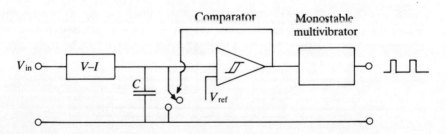

Fig. 6.24 A schematic circuit of one type of voltage-to-frequency converter.

If the carrier is a square wave, frequency modulation is accomplished by a *voltage-controlled oscillator* (VCO) or a *voltage-to-frequency* (V–f) *converter*. One form of VCO, the function generator, has been described in chapter 3. Others operate in a very similar way. The VCO, function generator, and some V–f converters produce a square-wave output. Many V–f converters, however, produce a train of pulses of constant height and length with a rate proportional to the applied voltage. A typical circuit is shown in figure 6.24. The input voltage is converted into a current, which charges a capacitor until a certain voltage is reached. This is sensed by a comparator, which discharges the capacitor ready for the next cycle. The comparator signal also starts a monostable multivibrator, which generates the output pulse.

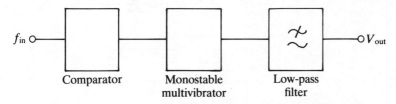

f_{in} V_{out}

           Comparator   Monostable   Low-pass
                           multivibrator   filter

Fig. 6.25 A schematic circuit of one type of frequency-to-voltage converter.

The reverse operation to the V–f converter is the *frequency-voltage* (f–V) *converter*, which is thus one form of FM demodulator. In the basic circuit shown in figure 6.25 the input frequency signal is made into a train of voltage pulses of equal amplitude and length at the input frequency using a monostable multivibrator. A low-pass filter then calculates the average value, which is proportional to the frequency. In practice charge pulses may be used instead of voltage pulses, but similar averaging is performed to obtain the average value. A phase-locked loop, which is described next, can also be used with a V–f converter in its feedback loop to give f–V conversion.

Phase-locked loop

The phase-locked loop (PLL) is a feedback circuit which can be used for several functions involving the manipulation of frequency signals. The basic circuit is shown in figure 6.26 and it can be obtained as an integrated circuit. It consists of a phase-sensitive detector (PSD) followed by a low-pass filter to give a low-frequency or d.c. output which is used to control the frequency of a voltage-controlled oscillator (VCO). The VCO output is used as the reference signal to the PSD. For a particular application either the voltage output V_{out} from the PSD and filter or the frequency output f_{out} from the VCO may be used. The VCO signal is normally a square wave.

To analyze the operation consider a constant-amplitude square-wave input signal at a fixed frequency and assume initially that the VCO is operating very near to this frequency. The loop will stabilize in a condition such that the phase difference between f_{in} and f_{out} is sufficient to generate a voltage V_{out} in the PSD which is that required by the VCO to keep its operating frequency. The size of the equilibrium phase difference is governed by the loop gain and this is largely determined by the V–f sensitivity of the VCO. The stability of the feedback loop is governed by the frequency

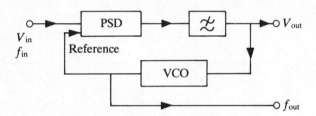

Fig. 6.26   A schematic circuit of a phase-locked loop.

response of the loop gain. If the input frequency changes, the system will adjust so that f_{out} follows f_{in} and the equilibrium phase difference and hence V_{out} will vary accordingly. If the natural frequency of the VCO is equal to f_{in} and hence $V_{out} = 0$, then there will be a phase difference of 90° between f_{in} and f_{out}. The VCO frequency will follow f_{in} until this phase difference reaches its maximum values 0 or 180°, when the loop will cease to work. The range of frequencies for operation, the *hold-in* range, will depend on the details of the circuit.

If the initial conditions are such that $f_{in} \neq f_{out}$ then the PSD produces an a.c. output signal at the difference frequency. If this difference frequency is not too far above the cut-off frequency of the low-pass filter, it will modulate the frequency of the VCO until $f_{out} = f_{in}$ and the loop becomes locked. In general the range of frequencies over which the loop can become locked, the *pull-in* range, is less than the hold-in range and a given circuit can be designed to optimize one of these ranges at the expense of the other.

The PLL can be used to improve a frequency signal since the low-pass filter will smooth out any changes in the PSD output so that f_{out} will be the time average of f_{in}. The PLL can be used directly as an FM demodulator since V_{out} will be directly proportional to the frequency difference between f_{in} and the natural frequency of the VCO, which is the frequency of operation when the loop is opened at $V_{out} = 0$. For this application the amplitude of the input signal must be kept constant so that an amplitude limiter must be used.

Frequency modulation can also be performed if the modulation signal voltage is added to the d.c. voltage in the loop controlling the VCO.

The PLL can also be used as an AM detector. If the input signal has a large signal-to-noise ratio, its amplitude can be made constant and then fed to the PLL. The PLL output frequency will be at the carrier frequency and this signal can be used as the reference signal for another PSD which is used to detect the original input signal. Thus, provided that the input S/N is not too low, the circuit will generate its own reference signal. Phase information is lost and the circuit has a performance intermediate between those of the full PSD and the linear detector.

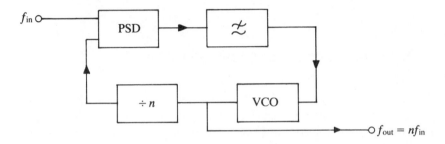

Fig. 6.27   A phase-locked loop circuit to generate a multiple of the input frequency.

The PLL can also generate harmonics such that $f_{\text{out}} = nf_{\text{in}}$ where n is an integer. The bistable elements, flip-flops, described in chapter 5, can be used to generate a subharmonic, $f_{\text{out}} = f_{\text{in}}/m$ where m is an integer, by frequency division. Although non-linear circuit elements allow a harmonic to be generated, the process is usually inefficient and also many other harmonics are also generated so that filtering and perhaps processing with a PLL may be needed to make the signal clearer. In the frequency range in which logic circuits can be used, harmonic generation can be performed by placing the easily accomplished subharmonic generation operation within the negative feedback loop. This is shown in figure 6.27. A high-frequency VCO is used at the harmonic frequency and its output is reduced in frequency by a frequency divider to produce a signal at the input frequency.

FREQUENCY SYNTHESIS

In this chapter we have seen that frequencies can be manipulated and that the following operations can be performed: nf, f/m, $f_1 - f_2$, $f_1 + f_2$, as well as filtering to separate individual frequency components, and the use of the PLL to average or 'clean' a frequency signal. It is therefore possible to generate a range of frequencies from a single very stable and accurately known frequency source such as a quartz oscillator or atomic standard. These output frequencies will have an accurately known frequency and phase relationship with each other and the original source, governed by the particular operations that have been performed. The operation is called *frequency synthesis*. The straightforward approach in which harmonics and subharmonics are generated and then the appropriate components added or subtracted to give the required frequency usually presents problems in filtering to distinguish the components, so that often the frequencies are used to modulate a carrier signal and the modulated signal is then manipulated.

PARAMETRIC OSCILLATORS AND AMPLIFIERS

The use of non-linear resistances has been described earlier in this chapter. There are also non-linear reactances. Although the saturation of the core of an inductance or transformer has been used to produce a voltage-variable reactance, the voltage-variable capacitance or *varactor* is most frequently used. This device has the conventional diode I–V characteristics at z.f. (d.c.) but it is designed so that its a.c., small-signal, capacitance in reverse bias is large and very voltage-variable. A typical variation is shown in figure 6.28. For typical devices the capacitance at $V = 0$ is between 10 and 1000 pF and the variation in capacitance is between about 4:1 and 20:1 over the allowed voltage range. The use of the varactor as an FM modulator or VCO has already been described.

If a large signal is applied to a varactor, its non-linear properties cause the generation of harmonics.

A common use of the varactor is in the *parametric amplifier*. This amplifier has low noise characteristics because it uses only reactances with low

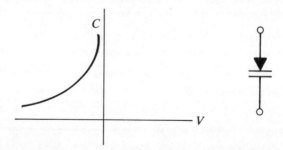

Fig. 6.28   The symbol and C–V characteristic of the varactor diode.

loss so that there is no thermal noise. The capacitor is in reverse bias so that no d.c. current flows and thus there is little shot noise. In the simplest form of parametric amplifier, the small-amplitude signal is applied to an LC tuned circuit resonant at the signal frequency. A separate large-amplitude signal at twice this frequency is applied to change the capacitance. The phase is such that the capacitance is decreased when the charge, Q_s, on the capacitance due to the signal is at a maximum and hence the signal energy $\frac{1}{2}Q_s^2/C$ is increased. The capacitance is restored when Q_s is zero, so that there is no signal change. Since the signal energy depends on Q_s^2, this operation can be repeated twice per cycle and the net result is an increase in the signal energy. This increase in energy is derived from the source, the pump, which modulates the capacitance.

INFORMATION THEORY

Information theory has a fundamental importance comparable to that of thermodynamics. There is considerable similarity between the measure of information and the statistical interpretation of entropy. An ability to measure the information content of a message, statement or picture is valuable for calculating the required memory or storage capacity that is needed in a system or the time and transmission rate that is needed to send it over a telecommunication system.

It is apparent that the term 'information' in its normal use is somewhat subjective, so that a message that is of great importance to one person or instrument may be of no interest or may not be understood by another. The same message content may be sent in a succinct or in a lengthy, verbose or redundant form. Thus the measure of information described here is always the maximum information content.

We consider the message to be split up into n elements. In each element, one of Q different symbols or distinguishable states can be placed. These Q states may be bits, digits, letters, colors or levels of intensity. Then the maximum information content is given by

$$I_{max} = n \log_2 Q \qquad \text{bits} \qquad (6.17)$$

For example, in a binary message, each bit may be 0 or 1 so that $Q = 2$ and $I_{max} = n$ bits. Thus the units are consistent with the binary digital usage. For a decimal number, $Q = 10$ and the maximum information content for an n-digit number will be $n \log_2 10$ bits. For a practical numerical message there will also be spaces and extra message elements to identify the purpose of each number. For an alphanumeric message Q will be large, with 26 letters, 10 digits, a space and perhaps punctuation marks. The standard teletype code ASCII (see chapter 10) uses seven bits for each message unit so that Q could have $2^7 = 128$ possible values. Real languages are very inefficient since all possible letters cannot be used in each space because only some combinations make known or pronounceable words. The information content is thus considerably less than the maximum.

More complicated messages can also be split up and the information content estimated. A picture, such as a television picture, can be split up into a number of individual elements defined by the spatial resolution. Each of the n elements can take one of a certain number Q of distinguishable intensity levels and colors so that the information content will be $n \log_2 Q$.

For a communication channel it is convenient to express equation (6.17) in the frequency domain and this is the *Shannon–Hartley law*

$$C_{max} = \Delta f \log_2 \left(1 + \frac{S}{N} \right) \qquad \text{bits/second} \qquad (6.18)$$

which gives the maximum information transfer rate, C_{max}, through a channel in terms of Δf, the channel bandwidth, and S/N, the power signal-to-noise ratio. A full derivation is given in most telecommunication texts. In a bandwidth Δf a total of n/second $= \Delta f$ distinguishable pulses can be sent and each has $Q = (N + S)/N$ distinguishable heights. This formula illustrates that a signal may be transmitted equally on a wide-bandwidth system as is used with FM at a lower S/N than on a narrow-bandwidth AM system.

FURTHER READING

F. R. Connor, *Modulation*, Edward Arnold (1982).
M. L. Meade, *Lock-in Amplifiers: Principles and Applications*, Peter Peregrinus (1983).
J. J. O'Reilly, *Telecommunication Principles*, Van Nostrand Reinhold (1984).
F. G. Stremler, *Introduction to Communication Systems*, Addison-Wesley (1982).
T. H. Wilmhurst, *Signal Recovery from Noise in Electronic Instrumentation*, Adam Hilger (1985).

7 BRIDGES

INTRODUCTION

The use of potentiometers and bridges is fundamental to electrical measurements. The same principle of balancing one effect against another to produce a null also applies to other measurement systems. However, active circuit techniques have made their use less frequent than formerly. For example, the high input impedance advantage of potentiometer voltage measurements has been superseded by high input impedance amplifiers and digital voltmeters. Also many commercial 'bridges' now use other techniques such as direct voltage-to-current ratio measurements. However, the basic principles underlying the operation of the potentiometer and the bridge are still necessary for the elegant and economic design of experiments.

THE POTENTIAL DIVIDER

The basic potential divider or potentiometer consists of two impedances in series (figure 7.1). If no current is drawn from the circuit by the load or detector at the junction of the impedances, then

$$V_2 = V_1 \mathbf{Z}_2 / (\mathbf{Z}_1 + \mathbf{Z}_2) \tag{7.1}$$

The voltage ratio is thus determined by an impedance ratio $\mathbf{Z}_1/\mathbf{Z}_2$. It should be noted that if V_1 is not an ideal source, or is not arranged to be kept constant by keeping $(\mathbf{Z}_1 + \mathbf{Z}_2)$ constant, then V_1 may vary. The full circuit consists of the Thévenin source voltage V_0 and its internal impedance $\mathbf{Z}_s$. The output impedance of the potentiometer is $\mathbf{Z}_1$ and $\mathbf{Z}_2$ in parallel, $\mathbf{Z}_1 \| \mathbf{Z}_2 = \mathbf{Z}_1 \mathbf{Z}_2 / (\mathbf{Z}_1 + \mathbf{Z}_2)$ if $\mathbf{Z}_s$ can be neglected.

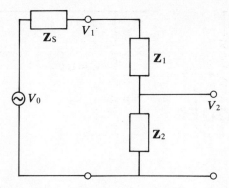

Fig. 7.1 The full potential divider circuit including the Thévenin equivalent circuit of the power supply.

Figure 7.2 shows some of the uses of the potentiometer. If a uniform resistance wire or chain of resistances (as shown in figures 7.2(a) and (b)) can be made accurately, then the output voltage is proportional to the distance x or the output position. Therefore, voltage ratios can be determined by resistance or position ratios independent of the source voltage or source impedance, as shown in figure 7.2(c). Note that for accuracy no current should flow through the output terminals. In many cases, impedances, and especially impedance ratios, can be bought or made with very high precision, accuracy, and uniformity, so that such methods can be powerful. However, digital voltmeters and frequency meters often enable much higher precision (number of digits on the output) and accuracy to be obtained, so that many measuring techniques are now based on these instruments. The general principle of generating a fraction of a voltage by means of a resistance chain is widely used. The same idea is also used in analog systems with other variables.

Figure 7.2(d) shows the use of a potentiometer for the measurement of an unknown voltage, $V(?)$, which has a high internal impedance. The potentiometer voltage is balanced against this voltage with a null detector. At the detector null, no current flows and the unknown and the potentiometer voltages are equal. Since no current flows the measuring system has an effective infinite input impedance. Since it is used at null, the detector need not have good linearity or dynamic range but just a high sensitivity for small signals.

Resistive potentiometers with a sliding contact are often used together with a voltage generator as a variable voltage source. In this case care should be taken that little current is passed through the contact since its resistance may vary with time to produce a noise voltage in the circuit. Similar problems can also arise if the device is used as a variable resistance between one end of the resistance and the sliding contact.

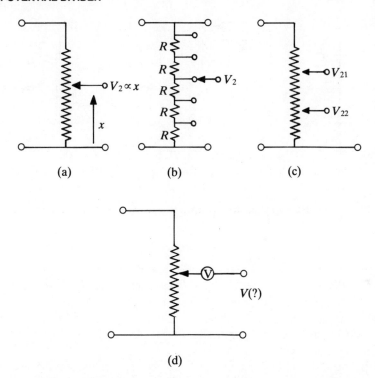

Fig. 7.2 Some uses of the potentiometer: (a) and (b) as a continuous or stepped voltage with position, (c) to measure a voltage ratio, and (d) to measure an unknown voltage with a large internal impedance.

Reactive potential dividers can also be used as shown in figures 7.3(a) and (b). These configurations are not so common as the resistive potentiometers since such components are not readily available in variable or tapped form and the input impedances depend on frequency. However, they do have the advantage that the components can be very ideal and it is easy to construct accurate ratios of capacitances and inductances since the values depend in a known way on their geometry.

The *autotransformer, ratio transformer* or *inductive ratio divider* shown in figure 7.3(c) is also a potentiometer, but the presence of a magnetic core coupling the two inductances produces a mutual inductance that gives it properties beyond that of the simple inductive divider. A current flowing in any turn produces a change in the magnetization of the whole core. Any flux change in the core produces an equal induced voltage in each turn round the core. The net result is that the voltage across each turn is equal although the currents applied to or drawn from individual turns may not be equal. The

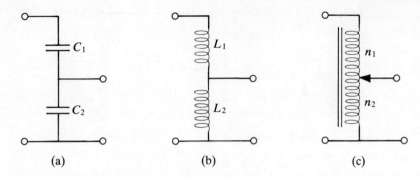

Fig. 7.3 Capacitive and inductive potential dividers (a) and (b) and the auto-transformer or inductive ratio divider (c).

effective output impedance is very small and the voltage ratio between any two terminal pairs in the circuit depends only on the number of turns between the pairs. The voltage ratio thus reduces to a simple counting of the turns. This high accuracy is achieved because of the large permeability that can be obtained in the magnetic core material. Hence good materials and a well designed magnetic circuit are needed.

Because of the low impedances involved, the circuit may be used as a voltage or a current device, and this will be developed later in the chapter. The autotransformer is also used as a power device (Variac) since it acts essentially as a variable turns-ratio transformer if the output tap can be moved. However, it should be noted that it does not have the same safety advantage of a transformer because there is a common earth connection between the input ('primary') and output ('secondary') circuits. Also for signal use the autotransformer will not break earth loops and does not have the high common-mode signal rejection of the transformer.

BRIDGES

The basic bridge arrangement is shown in figure 7.4. At balance the output voltage ΔV is zero and then

$$\mathbf{Z}_1/\mathbf{Z}_2 = \mathbf{Z}_3/\mathbf{Z}_4 \qquad (7.2)$$

For a.c. signals the bridge has to be balanced in amplitude and phase, so that two balance conditions are implied. These two conditions can alternately be described as balances of the in-phase and out-of-phase components of the signal or the resistive and reactive parts of the bridge. The balance or null condition gives the relationship between the impedances above and this is independent of the type of source, voltage or current, or its quality, magnitude or internal impedance. If the balance is not frequency-dependent, then the waveform or frequency stability of the source is also not important. Similarly the input impedance and linearity of the null detector are not important. The precision of the balance point is, however, dependent on the amplitude of the source and the detector sensitivity and noise. Optimum sensitivity is obtained for a high-impedance detector when $Z_1 = Z_2$ and $Z_3 = Z_4$.

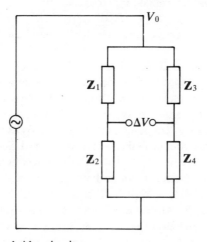

Fig. 7.4 The basic a.c. bridge circuit.

The bridge null detector can take many forms provided that it has high sensitivity and low noise. Since the high sensitivity is needed only at null, the detector response is sometimes made non-linear so that the effective gain is reduced for large off-balance signals (chapter 2). In an a.c. bridge a narrow-bandwidth r.m.s. detector is often used. Since there are two balance conditions, both the in-phase and out-of-phase (90° phase difference) signals must be nulled. If phase-sensitive detectors are to be used, two are needed with reference signals accurately at 90° to each other. In that case the phases of the reference signals should be chosen so that each of the phases is affected mainly by only one of the variable components of the bridge.

The bridge circuit may be used in two ways, *at null* and *near null*. When used *at null* the balance condition of equation (7.2), $Z_1/Z_2 = Z_3/Z_4$, is independent of many of the circuit components, as described before, and so it allows determination of an unknown impedance from a standard impedance and an impedance ratio or alternately from three known impedances. Thus only the values of passive components are used, the standard impedance can be of high accuracy or its value can be determined from first principles, and the ratio of two impedances may be very accurate although the actual values may not be known well. A suitable choice of bridge design will enable an impedance of a particular type and size, a large value inductance for example, to be measured by comparison with available standard impedances, say a resistance ratio and small variable capacitors. Such considerations often determine the choice of bridge.

The geometries of some of the more common designs of bridge are shown in figure 7.5. The Wheatstone bridge uses only resistances and can be used with either d.c. or a.c. excitation. The presence of stray reactances may require a small trimming capacitor across one arm to enable a perfect balance to be achieved using a.c. The direct comparison bridge uses a simple resistive ratio arm R_1, R_2 to compare the unknown impedance $C_3(?)$ with a known variable C_4. In general the specimen C_3 will be studied for its physical properties, which may include some loss. To balance the bridge, some loss will have to be introduced into the bridge arm containing C_4 and this can be done with either a parallel or a series known variable resistance. The parallel combination C_{4p}, R_{4p} and the series combination C_{4s}, R_{4s} are equivalent circuits and the choice will depend on whether large (parallel) or small (series) standard resistances are available. The Wien and Schering bridges give resistive and capacitive balances. The unknown may be either $C_3 R_3$ or $C_4 R_4$ in each case. The Hartshorn bridge balances the real mutual inductance, $M(?)$, and its loss, $r(?)$, against a standard mutual inductance, M, and a standard resistance, R. At null the voltage V is zero since the out-of-phase voltage due to $m(?)$ is balanced by that induced in M while the in-phase voltage due to the loss in $m(?)$ is balanced by the voltage developed across r. This circuit is used to study the permeability and loss in samples placed as cores within the unknown mutual inductance.

The use of a bridge *near null* is valuable for the observation of small changes in a component and especially in the comparison of the properties of two very similar components in order to investigate differences. Near null the offset voltage $\Delta V \propto \Delta Z / Z$, which is the fractional change in any of the components from the value at null.

The advantage of the bridge method can be seen. The detector has to measure ΔV to the accuracy needed in ΔZ. Without the bridge, Z and $Z + \Delta Z$ would have to be measured directly and subtracted. The direct measurement of V/I and $(V + \Delta V)/I$ would have to be made to a very high precision if $\Delta Z \ll Z$ and hence $\Delta V \ll V$.

To illustrate the advantages of the bridge method in experiments, consider a simple comparison bridge with equal resistances in the ratio arms, $R_1 = R_2$, the specimen in arm 3 and its balancing variable impedance in arm 4 as in figure 7.5(b). After the bridge has been balanced under one condition, the offset voltage gives a measure of the deviation of the sample impedance from the reference impedance value. Phase-sensitive detectors may be used

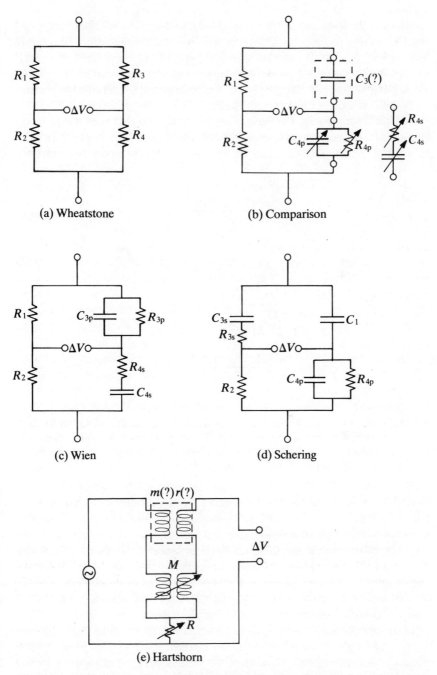

Fig. 7.5 Some common a.c. bridge configurations: (a) Wheatstone bridge, (b) comparison bridge, (c) Wien bridge, (d) Schering bridge, and (e) Hartshorn bridge.

to measure the in-phase and out-of-phase components of the offset signal, and with a suitable choice of bridge these will indicate the deviations of the real and imaginary parts of impedance. An example of the use of this technique is in the investigation of phase transitions. As the temperature is altered through the transition, there may be small changes in the physical properties such as resistance or dielectric constant.

A direct comparison technique can often be used to reduce the effect on the samples of those experimental variables not being investigated. Consider two samples, S_3 and S_4, as nearly the same as possible, placed in two arms of a

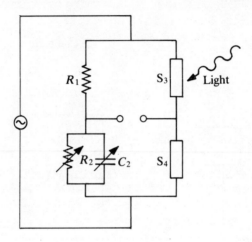

Fig. 7.6 A comparison bridge for the measurement of small differences between nearly identical specimens, S_3 and S_4. After the bridge has been balanced in the dark, the off-balance signal gives a measure of the change in the impedance of S_3 with the exposure to light.

bridge as shown in figure 7.6. Because of the slight differences between the samples, the bridge will need to be balanced by the addition of variable components in one of the resistive ratio arms, R_2C_2. The effect of one experimental variable, say light, on the impedance of the specimen can now be investigated by applying it to only one of the two samples. The off-balance signal gives a measure of the effect of the light, as described before. The advantage of this arrangement is that all other variables will affect both samples equally, so that they will not alter the balance. Thus the temperature of both samples may be changed with no effect on the output. This technique is the same as that used by biological, medical, and social science investigators, when the effect of a certain variable is being studied on a certain population. A control or reference population is chosen similar in as many respects as possible to the first except in the exposure to the particular experimental variable.

BRIDGE DESIGN

The d.c. bridge has the advantage of simplicity since only the resistive balance condition need be made and also the detector bandwidth can easily be made very narrow with a simple RC low-pass filter. However, these advantages are usually less than the general disadvantages of using d.c. circuits. At d.c. (z.f.) instruments have poorer performance than similar a.c. instruments. There are large noise signals and drifts due to aging and temperature changes in both instruments and the circuit.

The a.c. bridges suffer from problems with earths, pick-up, and stray impedances. The resolution of these problems presents a valuable example of circuit design. It should be remembered that the precision of a bridge balance may be 1 part in 10^6, so that very careful techniques are needed.

Bridge earths

The importance of a single clear circuit earth in any low-level circuit was emphasized in chapter 4. A simple bridge circuit is shown in figure 7.7. It can be seen that in this conventional circuit both the source and the detector cannot have one terminal in common or connected to the circuit earth. At the most only one of the links A or B may be made, or impedance Z_4 is shorted. If link B is made then the source will have to be 'floating' with battery power or a good isolated power supply. Alternately, an isolation transformer can be placed between the source and the bridge so that only the source differential-mode signal is transmitted. Similarly, if link A is made, the amplifier must be a good-quality differential amplifier with a large common-mode rejection ratio (CMRR) (chapter 4). This can also be achieved by using a transformer input,

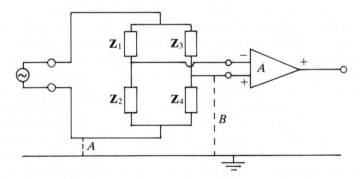

Fig. 7.7   A simple bridge circuit illustrating the problems involved in earthing one or more points in the circuit.

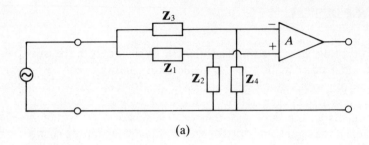

(a)

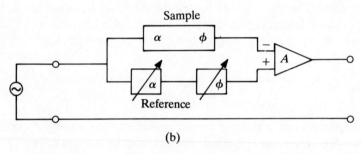

(b)

Fig. 7.8 In (a) the basic a.c. bridge circuit is redrawn to show the signal being passed
along two parallel paths and the output signals subtracted. This is compared
in (b) with a schematic view of other comparison methods.

since transformers only transmit the differential-mode signal, or by using a
high-quality instrumentation amplifier. Such amplifiers have well balanced
inputs with high CMRR.

Because of stray impedances, sources and detectors operating at high
frequencies cannot be made with large isolation from earth, so that other
bridge designs are used. If the bridge design of figure 7.7 is redrawn as in
figure 7.8(a) it appears as a signal injected into two parallel paths Z_1 and Z_2
going to the non-inverting input and Z_3 and Z_4 going to the inverting input.
The amplifier subtracts the received signals and a null is achieved if the signals
are of equal amplitude and phase. There is a great similarity with other
comparison methods such as those used in optical systems, especially inter-
ferometers. In figure 7.8(b) the principles of the method are shown. The
signal is applied equally to two parallel circuits or signal paths. In the sample
circuit the signal is altered in amplitude and phase; in the reference circuit the
amplitude and phase are adjusted by a variable attenuator, α, and phase-
shifter, ϕ. The two output signals are subtracted (or added if ϕ includes an
extra π shift) and α and ϕ are adjusted for a null. The set values of α and ϕ thus
give a measure of the attenuation and phase-shifts through the sample circuit
and hence the sample properties.

The Twin-Tee network shown in figure 7.9 is one of many bridge arrangements where this technique is used so that the source, circuit, and detector all have the same earth. Often such circuits have a frequency-dependent null and thus also act as rejection filters (chapter 4). The combination of the signals is done here at the amplifier input. The unknown is usually one of the components that have one terminal at earth potential. The general technique can be easily adapted for use with active circuit elements. For example, an

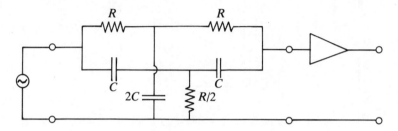

Fig. 7.9 The symmetrical RC Twin-Tee bridge.

operational amplifier summer may be used to combine the signals from the two signal paths or a variable all-pass network could be placed in the reference arm in series with a variable-gain amplifier.

Pick-up

In chapter 4 it was shown that when designing circuits with low-level signals it is necessary to reduce interfering signals or 'pick-up' by keeping the circuit compact and by adding appropriate magnetic and electrostatic screens connected to the circuit earth. Such a system is shown for a bridge in figure 7.10. Note that there are breaks in the screens to eliminate earth loops. The addition of these screens will increase the stray capacitance of each point of the circuit to earth. Some of these stray capacitances affect the bridge null condition. Thus although screening improves the signal-to-noise ratio and allows higher resolution in the setting of the null, it may reduce the absolute accuracy. Solutions to this conflict will be described later.

Stray impedances

The most important stray impedances are the capacitances. For a single bridge circuit with one source terminal earthed and a differential input detector, the capacitances to earth can be represented by the three

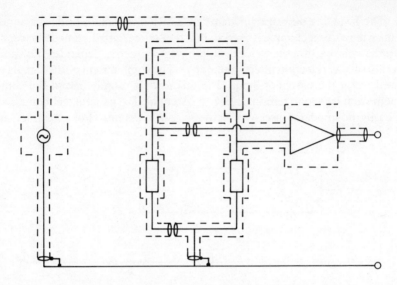

Fig. 7.10 A bridge circuit with electrostatic screen to reduce capacitive pick-up. There are breaks in the screen to prevent earth loops.

components shown in figure 7.11. Capacitance C_1' only loads the source but C_2' and C_3' appear in parallel with the bridge impedances and hence alter the balance conditions. In principle, capacitors could be placed across the other arms so that the total stray capacitance will be balanced and hence there would be no net effect. However, if both source and detector are in differential mode, then the Wagner earth technique allows this to be done very simply.

The *Wagner earth* circuit involves an extra pair of arms to the bridge, $\mathbf{Z}_5$ and $\mathbf{Z}_6$, as shown in figure 7.12. By adjusting impedances $\mathbf{Z}_1$ and $\mathbf{Z}_5$, say, the bridges $\mathbf{Z}_3, \mathbf{Z}_4, \mathbf{Z}_5, \mathbf{Z}_6$ and $\mathbf{Z}_1, \mathbf{Z}_2, \mathbf{Z}_3, \mathbf{Z}_4$ are balanced in turn by alternating

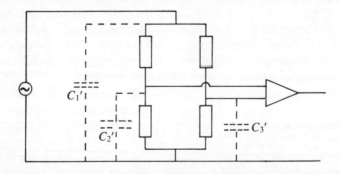

Fig. 7.11 The three possible stray capacitances in a bridge circuit.

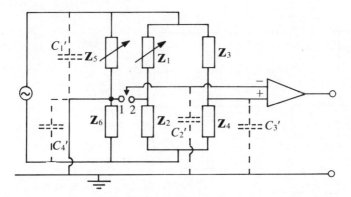

Fig. 7.12 The Wagner earth, Z_5 and Z_6, added to the basic bridge together with all the possible stray capacitances.

the switch positions 1 and 2. The junction of impedances Z_5 and Z_6 is made the circuit and shield earth. The junctions between Z_1, Z_2 and Z_3, Z_4 are thus virtual earths at the null setting. The stray capacitances to earth are as shown. Of these C_1' and C_4' appear across Z_5 and Z_6, which are not part of the precision components of the bridge. Capacitances C_2' and C_3' have the same potential at each end and so do not contribute to the circuit. The differential detector amplifier also does not experience a common-mode signal and so it need not have a good CMRR.

THE TRANSFORMER BRIDGE

The transformer bridge avoids many of the problems of pick-up and stray capacitances that have been described above by using the properties of the ratio transformer. The basic circuit is shown in figure 7.13. The unknown impedance $Z_3(?)$ is balanced by a variable Z_4 in one pair of arms while the other ratio arm consists of a ratio transformer with a voltage ratio given by the turns ratio n_1/n_2. Thus at null $Z_3/Z_4 = n_1/n_2$. The ratio is very precise because it depends only on the value of the turns ratio, which is a simple ratio of integers. The stray capacitances are shown. One appears across the detector input and just reduces its sensitivity without affecting its null. The other two appear across the ratio divider windings, but since the individual turns are tightly coupled to the core to give a very low effective output impedance these stray capacitances have very little effect.

Variants of the basic circuit are shown in figure 7.14. In figure 7.14(a) the drive signal is coupled into the ratio arms by transformer action through the

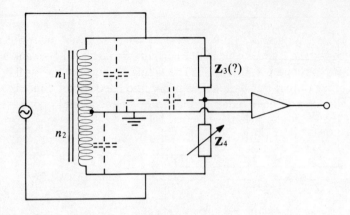

Fig. 7.13 The basic transformer bridge.

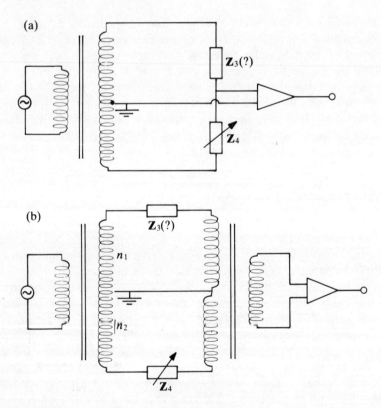

Fig. 7.14 Variants of the basic transformer bridge with transformer coupling of the drive signal in (a) and also in (b) a transformer used as a differential current detector.

core. This increases the isolation of the source. In figure 7.14(b) a transformer is used for the differential detector. The arms with turns n_1, n_2 are low-impedance voltage sources which drive currents through the upper and lower circuit loops containing $Z_3(?)$ and Z_4. The circulating currents induce flux into the core of the output transformer and hence into the detector. Since the two primary windings of the output transformer are wound in the opposite sense, a null can be obtained when the currents have an equal and opposite effect. The primary windings can be considered as having a low input impedance so that the currents in the two loops are proportional to n_1/Z_3 and n_2/Z_4. At null $Z_3/Z_4 = n_1/n_2$.

The transformer bridge may be used in many ways to take advantage of the accurate integral ratios derived from the individual turns. Also there is the possibility of deriving several related, but independent, signals from separate secondaries on the same core and adding or subtracting signals by coupling them into the core of the output transformer. If a good-quality core is chosen and care is taken in winding the coils, accurate bridges can easily be made. Transformers become less useful at frequencies above about 1 MHz when they become non-ideal owing to core losses, resistive losses in the windings, and stray inductances and capacitances.

The basic bridge circuit involves the conventional two-terminal impedance shown in figure 7.15(a). Because the transformer bridge is affected very little by stray impedances to earth, it can use the three-terminal impedance shown in figure 7.15(b). The third terminal is connected to the

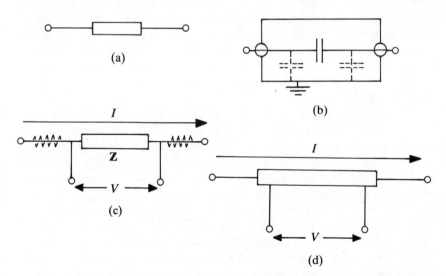

Fig. 7.15 (a) The two-terminal impedance, (b) the three-terminal impedance with a screen, (c) the four-terminal impedance which eliminates the effect of the lead impedances, and (d) a modification of the four-terminal connection to eliminate the effect of any contact resistance.

screen. In some measurements the stray impedances of the wires to the circuit impedance become significant so that a four-terminal measurement is needed as shown in figure 7.15(c). Here a current is passed through the specimen and the stray series resistances but only the voltage drop across the impedance itself is measured using a high input impedance voltmeter which will not disturb the current flow. There are bridge configurations that can perform a four-terminal measurement but usually a direct V–I measurement is made of such an impedance.

In many measurements of the resistance of physical specimens such as semiconductors it is necessary to prevent the measurement of the significant resistances of the contacts between the specimen and the leads to it. In this case the modification of the four-terminal measurement shown in figure 7.15(d) is used. Current is passed through one pair of terminals and the potential drop along the bulk of the specimen is measured with a high input impedance voltmeter. In this way any potential drop at the current contacts is not measured and, since no current flows through the voltmeter, there is no potential drop across any resistances at the potential contacts.

ACTIVE BRIDGES

The operational amplifier techniques described in chapter 2 enable active devices to perform operations on signals to an accuracy of 1 in the loop gain, which may be 10^6 or 10^8 in high-quality devices. Examples of such applications are in the use of the Miller effect to simulate a capacitance $(A + 1)C$ or a resistance $R/(A + 1)$ as shown in figure 7.16. A variable capacitance can therefore be produced using a single standard capacitance and the resistance ratio which defines A.

A voltage may be transferred accurately with a buffer amplifier or converted from a differential voltage with a good differential amplifier. In this way four-terminal measurements may be performed. A simple example of a direct comparison four-terminal circuit is shown in figure 7.16(c).

Many impedance measurements need to be made automatically so that the results can be connected directly to a computer. The high accuracy and precision of bridge methods are often needed but conventional bridges are not easy to balance automatically. One active feedback method is shown in figure 7.17. The variable Z_4 is set near the value of the unknown $Z_3(?)$. The bridge is not balanced but the detector amplifier operates at null. It produces a null in the output transformer by injecting a suitable feedback signal through R_2 into another primary coil. The output voltage of the amplifier is thus an accurate measure of the out-of-balance signal. The in-phase and out-of-phase components of the signal are measured using phase-sensitive detectors with

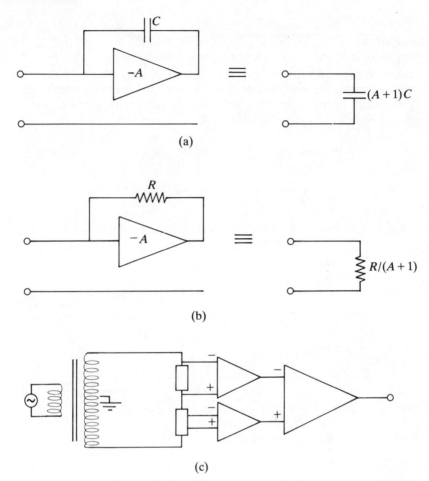

Fig. 7.16 Examples of active bridge techniques: (a) an active capacitance, (b) an active resistance, and (c) a transformer bridge using differential amplifiers to compare two four-terminal impedances with different connections.

the bridge excitation signal, and this signal shifted in phase by $\pi/2$, as references. The two PSD output signals give a measure of the difference between the real and imaginary components of $\mathbf{Z}_3(?)$ and $\mathbf{Z}_4$.

Fully automatic impedance measuring circuits use more direct techniques. A capacitance meter is shown in figure 7.18. The capacitance is charged to a fixed voltage and then discharged through a known resistance. The time taken to discharge between two fixed reference voltages is measured by counting the clock pulses between the times given by the comparator output signals. This circuit cannot measure the loss in the capacitor.

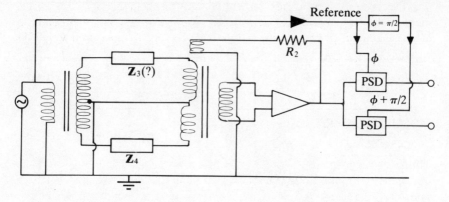

Fig. 7.17 An example of an active transformer bridge with feedback circuit to give automatic balancing.

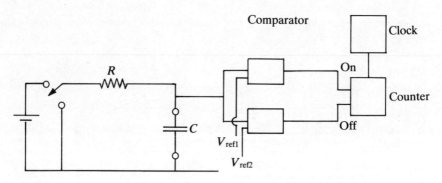

Fig. 7.18 A simple capacitance meter based on the charging time of an RC circuit.

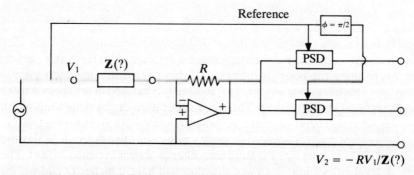

$$V_2 = -RV_1/\mathbf{Z}(?)$$

Fig. 7.19 A schematic automatic impedance meter in which a constant voltage is applied across the impedance $\mathbf{Z}(?)$ and the amplitudes of the in-phase and out-of-phase current components are measured.

Precision automatic impedance meters often use a direct V–I measurement as shown in figure 7.19. A voltage is applied to the component and the in-phase and out-of-phase components of the current are measured with PSD circuits.

MODULATION METHODS

The bridge arrangement is able to give an accurate measure of the difference between two impedances. This can be combined with the low noise level, high interference rejection, and narrow bandwidth detection properties of the phase-sensitive detector (PSD) (chapters 4, 6 and 9) to give a range of very important measurement techniques in which one of the experimental variables is modulated.

The simplest instrument of this type is the *chopper amplifier*, which was described in detail in chapter 6. In this instrument the d.c. (z.f.) signal is converted into an a.c. signal which is amplified by an a.c. amplifier and then converted back into a d.c. (z.f.) signal. D.c. (z.f.) amplifiers have poor low-level performance compared with similar a.c. amplifiers because of the large low-frequency noise, drift, and temperature effects that occur at low frequencies. The chopper or amplitude modulator is a simple switch that converts the d.c. (z.f.) signal to a square wave with a proportional amplitude. It must be of high quality.

To discuss the value of modulation methods for the design experiments, we will consider a specific example of a specimen with a resistance $R = R_0 + R(B)$, which has a component $R(B)$ that varies with magnetic field, B, and a field-independent value R_0. The bridge aspects will not be considered initially but this improvement will be added later.

The measurements could be done by a simple d.c. (z.f.) voltage measurement if a known current is passed through the specimen. This is shown in figure 7.20(a). However d.c. (z.f.) amplifiers do not have such a good performance as a.c. amplifiers. The resistance can be measured using a.c. if an a.c. current is applied and the a.c. voltage is detected. This is a better method of overcoming the poor performance of d.c. (z.f.) amplifiers than using a chopper amplifier since any d.c. (z.f.) voltages generated in the specimen are not amplified in this method. The a.c. amplification can be done simply with an amplifier and band-pass filter as shown in figure 7.20(b). However this a.c. measurement can be improved by using a phase-sensitive detector (PSD) and low-pass filter to replace the band-pass filter as shown in figure 7.20(c). The noise level is thus improved and the filter will have a higher Q and will be automatically centered at ω_1, the drive signal frequency. These three methods are simply different ways of performing a simple resistance measurement by

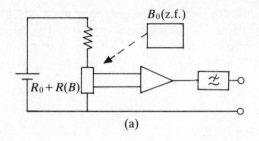

(a)

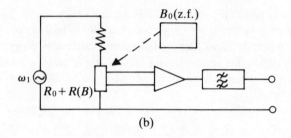

(b)

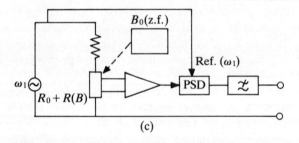

(c)

Fig. 7.20 Examples in the use of modulation methods to investigate a magnetic-field-sensitive resistance. In each case a current is applied and the potential drop is measured: (a) direct current applied and z.f. voltage measured, (b) alternating current applied and the alternating voltage measured with a narrow band-pass filter system, and (c) the circuit of (b) improved using a phase-sensitive detector to reduce the bandwidth.

the ratio of the voltage to current. The applied current in this case is shown as a voltage source together with a large series resistance. To measure any field dependence, accurate values of $R_0 + R(B)$ at each field must be measured, and this will require great precision if $R(B) \ll R_0$.

If the field-dependent part of the resistance, $R(B)$, is of most importance, then that component may be investigated separately. Consider the circuit of figure 7.21(a). Here a d.c. (z.f.) current is passed through the specimen and an a.c. magnetic field $B_2 \sim \cos \omega_2 t$ is applied. The voltage across the sample has a

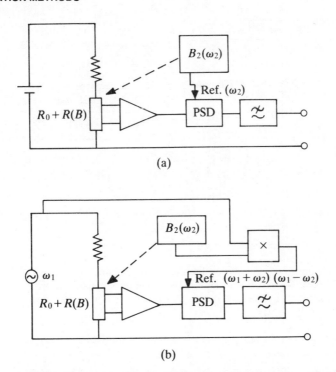

Fig. 7.21 To extract out only the magnetic-field-dependent part of the resistance, an alternating magnetic field may be used with a phase-sensitive detector. In (a) the specimen current is at z.f. (d.c.) while in (b) an alternating current is applied.

d.c. component proportional to R_0 and an a.c. component at a frequency ω_2 proportional to $R(B)$. If the amplifier contains a high-pass input filter so that the d.c. (z.f.) signal is not passed, then the output signal will be proportional to $R(B)$ only. Since the whole resistance is not being measured, the accuracy of the measurement of $R(B)$ will be that of the a.c. signal and can be high. A PSD system will again produce the best results. There can be a slight improvement in performance if the input current is a.c. rather than d.c. as shown in figure 7.21(b). If the current $\sim \cos \omega_1 t$ and the field $\sim \cos \omega_2 t$ so the resistance change $\sim \cos \omega_2 t$, then the output voltage $\sim \cos \omega_1 t \cos \omega_2 t \sim \cos(\omega_1 + \omega_2) t + \cos(\omega_1 - \omega_2) t$. For optimum detection the reference signal to the PSD must also contain the same components in the correct phases and this can be produced by multiplication as shown. This is called the double a.c. method.

The modulation technique just described separates $R(B)$ and R_0. This can also be done with a bridge method as shown in figure 7.22. A separate, but very similar, specimen is placed in the comparison arm of the bridge and is kept under the same conditions as the sample itself except for the exposure to

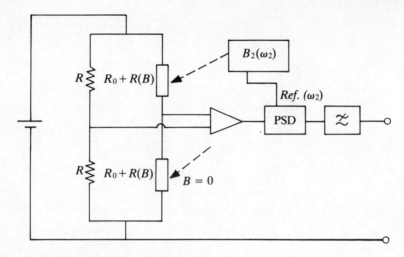

Fig. 7.22 The measurement can be made stable against extraneous variables if a
bridge arrangement is used to compare the specimen, which is subjected to
a magnetic field, with an identical specimen in an identical environment
except for the field.

the magnetic field. A d.c. (z.f.) magnetic field could be used and similar
results are obtained to those from the simple modulation technique. The
effect of the component R_0 is cancelled by the bridge. The unbalance signal is
only due to $R(B)$. A modulation method is preferred in which an a.c.
magnetic field $B_2(\omega_2)$ is applied. The unbalance signal has both d.c. (z.f.) and
a.c. components. The measurement of the a.c. component by PSD techniques
is preferred. The advantage of the bridge configuration is that other variables
(such as temperature, light, and even unmodulated magnetic fields) can be
arranged to affect both specimens equally and so their influence will not
unbalance the bridge or appear in the output signal. Even without the bridge,
only such effects at the PSD reference frequency will have an effect.

　　In these circuits it has been assumed that the total magnetic field has been
modulated and that $R(B)$ is linear in B. The system is therefore similar to a
system in which B is turned on and off and the difference signal is investigated.
The power of modulation methods is, however, revealed when the specimen
has a non-linear $R(B)$ variation.

　　Consider the circuit of figure 7.23(a). A bridge arrangement could be
used but the simple circuit has been presented for clarity. The applied
magnetic field now has two components: B_0(z.f.) at z.f. and $B_2(\omega_2)$ at ω_2. If
the resistance variation is as shown in figure 7.23(b) then the a.c. output at ω_2
depends on $R(B)$ and not R_0. For a sine-wave modulation of B, there is an a.c.
resistance modulation and hence, for a z.f. applied current, an a.c. output

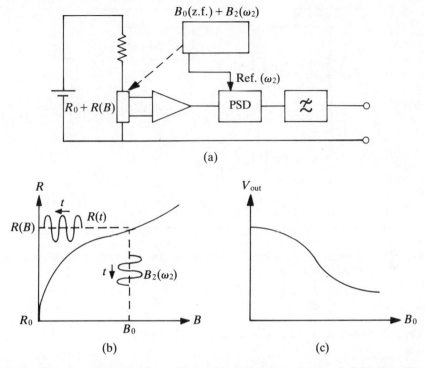

Fig. 7.23 A combination of a small a.c. and a large constant magnetic field allows the slope of the R–B curve to be measured directly.

voltage at ω_2 which can be detected. The transfer curve $R(B)$–B shows that the amplitude of the output is proportional to the slope, or to the differential of the curve dR/dB evaluated at the bias field B_0. Since the differential corresponds to multiplication by $j\omega$, or a high-pass filter, this technique is valuable for emphasizing variations in R that occur rapidly with B, such as resonances. The modulation amplitude must be less than the extent of such variations.

If the same experiment as that shown in figure 7.23 is performed but the reference signal is at $2\omega_2$, then the second derivative d^2R/dB^2 can be measured. The reference signal at $2\omega_2$ can be obtained by squaring the applied signal and passing it through a high-pass filter to reject the d.c. (z.f.) component. If

$$R = R_0 + R(B) = R_1 + A_1 B + \tfrac{1}{2} A_2 B^2 + \ldots$$

then

$$\frac{dR}{dB} = A_1 \qquad \frac{d^2R}{dB^2} = A_2 \qquad \text{etc.}$$

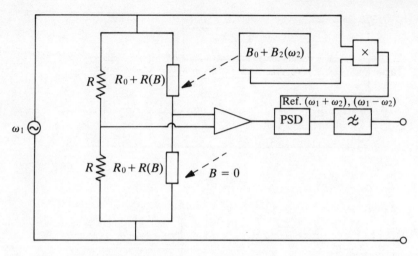

Fig. 7.24 An example of a double a.c. modulation method with the specimen in a comparison bridge arrangement.

The output signal will be proportional to $R(B)$, which for

$$B = B_0 + B_2\cos\omega_2 t$$

becomes

$$A_1(B_0 + B_2\cos\omega_2 t) + \tfrac{1}{2}A_2(B_0 + B_2\cos\omega_2 t)^2 + \ldots$$

$$= A_1 B_0 + \tfrac{1}{2}A_2 B_0^2 + \ldots + A_1 B_2\cos\omega_2 t + A_2 B_0 B_2\cos\omega_2 t + \ldots$$
$$+ \tfrac{1}{2}A_2 B_2^2\cos^2\omega_2 t + \ldots$$

$$= A_1 B_0 + \tfrac{1}{2}A_2 B_0^2 + \tfrac{1}{4}A_2 B_2^2 + \ldots$$
$$+ A_1 B_2\cos\omega_2 t + A_2 B_0 B_2\cos\omega_2 t + \ldots$$
$$- \tfrac{1}{4}A_2 B_2^2\cos 2\omega_2 t + \ldots$$

The $2\omega_2$ term has an amplitude proportional to $A_2 = \mathrm{d}^2 R/\mathrm{d}B^2$. However it should be noted that the ω_2 term also has a component proportional to A_2 so that in the measurement of any particular derivative care should be taken that the other derivatives are not so large as to have a significant effect.

All the various aspects of the modulation technique described may be combined and figure 7.24 shows a double a.c. modulation method using a bridge and also a magnetic field bias. Although such systems may be complicated, they can have advantages over the simple systems in signal-to-noise ratio, as the filtering can be optimized.

FURTHER READING

B. A. Gregory, *An Introduction to Electrical Instrumentation*, Macmillan (1981).
B. Hague and T. R. Foord, *Alternating Current Bridge Methods*, Pitman (1971).

8 TRANSDUCERS AND DATA ACQUISITION

INTRODUCTION

In an experiment, the quantity under investigation is normally measured with a particular instrument designed to obtain an accurate value of the quantity with as little disturbance to the experiment as possible. In a simple instrument, such as a traveling microscope used to measure small displacements, the output value is calculated from the difference of two readings taken visually from a scale after manual setting. A more advanced instrument will not require manual setting but gives a numerical readout of the value.

In a more sophisticated experiment, an accurate signal in the form of a voltage or current proportional to the measured displacement might be more convenient. This method may reduce observer error, increase the speed of measurement, and provide frequent or continuous reading, recording and display of the information. Electronic processing may allow further manipulation of the signal and improvement of the signal-to-noise ratio.

The next logical step is to use the great power of computers and computer systems to memorize, record, and manipulate the data and to administer the experiment by performing operations in sequence and then to control the apparatus by stabilizing or changing the experimental variables in response to the results obtained. The obvious ability of computers to carry out complicated instructions has been widely used for processing data in the form of numbers that are supplied manually at a keyboard. However, the power of the system is considerably enhanced if the data are supplied directly from automatic measuring instruments. In this chapter we will consider the devices and circuits that enable a clear measure of a quantity to be obtained, converted to a suitable analog or digital form, and transferred within the measurement system. The inverse operation whereby a signal from the measurement system is used to change an experimental variable is also considered.

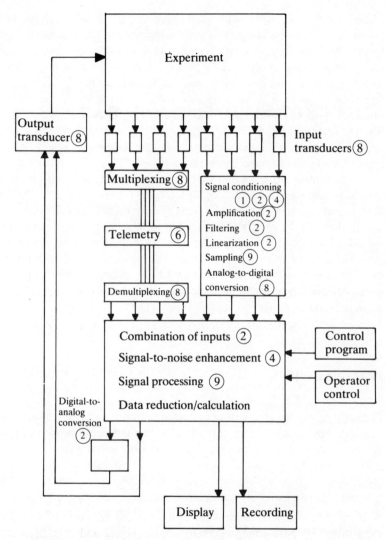

Fig. 8.1 An outline diagram of the constituent parts of a measurement system. The numbers refer to the chapters in which the topics are discussed.

A complete system for acquiring data can take many forms depending on the particular quantities to be measured. Thus, any description can easily be either too general to be helpful or too specific to be applicable to other systems. The principal elements and operations involved in such a system are shown in figure 8.1, together with the chapters in which each is discussed.

The experimental quantities are measured with transducers (chapter 8). The individual output signals are sent to the main body of the apparatus directly or by some form of telemetry involving modulation (chapter 6). The transmission may be along individual wires or through one channel by some form of multiplexing (chapter 8). During this data acquisition stage, the signal may be manipulated into a form that is a faithful function of the measured quantity and is suitable for transmission and further processing. These operations may be buffering, amplification, common-mode signal rejection, filtering, linearization, current-to-voltage conversion (chapter 2), interference rejection (chapter 4), analog-to-digital conversion (chapter 8), and sampling (chapter 9). These processes may be done next to the transducer or after transmission to some central unit.

The central experimental unit may combine together the signals from several transducers, and enhance the signal-to-noise ratio by filtering (chapter 4) or signal averaging (chapter 9). Finally data reduction can be performed by calculations on the results. The initial or reduced data may be displayed and stored. If the central unit is to be used to send control signals to stabilize (chapter 2) or alter the experimental variables, there will be further transmission of signals from the central unit to an output or control transducer, which can alter the variable, with perhaps intermediate signal processing such as digital–analog conversion (DAC) (chapter 2).

TRANSDUCERS

Transducers or *sensors* are devices that convert one variable into another. For example, thermometers convert a measure of temperature into a more convenient variable: a mercury-in-glass thermometer converts a temperature into a displacement using the difference in thermal expansion between mercury and glass; a platinum resistance thermometer converts a temperature into resistance using the temperature coefficient of resistance; and a thermocouple converts a temperature difference into a voltage. Most transducers have an electrical signal as one of the variables because of its versatility and convenience and we will concentrate on these. In many cases, the conversion between variables is done in two stages with an intermediate variable so that there is a *primary transducer* and a *secondary transducer*. For example, some microphones, which convert air pressure changes to electrical variables, operate by the air pressure acting on the area of a diaphragm to produce a force which acts against the elasticity of the diaphragm (Hooke's law) to produce a proportional displacement. The displacement is detected electrically, often by the capacitance change between the diaphragm and a fixed plate.

A transducer may be described as an *input transducer* or an *output transducer* if it takes the information into the measuring system from the experiment or out of the system to alter the experimental variables. Examples of input transducers are thermometers, microphones, pressure sensors, and rotary encoders. The corresponding output transducers are heaters, loudspeakers, pumps and motors.

Another possible division of transducers is between *active* or *self-generating transducers* and *passive* or *modulating transducers*. The terms 'active' and 'passive' can be confusing as they do not correspond to the usage in electrical circuits. In a self-generating transducer, the signal power is developed from the signal source or experimental variable. Examples are the mercury-in-glass thermometer and the thermocouple. A modulating transducer changes its properties in response to a change in the experimental variable but the change only becomes a signal if an external power source is applied. Thus a platinum resistance thermometer needs an external electrical source in order that the resistance change can be revealed as a voltage or current change.

A discussion of transducers designed to measure even one quantity is a major undertaking because there are usually many different types, using different mechanisms and with different advantages and disadvantages. A full discussion would also need to consider the system in which it is to be used and the purpose of the measurement. Here we will concentrate on the general principles involved with all transducers but give some specific examples. The quality of a transducer and its suitability in a given experiment are very important since these factors will control the optimum results that can be achieved, however much signal processing is done later.

The operation of a transducer may be considered in three stages: it responds to the value of the input quantity and in turn it will also have some effect on the input quantity; it converts the input variable into an output variable; and finally this output quantity affects and is affected by the receiving system.

Input criteria

Once a transducer has been chosen for the particular input quantity that is to be measured, the main consideration is that the *usable range* of the transducer for that variable should be adequate for the range expected. Related to this is the *over-range* or magnitude of the variable that can be suffered by the transducer without damage.

A less obvious property is the 'input impedance' of the transducer with respect to the input variable. For an electrical circuit manipulating voltage signals, we require that the input impedance of a receiving stage should be large enough that it will not load the source and hence there will be no signal loss between the source and the receiver. An analogous argument can be made for the transducer. The input properties of the transducer must be such that it does not load or affect the experimental quantity so that a lower reading is obtained than could be obtained by an ideal instrument. Examples of this are that the thermal capacity of a thermometer should be negligible compared with that of the system, otherwise the introduction of the thermometer will add, or remove, sufficient heat to alter the temperature of the system by the act of measurement. Similarly, the active volume of a gas pressure transducer must be small compared with the volume of the experimental chamber.

Transfer criteria

The relationship between the input quantity (Q_i) and the output quantity (Q_o) is given by some transfer function $Q_0 = f(Q_i)$ as shown in figure 8.2. This should ideally be a simple, well established, and stable function. However, it

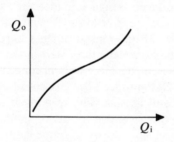

Fig. 8.2 A typical transfer function between the input and output, Q_i and Q_o, variables of a transducer.

is not now extremely important that it is a simple function since analog or digital computers can easily make a suitable calculation in order to modify the output values so that the overall transfer function, including the transducer and calculation, is of the desired form. Usually, however, the transducer operates on some simple physical principle so that a straightforward linear transfer function can be obtained. In this case an alternative description is the *sensitivity* $S = dQ_o/dQ_i$ or the *scale factor* $1/S$. These quantities will, in general, have mixed dimensions.

Errors

In a real transducer, the actual relationship between the input and output quantities will not be exactly the same as the assumed or ideal transfer function. These departures from the ideal are called 'errors' and can be divided into *static errors*, which do not depend on the time variation of the input and output signals, and *dynamic errors*, which do. Both may change with time as the device ages and its properties alter.

If we consider, for simplicity, a linear transfer function, the static error departures from this ideal form can take the form of an *offset error* or an added constant, a *factor error* corresponding to a scale change or a *non-conformity* or *distortion* which is a change in the shape or a departure from the ideal shape. These are shown in figure 8.3. For the special case of a linear transfer function, the non-conformity becomes a *non-linearity*. Small deviations from the linear can often be expressed as coefficients in a power expansion in Q_i.

Many transducers and devices show an output value that is not a unique function of the input but depends to some extent on the previous values of the

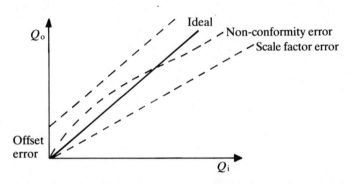

Fig. 8.3 Typical departures from the ideal linear transducer characteristic.

input. This is called generally *repeatability* or *resettability* but for specific transducers where the effect can be attributed to actual processes it might be called *hysteresis, backlash, deadspan* or *stiction*. These are shown in figure 8.4. Hysteresis and backlash indicate that an open loop develops in the transfer curve when the input quantity is cycled. Backlash, deadspan, and stiction indicate that the input variable must change by a non-zero amount before the output changes. An example of backlash is that due to slackness between the teeth of two gears. Initially no power will be transmitted on reversing the direction of motion. Stiction is used to refer to the specific case where the presence of static friction, which is usually larger than dynamic friction, requires that a large change in the input signal is needed to alter the output value although, once the system has moved, the output variable will reach the appropriate value.

Although each of these effects may be characterized in some quantitative way, they are often all collected together to give a maximum error from all causes. It should be noted that all these static errors are usually given as a *percentage of full scale* so that, if the transducer is used over only a small part

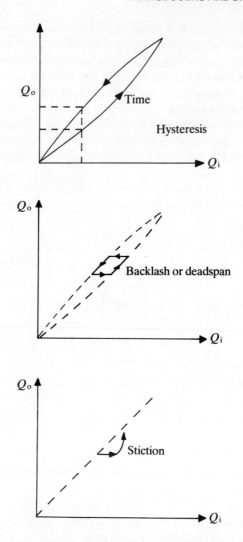

Fig. 8.4 Characteristic curves to illustrate hysteresis, backlash or deadspan, and stiction.

of its usable range, a large percentage error in the output signal may be expected. Other methods of expressing the quality of the transducer with respect to the fineness by which different readings can be discriminated are the *signal-to-noise* (power) *ratio* and the *resolution*.

The *dynamic errors* are due to the rate of change of the signal. These can best be described by drawing an analogy with a mechanical system such as the displacement of a mass in response to a force. There will be an effect at the output Q_o due to inertial effects and these will depend on $d^2 Q_i / dt^2$, and there will be effects caused by the dynamic friction which varies as dQ_i/dt. A well designed transducer will be critically damped so that there is little oscillation or overshoot as the output value approaches its new equilibrium position and this value is reached in the shortest time. Often the damping dominates over the inertial effects so that the system response will be $\sim\exp(-t/\tau)$ and can be described by the time constant τ.

Other time-varying effects at the output are the a.c. or high-frequency fluctuations or *noise* and the d.c. or low-frequency changes, which are normally referred to as lack of *stability*. These effects exist even with no input signal. The noise may be caused by many effects, but the ultimate sensitivity of the transducer will be governed by processes analogous to the thermal fluctuation noise and shot noise described for electrical systems in chapter 4.

The stability may be assigned specifically to the offset or scale factor changes and can sometimes be identified with specific causes such as aging or temperature or humidity changes, in which case the specifications can be stated suitably.

Output criteria

The type of output quantity is usually specified by the application but even if the discussion is restricted to an electrical output signal it can take several forms. The signal may be a voltage or current, analog or digital. In analog form the information may be the amplitude of a d.c. signal or an a.c. signal with a sine or square waveform. Also it could be the frequency of a sine or square wave of constant amplitude. In digital form the signal may be coded in some binary system.

Equivalent circuits

The input and output sections of the transducer have already been described in terms of a Thévenin equivalent circuit using the relevant variables Q_i and Q_o. This assumes that these systems are linear. Using the transfer function, a full two-port or two-terminal pair equivalent circuit can be introduced to characterize the transducer.

The Z-parameter equivalent circuit is that shown in figure 8.5. The electrical notation has been kept but I_1V_1 and I_2V_2 represent the appropriate physical variables for the particular quantities Q_i and Q_o. The 'transfer impedances' $\mathbf{Z}_{11}$ and $\mathbf{Z}_{12}$ are numbers of mixed dimensions which represent the transfer of information from the input variables to the output variables and the output variables to the input variables. They represent the transducer action and ensure that the quantities on each part of the equivalent circuit are those appropriate to that system. Other two-terminal pair equivalent circuits

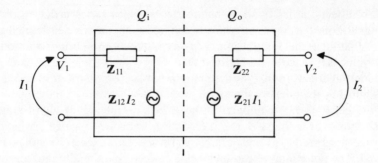

Fig. 8.5 The Z-parameter equivalent circuit of a transducer. The input and output
variables are different and will, in general, have different dimensions. The
circuits are the electrical analogs of the physical systems.

may be used. An alternative technique is to use a transformer as the equivalent circuit element to link the input and output systems. The 'turns ratio' of the transformer then has dimensions and supplies the information contained in the transfer function.

DISPLACEMENT TRANSDUCERS

A general description of all types of transducer would be very long so that examples will be given only of displacement electrical transducers. These are very sensitive and illustrate some general principles. Displacement transducers are common since they are often used as the secondary transducer in a compound device.

If the output is electrical, many common displacement transducers involve altering an impedance.

Resistance displacement transducers

The simplest displacement transducer for linear or rotary motions is the potentiometer (figure 8.6). A direct or alternating current flowing through the resistance produces a uniform voltage drop along the length. For an accurate reading, a voltmeter with a high input impedance is needed. Although simple and rugged, this device relies on careful manufacture to provide a uniform resistance along the length. Wear with use may also change the resistance uniformity. There may also be self-heating due to the bias current, so that any temperature sensitivity may be enhanced. The device can also produce noise at the wiper due to imperfect contact. The effect of this fluctuating resistance will be small if little current flows through the contact. A more fundamental problem with this type of device for very precise use is that it will be inherently noisy because of the thermal (kT or Nyquist) noise produced in the resistance itself.

Another commonly used resistive device is the *strain gage*. This is a specially made resistance that has a large resistance change under an elastic strain. The gage is often used as a secondary transducer. When fixed to an

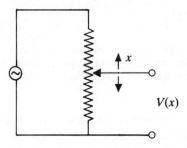

Fig. 8.6   A resistance displacement transducer connected as a potential divider.

elastic support such as a diaphragm, it acts as a pressure gage, and when fixed to a bar or ring, it acts as a force gage or *load cell*.

If the strain gage resistor is a uniform rod of length L, cross-sectional area A, and resistivity ρ, then the resistance is $R = \rho L/A$. The resistance changes on straining because of a change in the geometry and a change in the resistivity. The gage factor is

$$G = \frac{\Delta R/R}{\Delta L/L} = 1 + 2\nu + \frac{\Delta\rho/\rho}{\Delta L/L}$$

Here

$$\nu = -\frac{\Delta d/d}{\Delta L/L}$$

is the Poisson ratio of the material, which describes the change Δd in the lateral dimension d due to a longitudinal elongation ΔL. This ratio is usually between 0 and 0.5. The geometric term in G, $1+2\nu$, is thus between 1 and 2. In some materials there is a change in the electrical properties when they are strained so that the resistivity term $(\Delta\rho/\rho)/(\Delta L/L)$ may be over 100.

Although the resistance, and hence resistance change, may be measured directly, the more sensitive gages are usually also very temperature-dependent so that they are used in bridge arrangements either in pairs or with gages in all four arms. In figure 8.7(a) one transducer R_1 is subjected to the

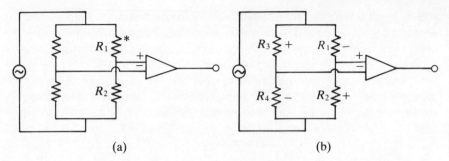

(a)   (b)

Fig. 8.7 A strain gage may be connected as a single device R_1 in a bridge circuit as in
(a), but temperature, pressure, and other effects are reduced, and the
sensitivity and linearity are increased, if two or four gages are connected in a
bridge arrangement and exposed to positive and negative strains as in (b).

strain and R_2 is a reference unit kept under conditions that are identical to
those of R_1 in as many respects as possible other than the strain. Often the
strain element (such as a diaphragm) has one side in extension and the other in
compression, so that in the full bridge arrangement shown in figure 8.7(b) the
gage arms R_2 and R_3 can be placed on one side and R_1 and R_4 on the other. The
output signal is thus enhanced while thermal effects are balanced out.

Inductance displacement transducers

Most inductance displacement transducers operate by detection of the change
in self- or mutual inductance of a coil when a ferromagnetic core is moved in
its field. These devices have a large sensitivity because of the extremely high
permeability (10^3–10^4) that can be obtained in such core materials. These
transducers also have low noise since the electrical circuit has little resistance
and the eddy current and hysteresis loss in the core, which can contribute to
the thermal and excess noise, can be made small.

Devices using a simple inductance are not very linear and so are used only
as simple presence detectors. The ferromagnetic object moves to alter the
amount of air gap in the core magnetic circuit in figure 8.8.

The most useful inductive displacement transducer is the *linear variable
differential transformer* (LVDT), which consists of two mutual inductances
with a common ferromagnetic core. The core moves inside a primary coil,
which produces a uniform a.c. magnetization along its length, and a pair of
secondary coils connected in series opposition as shown in figure 8.9. When
the core is symmetrically placed, equal and opposite signals are induced in the
secondary coils. When the core is displaced, the net signal increases with
either 0° or 180° phase. Although the a.c. output may have an amplitude
minimum at the center, where only the stray out-of-phase ($\pm 90°$) signal gets

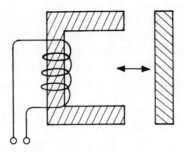

Fig. 8.8 A simple inductive displacement transducer.

(a)

x

V_{out} (a.c.) V_{out} (d.c.)

PSD

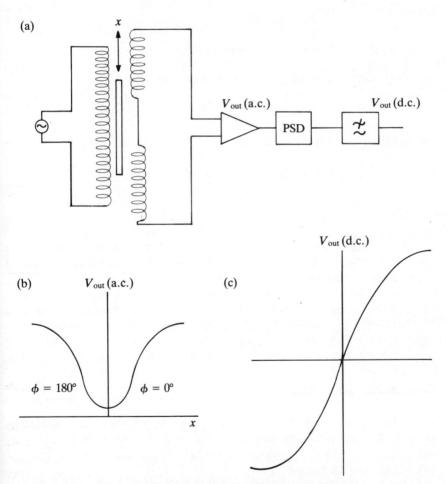

(b) V_{out} (a.c.)

$\phi = 180°$ $\phi = 0°$

x

(c) V_{out} (d.c.)

Fig. 8.9 The linear variable differential transformer design and circuit are shown in (a). The output signal amplitude is shown in (b) and the output after phase-sensitive detection in (c).

through, the use of a phase-sensitive detector (chapter 6) enables a good linear relationship between the displacement and the output to be developed.

The use of a differential technique increases the linearity of the transducer since even-order non-linearities are balanced out. Consider a pair of devices with characteristics V_{out} for a displacement x:

$$V_{out}(1) = A_1 + B_1x + C_1x^2 + D_1x^3 + \ldots$$
$$V_{out}(2) = A_2 + B_2x + C_2x^2 + D_2x^3 + \ldots \tag{8.1}$$

Then if they are connected differentially, the displacement for one is $-x$ and for the other x, so that

$$V_{out}(1) = A_1 + B_1x + C_1x^2 + D_1x^3 + \ldots$$
$$V_{out}(2) = A_2 + B_2(-x) + C_2(-x)^2 + D_2(-x)^3 + \ldots$$
$$= A_2 - B_2x + C_2x^2 - D_2x^3 + \ldots$$

and the differential output signal is:

$$V_{out} = V_{out}(1) - V_{out}(2)$$
$$= (A_1 - A_2) + (B_1 + B_2)x + (C_1 - C_2)x^2 + (D_1 + D_2)x^3 + \ldots \tag{8.2}$$

If the devices are matched, then the coefficients of the two devices, A_1 and A_2, B_1 and B_2, C_1 and C_2, etc., will be very similar to give very small net coefficients for the terms even in powers of x.

The LVDT has no electrical moving contacts so the precision of the physical displacement is as good as the mechanical suspension and friction. The device has low noise and a large signal so that it can be optimized for a high sensitivity or a large linear range.

Capacitance displacement transducers

Capacitance transducers have very good characteristics and are widely used for very high-precision and high-sensitivity measurement because of their very low noise and the precision with which their characteristics may be calculated from the geometry.

The basic methods are shown in figure 8.10 and 8.11 for parallel-plate capacitors. In figures 8.10(a) and (b), the effective area of the capacitance is altered by offsetting the plates or inserting an earthed screen. The capacitor

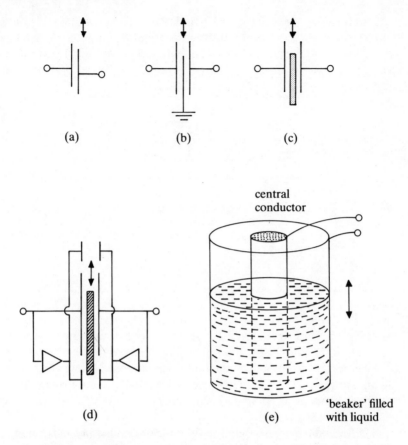

Fig. 8.10 Various configurations for variable-capacitance displacement transducers. The displacement measure is of one electrode in (a), a screen in (b), a dielectric slab in (c) and (d), and a liquid level in (e).

plate spacing must be kept constant. In figure 8.10(c) a material of high dielectric constant is placed between the plates to increase the capacitance. In this case the extra sensitivity gained must be balanced against the increase in noise due to any loss in the dielectric and the reduced capacitance since the plate separation must be larger. In these geometries, the linearity is not very high because of the shape of the fringing fields at the capacitor edges. This problem is reduced by the addition of guard plates which are kept at the plate potentials but are driven from a separate source so that their current contribution and hence their capacitance is not measured (figure 8.10(d)). A cylindrical geometry (figure 8.10(e)) is often used for liquid depth gages and this reduces the fringe field effects and also provides screening since one plate surrounds the other.

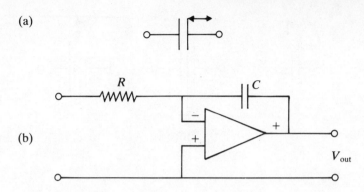

Fig. 8.11 The capacitive transducer shown in (a) can be very sensitive but the capacitance change is inversely proportional to the separation of the plates. The circuit shown in (b) produces an output voltage proportional to the separation.

The geometry shown in figure 8.11(a) has the potential for the highest sensitivity since $C = \epsilon_0\epsilon_r A/d$ and $dC/dd = -\epsilon_0\epsilon_r A/d^2 = -C/d$, where A is the effective plate area and d is the separation. The limits to the increase in the sensitivity by reducing d are the practical geometric alignment necessary to keep d uniform and the breakdown field of the dielectric between the plates. This geometry also produces a non-linear capacitance change with displacement. However, this can be overcome by placing the capacitance as the feedback element of an operational amplifier integrator as shown in figure 8.11(b). Then $V_{out} \propto 1/C \propto d$.

Differential methods significantly improve the linearity and examples are shown in figures 8.12(a) and (b). In a circular-plate geometry the method shown in (a) is often used as a pressure gage with fixed outer plates and an earthed diaphragm between. If the capacitors form two arms of a bridge, then the off-balance signal is proportional to the displacement.

The transformer bridge arrangement shown in figure 8.12(c), and described in detail in chapter 7, is particularly useful for such capacitance measurements. The transducer capacitance is usually small. To reduce pick-up the leads will be screened and coaxial, but this increases the stray capacitance to earth. The transformer bridge and the charge amplifier shown in figure 8.13 are insensitive to such stray capacitances.

Optical displacement transducers

Optical methods are frequently used for transducers because they are compact, sensitive, and reduce the possibility of electrical pick-up because the optical signal breaks the electrical circuit and hence any earth loops.

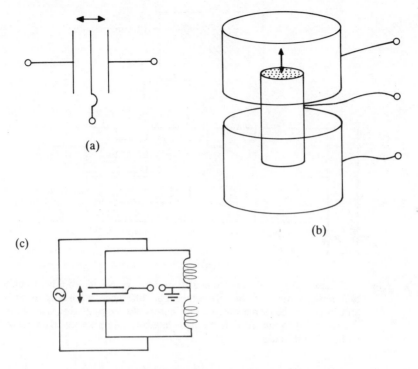

(a)

(b)

(c)

Fig. 8.12 Differential capacitance displacement transducers are more linear than non-differential configurations.

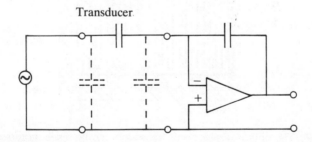

Transducer

Fig. 8.13 The charge amplifier circuit is insensitive to the stray capacitances to earth from each plate of the capacitive transducer. The output is proportional to the transducer capacitance.

The common solid-state optical detector is the photodiode. When this junction is reverse-biased, into its low conductance state, it produces a current proportional to the intensity of the light falling on it. Matched pairs or arrays of such detectors can be made by simultaneous production on a single piece of semiconductor.

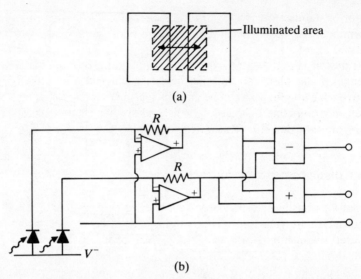

(a)

(b)

Fig. 8.14 A differential optical displacement transducer consisting of a light beam that moves across two photodetectors. The difference in the outputs gives a measure of the displacement. The sum is also computed in the circuit shown in (b) to ensure that the light intensity and photodetector sensitivities do not change.

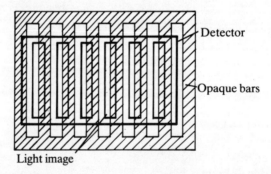

Fig. 8.15 The optical displacement transducer can be made more sensitive if the effective edge length is increased by making both the detector and optical image a set of parallel bars.

A typical differential displacement transducer is shown in figure 8.14. A uniform beam of light illuminates the edge region of two photodiodes. The circuit consists of a pair of current–voltage converters followed by analog difference and summing circuits (chapter 2). The difference signal is proportional to the displacement of the light spot. The sum signal can be used to monitor or stabilize the total light source intensity. The system relies on the uniformity of the light beam and the diode response across the displacement direction.

It should be noted that the system depends on the light spot overlapping the edge of the photocell and can hence be enhanced by increasing the effective edge length. This can be done by placing a set of opaque bars across the cell and projecting an image of the light source, which also consists of a set of bars, onto the detector. This is illustrated in figure 8.15.

Output displacement transducers

The output transducer usually does not have to be of as high quality as the measuring, input transducer. This is because its effect on the system can be measured by an input transducer rather than precisely determined by the signal supplied to the output transducer. Alternately, the output transducer may be incorporated within a negative feedback loop where its exact properties are of less importance (chapter 2). Its effect on the system is controlled by the signal from a transducer monitoring the system. In general, if the output transducer has to provide significant power, then it cannot also easily be designed to be of high precision.

The output displacement transducers that are most developed are motors with gears and a pulley and belt or screw arrangement to convert the rotary motion into a translational motion. For experimental work, the motors are usually pulse-operated to give a well defined angular rotation, as in the stepping motor (see later in this chapter). For use within a feedback loop, the motor must have a low moment of inertia and be highly geared with little backlash so that there is little delay during its acceleration or reversal of direction, which would be equivalent to the introduction of a phase-shift within the loop or a limitation of the high-frequency response.

Current-to-force transducers may be used to move an object with little precise control as in the power *actuator* or *solenoid*. A linear displacement transducer may be made by applying the current-to-force transducer to a linear spring element which converts the force to a displacement. The force is usually developed on a current-carrying conductor in a uniform magnetic field as in a *moving-coil transducer* such as is used in the loudspeaker.

DIGITAL TRANSDUCERS

The transducers described so far are analog devices since they produce a continuous range of output values. Digital signals are usually preferable for transmission without degradation and for manipulation by computers. There

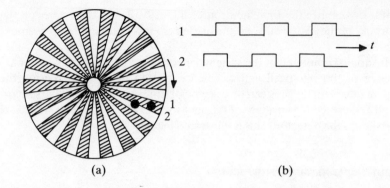

Fig. 8.16 An incremental rotary encoder with offset detectors (a). The relative phase of the two output signals (b) indicates the direction of rotation.

are transducers that have inherent digital operation and output signals. To detect a rotary angular position, a *shaft-angle encoder* is used. This has fixed to the shaft a disk with transparent and opaque sectors (figure 8.16). These are detected with a lamp-photocell combination shining through the disk. Each sector is thus detected and can be counted. Reflective and transmission versions can be made. A typical resolution is 1000 per revolution. These are often used to generate a pulse train and the frequency is compared with a reference frequency in order to provide a control signal to a motor to produce a constant speed.

The device described above is an *incremental encoder* and has the disadvantages that it cannot sense the direction of motion or the absolute angular position, just changes in position. To sense the direction of rotation another photocell can be located, displaced by half a sector and the relative phase of

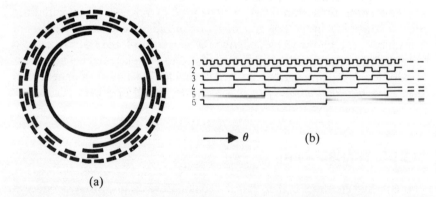

Fig. 8.17 An absolute angular encoder (a) with the output signals from the detectors as a function of angle (b). This encoder is in simple binary code.

the two detector outputs compared. A continuous count must be kept of the pulses and the direction in order to measure the position of the shaft.

The *absolute angular encoder* is more complicated and for a resolution of 2^n per revolution it needs n photocell–lamp pairs, each detecting an encoder with different resolution. A six-bit binary encoder is shown in figure 8.17. Other codes may be used. The output binary n-bit signal gives the shaft position uniquely.

The equivalent output incremental digital rotary transducer is the *stepping motor*. The stator and the rotor each have a large number (perhaps 100) equivalent poles so that there are many positions of equilibrium where

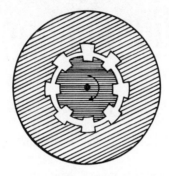

Fig. 8.18   The construction of a multipole armature and stator stepping motor.

the magnetic circuit is complete and the magnetic energy is a minimum (figure 8.18). The transition between states and hence the angular position is changed by applying suitable pulses to change the magnetization of the core. The phase of the pulses specifies the direction of rotation.

FRINGES

Many physical effects produce an output that consists of quanta or pulses which need only to be counted. Interference effects involving waves produce maxima and minima which may be counted. For example, in a Michelson *interferometer* the displacement of one mirror by half a wavelength changes the path length in that arm by one wavelength and the interference pattern moves by one fringe. Thus a photodetector can be used to count the maxima and hence displacements in units of one half-wavelength. The wave can be light, microwaves or sound, depending on the resolution required. Usually the fringe variation is sinusoidal with the relative phase of the interfering

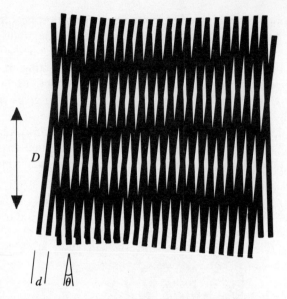

Fig. 8.19 Moiré fringes of spacing D for gratings with spacing d at an angle of θ.

waves so that is possible to detect displacements much smaller than that due to a single fringe.

Moiré fringes can be used to detect displacements. A simple example is shown in figure 8.19. Two identical sets of gratings consisting of equal transparent and opaque bars with spacing d are superimposed at a small angle θ. When illuminated, the light transmitted shows wide bands or fringes perpendicular to the average direction of the gratings. The spacing is $D = d/\theta$. The fringes are displaced by one cycle D for each displacement d of the gratings. The movement is thus magnified by $1/\theta$ and the fringes can be counted easily. Similar effects can be obtained with gratings of more complex geometry.

Another wave phenomenon, the Doppler effect, can be used as the basis of a frequency output velocity transducer. A wave reflecting from a moving object changes its frequency in proportion to the velocity of the object. Thus, if the returning signal is mixed (chapter 6) with a signal derived from the source, the difference frequency gives a direct measure of the velocity and can be evaluated as pulses per second.

SIGNAL CONDITIONING

At the beginning of this chapter, the basic elements of a system for acquiring measurement signals were outlined. Between the transducer and the main signal processor and controller may be placed instruments to improve the signal. Many of these operations are described more fully elsewhere in this book, but are outlined here for completeness.

Preamplifier and signal converter

The signal is most vulnerable to degradation by loading and interference during its transmission between the transducer and the central processor. Where possible, the signal is made as large as possible and given a clear waveform before transmission. For this purpose amplifiers and signal-conditioning circuits are placed near to the transducer. The disadvantage of this is that there is extra complexity in the circuit since power has to be supplied to these circuits, usually from the central unit. Also the transducer may be in an environment that is hostile to active devices.

If the signal is in the form of an analog voltage, a low-noise, high input impedance preamplifier is needed. The output of the transducer may actually be a current so that a current-to-voltage converter may be required as for the photodetector. In some systems the interference and signal degradation may be reduced by transmitting the signal in the form of a current from a high output impedance source to a low input impedance receiver. For high-frequency signals, the source and receiver impedances must be matched to the characteristic impedance of the transmission line (chapter 11).

As part of the signal-conditioning process, care must be taken to eliminate possible problems of pick-up by balancing the signals with respect to earth and removing earth loops where possible. There are many possible combinations of transducer and amplifier, each of which may be earthed or floating, common-mode or differential. The principles have been described in chapter 4, where the value of the instrumentation amplifier, isolation amplifier, and analog or digital optical links have been outlined. Improvements in the signal-to-noise ratio can be obtained at this stage by filtering.

Linearization

The output signal of a transducer is defined by the transfer function, but the central signal processor or recorder may require a different function of the experimental variable. For example, the transfer function may have a small degree of non-linearity which, if removed, would enable further operations on the signal to be performed very simply. Similarly, an intensity signal, $V \propto Q_i^2$, might be more useful than an amplitude signal, $V \propto Q_i$, derived directly from the transducer. The analog non-linear circuits needed for these non-linear operations have been described in principle in chapter 2. Alternately, the operation may be performed digitally by a computer once the signal has been put into digital form.

MULTIPLEXING AND TELEMETRY

The transmission of the transducer signal to the central processor or an analog–digital converter (see later) can be done over a pair of wires, a light beam or perhaps a radio signal. If this *channel* is not being used continuously in a fast data transfer but measurements are only made periodically, then several signals may be sent over the same channel either at different times or at the same time but coded or modulated in such a way that they can be separated unambiguously at the receiver. This is outlined in chapter 6. This process is called *multiplexing* and the transmission process *telemetry*.

The simplest arrangement is, for example, when several transducers are being used but their outputs are changing slowly so that they can be read in succession by a single voltmeter. Such a multiplex arrangement can be done with a single line as shown in figure 8.20(a) for signals I_1, I_2, I_3, and I_4 or with a pair of lines if good isolation is required, as shown in figure 8.20(b). The switches can be relay contacts or semiconductor (analog) switches, which consist of FET channels that can be turned 'on' or 'off' (low or high resistance) with a control gate voltage. The impedances of the switch, both along the

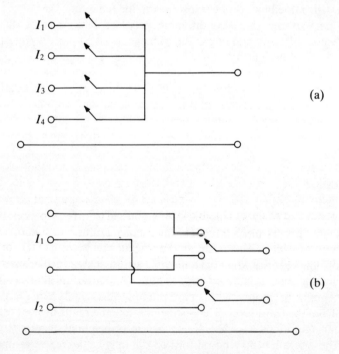

Fig. 8.20 Single (a) or differential input (b) multiplexers.

signal path and to earth, should be suitable to prevent the loss of signal to the accuracy required. Usually a logic circuit is incorporated in the control circuit so that only one path is connected at any time.

ANALOG–DIGITAL CONVERTERS

Most signal sources produce an analog signal, whereas for display, signal processing, or recording a digital signal is often preferable. The digital signal can be transmitted, recorded, and manipulated mathematically with much higher accuracy than an analog signal. However, it has the disadvantages that

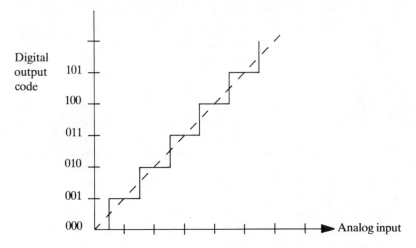

Fig. 8.21   The transfer function of a digital-to-analog converter.

the processes are often slower than analog computation and there is a loss in resolution in the conversion from an analog signal to a digital binary signal. This is illustrated in figure 8.21, which shows that each digital output signal corresponds to a range of possible input signals. The reverse process, digital–analog conversion, was described in chapter 2.

Here we will consider the *analog–digital converter* (ADC) operation using the example of a voltage input and pure binary output. A binary coded decimal (BDC) or other coded output can be obtained by the code conversion methods outlined in chapter 5. There are many types of analog–digital conversion techniques, some of which are optimized for rapid conversion to match the fast operation rate of the computer and normally have a pure binary output to connect directly into the computer. Some others are designed to be measuring instruments with good input qualities and noise rejection but with slower operation. The output is often in BCD form since a digital display is provided. The former are usually called ADCs while the latter are called *digital voltmeters* (DVM).

It should be emphasized that ADCs in general and DVMs in particular have properties that are considerably different from, and usually better than, an equivalent analog instrument such as a voltmeter or an amplifier followed by a voltmeter. The method of operation ensures a very high input impedance, a good linearity, and often high resolution and accuracy.

Voltage–frequency converter

The voltage–frequency converter produces a stream of constant-amplitude pulses or a square wave with a frequency proportional to the input voltage. Since the pulses can be counted, it acts as an ADC. However, it can be used in other ways. If the output is a square wave or sine wave it is called a voltage-controlled oscillator and forms the basis of the function generator (chapter 3).

The voltage–frequency converter may also be considered as a frequency modulator (chapter 6). Usually the term FM is used for systems in which the modulation of the frequency is only a small proportion of the carrier frequency, whereas with the voltage–frequency converter, the fractional modulation is large, or the frequency itself is proportional to the input voltage. The frequency signal is very convenient for transmission since it is a two-level or binary signal and hence will not be easily degraded. At the receiver, the signal may be either counted or converted back to an analog signal with a frequency–voltage converter.

In some transducers, an impedance change is converted into a frequency change by making the impedance one of the active feedback components in an *LC* or *RC* oscillator.

The usual conversion principle is shown in figure 8.22. The input voltage is converted into a current which charges a capacitor up to some reference voltage level supplied to a comparator. The capacitor is then either discharged rapidly by shorting its terminals or it is made to discharge at the same rate as the charging rate by changing the sign of the current. The period of each cycle is inversely proportional to the input signal. An output pulse of a fixed length is produced after each cycle by a monostable multivibrator (chapter 3), so that the pulse rate or frequency is proportional to the input voltage. The input signal range can easily be altered by changing the value of the charging capacitor.

The comparator has to have a high input impedance and some hysteresis and the switch has to have a low on-resistance so that the capacitor discharges completely during the reset period.

Variations of the basic circuit can be made. The input circuit, up to the comparator input, can be replaced by an active integrator (chapter 2). If the

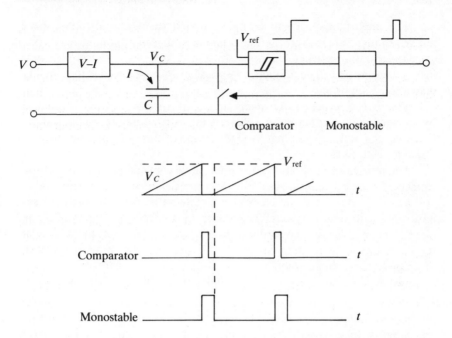

Fig. 8.22 The schematic circuit and waveforms of a typical voltage-to-frequency converter.

input current is made to charge and discharge alternately the capacitor between two fixed values of V_{ref}, then the comparator output is a square wave at the output frequency rather than a pulse train.

In another version shown in figure 8.23, the comparator reference voltage is set to a very low value so that, whenever the integrator output changes by this amount, a constant pulse of charge (voltage × time across a resistance R_1) is sent into the input to set the integrator back to zero. The pulse rate is thus proportional to the input voltage averaged over the integrator time constant.

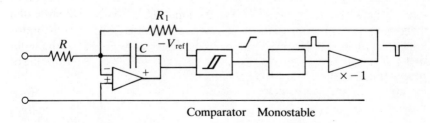

Fig. 8.23 The schematic circuit of a charge feedback voltage-to-frequency converter.

The important specifications for voltage–frequency converters are the linearity and offset (zero error). The frequency range may limit the resolution since the counting instrument is normally restricted to plus or minus one count in the counting time. The frequency response to an a.c. signal and the stability may also be important.

The reverse process, *frequency–voltage conversion*, is usually achieved by converting each input pulse, or cycle, into a constant-size (amplitude × time) voltage pulse. The time-average voltage of this pulse train is proportional to the frequency.

The integrator methods of analog-to-digital conversion have an intrinsic capacity for high linearity, resolution, and precision compared with analog voltmeters. The input circuit element is an integrator. Since the output rises uniformly with time, any small signal can, in principle, be observed if the measurement is carried out for long enough time. In practice, the quality of the integrator is the limiting factor. One integrating ADC has already been described, the voltage–frequency converter shown in figure 8.23. In this circuit the integrator operates with null input, which ensures good performance.

Single- and dual-slope ADCs

A *single-slope integrating ADC* circuit is shown in figure 8.24. A high-quality ramp voltage is generated by a reference voltage, $-V_{ref}$, and an active integrator. At the start of the integration cycle, a counter starts to count the pulses from a clock. When the integration reaches the input voltage V_{in}, a comparator turns the counter off and resets the integrator. The count is proportional to the input voltage and is displayed. After a delay, the cycle recommences. The range can be charged by changing the RC value and hence the ramp rate.

The *dual-slope integrating ADC* circuit has many advantages over the single-slope method. The circuit is shown in figure 8.25. The input signal is integrated for a fixed time t_1 specified by the range and measured by a fixed number of cycles of the clock and counted by counter 1. At the end of time t_1, the integrator is switched to integrate a reference voltage, $-V_{ref}$, of the opposite sign to the input voltage. The integrator ramps down and the comparator detects the return of the integrator output voltage V_C to zero. Counter 2 measures this second integration time, t_2, using the same clock. Since $t_1/t_2 = |V_{ref}/V_{in}|$ we get $V_{in} = |V_{ref}| \times t_2/t_1$; the input signal is thus proportional to the count corresponding to the time t_2. The accuracy of this circuit relies on the balance provided by the upward and downward integration stages, so that the linearity of the integrator is not very critical. The actual value of the clock frequency is also not critical, provided $t_1 \approx t_2$. Also the comparator can be accurate since it detects zero voltage and hence experiences no common-mode signal at

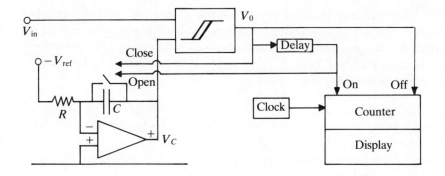

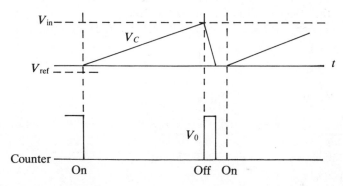

Fig. 8.24 The schematic circuit and waveforms of a single-slope integrating analog–digital converter.

threshold. Again, the most important quantities are the noise and stability of the integrator.

One particularly valuable property of this circuit arises if the integration time t_1 is made a multiple of the period of any unwanted a.c. input signals such as the common power supply (line) frequency (50 or 60 Hz) or its harmonics. If $t_1 = n \times 1/50$ s, integral numbers of cycles are integrated to give zero effect at the output. Thus the system acts like a detector with a frequency response that is large at z.f. but has nulls at 50 Hz and its harmonics as shown in figure 8.26. The conversion time is consequently very long.

Integrating ADCs are made that can reduce the effects of input offset voltages and drifts by the introduction of stages in each cycle in which such signals are measured and their values stored in either analog or digital form for subtraction from the final output signal.

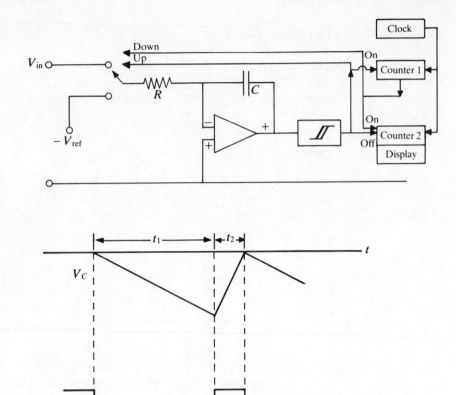

Counter 1   On   Off

Counter 2   On   Off

Fig. 8.25   The schematic circuit and waveforms of a dual-slope integrating analog–
digital converter.

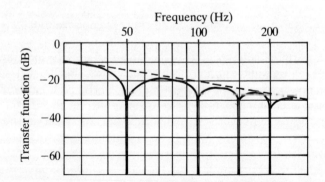

Fig. 8.26   The transfer function of the dual-slope ADC with an integration time of
1/50 s.

Feedback ADCs using DACs

The DACs described in chapter 2 are simple devices that can be made to be very fast and accurate. ADCs can be made that include a DAC within a negative feedback loop which sets the DAC analog output value to be as near as possible to the input voltage. Then the DAC digital input signal is the required ADC output signal. There are two basic designs.

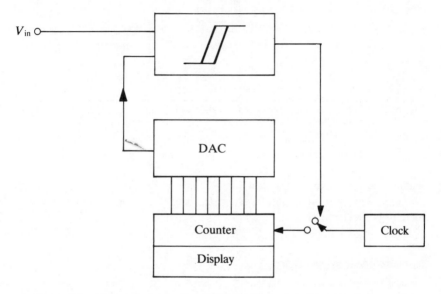

Fig. 8.27   The schematic circuit of a counting analog–digital converter.

In the *counting ADC*, shown in figure 8.27, the digital control to the DAC changes its value by increments equal to the DAC step size. In the simple case, the digital signal is set to zero and then counts upward until the output of the DAC is observed by the comparator to be equal to the input signal. This is obviously slow and each measurement will take a different time to complete. In a modified version, the counter can count upward and downward, and the comparator controls the direction of the count. This is a fairly fast technique if the signal is slowly changing and the converter then tracks the input signal.

In the *successive approximation ADC*, shown in figure 8.28, a more rapid method of setting the DAC is used. If there are n bits to be set, the counting ADC described above has to consider each of the 2^n possibilities in sequence until one is found to be correct. However, each bit has only two possibilities corresponding to a total of n choices. The successive approximation ADC tests each bit of the DAC, starting with the most significant bit (m.s.b.), and

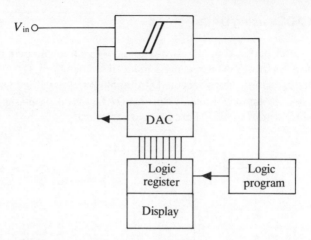

Fig. 8.28 The schematic circuit of a successive approximation analog–digital
converter.

leaves it set if the analog output signal from the DAC is less than the input
voltage. The setting is thus very rapid since only n setting operations
have to be performed.

Parallel comparator ADC

The fastest design of an ADC involves an arrangement of parallel comparators, each set at a reference voltage corresponding to one of the incremental
ADC levels. These can be derived from a potential divider chain as shown in
figure 8.29. In operation, all of the comparators up to a certain level will give
an output. The time taken is that for only one setting operation since all n
comparators act at once. This will need a digital encoder in order to give a
suitable binary output. Since n comparators are needed, the size, complexity,
and cost of this type of ADC restrict its use.

ADC specifications

The ADC produces an inherent loss of resolution. The digital output is
quantized although the anlog input is continuous. The ADC is designed to
make the transition at a voltage such that the step is symmetrical about its
nominal analog voltage. Thus the quantizing resolution is $\pm\frac{1}{2}$ l.s.b. if we use a
pure binary signal as shown in figure 8.20. For counting ADCs, the equivalent
resolution is ± 1 count. The absolute resolution is fixed by the maximum range

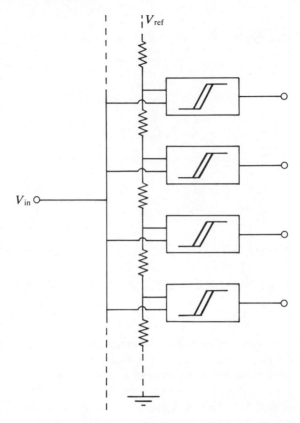

Fig. 8.29 The schematic circuit of a parallel comparator analog–digital converter.

and the number of steps or bits. The fractional resolution of a voltage thus depends on its proportion of the full-scale voltage.

A real ADC characteristic may depart from the ideal in many ways. An important measure of the departure is the *differential linearity*, which is the size of each step. If this is greater than ±1 bit, the steps will no longer be monotonic. As well as these static errors, there are dynamic errors such as the conversion or settling time, noise, and stability.

For a specific purpose, it is possible to make the analog–digital conversion non-linear in order that each digital code has a more equal probability of occurring. For example, if speech is to be digitized, there need be fewer levels at the high amplitudes since these occur infrequently and the ear is less sensitive to them. If the signal is to be reconstructed later by a complementary digital–analog process, then little information will be lost. This process is called *companding* and an example is shown in figure 8.30.

The digital signal in the converters described is produced as a parallel-bit

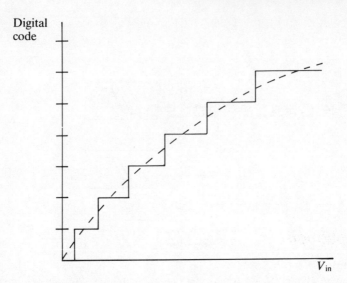

Fig. 8.30 The transfer characteristic of a non-linear analog–digital converter.

byte. It can be converted into bit-serial using a shift register. If a computer is connected directly to the converter, it will give a command and the byte will be transferred into its data registers or onto its data bus.

In many cases, there is not a dedicated, direct or semipermanent connection between the ADC and the computer, but the computer is designed to accept suitable digital signals from a selection of instruments. A standard bus for transfer of data and commands between a computer and digital instrument is described in chapter 10.

FURTHER READING

K. G. Beauchamp and C. K.Yuen, *Data Acquisitions for Signal Analysis*, Allen and Unwin (1980).

G. B. Clayton, *Data Converters*, Macmillan (1982).

A. J. Diefenderer, *Principles of Instrumentation*, Saunders (1979).

J. D. Garratt, 'Survey of displacement transducers below 50 mm', *J.Phys. E* **12** (1979) 563–73.

R. W. Henry, *Electronic Systems and Instrumentation*, Wiley (1978).

B. E. Jones, *Instrumentation, Measurement and Feedback*, McGraw-Hill (1977).

J. Millman, *Microelectronics*, McGraw-Hill (1977).

A. de Sa, *Principles of Electronic Instrumentation*, Edward Arnold (1981).

P. H. Sydenham, *Transducers in Measurement and Control*, Adam Hilger (1984).

9 SIGNAL PROCESSING

INTRODUCTION

The power of electronic function circuits to manipulate signals has been shown in earlier chapters. This signal processing has been described in analog form and for many purposes this is most appropriate since the method is simple, accurate, and rapid. Analog filters, integrators, and summers are very valuable circuit elements. However, there are many powerful ways of manipulating signals (enhancement of signal-to-noise ratio, and complex filtering, for example) that cannot easily be done in analog form.

The principal technique for carrying out these operations is to convert the time-varying input signal into a series of discrete digital values and to manipulate these numbers in a computer. This stream of values, usually equally spaced in time, is called a time series and is described in appendix 5 to expand the analysis in this chapter. Since the result is needed rapidly a 'dedicated' computer is preferably used to perform just the desired calculation. For some operations, if speed and simplicity are needed, there is a solution intermediate between the strictly analog and digital in which the signal is divided into discrete time sections by a 'chopper' or switch and these analog pulses are processed by analog circuits. An example of this approach is the phase-sensitive detector (PSD) which was described in chapters 4 and 6 as a filter and a modulator. Here it will also be described but as an analog signal averager or correlator.

SAMPLE AND HOLD

An analog–digital converter (ADC) needs a constant input signal during the period that it is digitizing. In some cases the input signal will change by less than the resolution of the ADC during the conversion time, so that digitization can be direct. Usually high-resolution digitization is needed, so the signal has to be held constant at the input of the ADC. This is achieved with a *sample and hold* (SH) or *track and hold* circuit.

The output of this circuit follows (tracks) the input until addressed. The output signal at this time is then held until a command is given to restore the track mode. In figure 9.1 samples are shown taken at times t_1, t_2, t_3, etc., and tracking is restored at times t'_1, t'_2, t'_3, etc.

Circuits to perform the SH function are shown in figure 9.2. In the simple circuit of figure 9.2(a), during the tracking mode, the capacitor C is charged

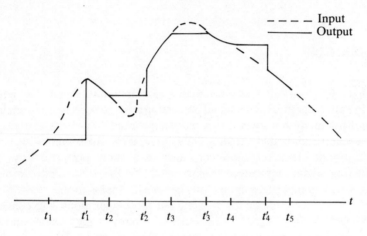

Fig. 9.1 The input and output waveforms of a sample-and-hold circuit which holds at times t_1, t_2, t_3, etc., and releases to start the next sample at times t'_1, t'_2, t'_3, etc.

rapidly through the series combination (r) of the small switch on-resistance and the small output resistance of the input buffer amplifier. The source circuit is thus not loaded and the capacitor voltage follows the input voltage rapidly with a time constant rC. After the switch is opened at the sampling time, the charge on the capacitor decays only slowly through the resistance (R) of the parallel combination of the switch leakage resistance and the input resistance of the output buffer amplifier. The ratio of the hold time to sample time for a given accuracy thus depends on R/r. The exact limits of the sample-and-hold times depend on the precision needed, the necessary constancy during the hold time ('droop'), and any transient effects and pick-up during the switching process. The switch is usually an electronic switch consisting of an FET or diode gates. In practice, the output buffer amplifier effect on the capacitor charge is best described by a constant leakage current owing to the amplifier input bias current. Amplifier offset voltages

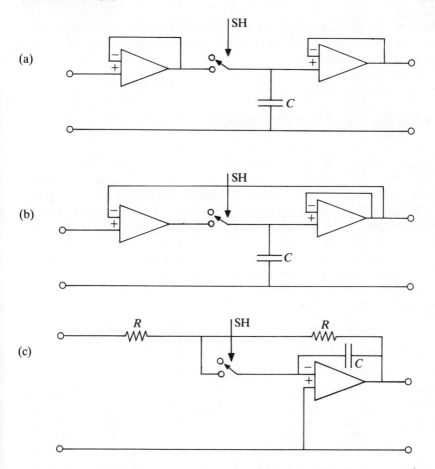

Fig. 9.2 Typical sample-and-hold circuits (a) and (b) with an integrating sample-and-hold circuit (c).

also add to the signal. If the leakage current is a limiting factor, a large capacitor improves the hold time but increases the track charging time constant. High-quality capacitors are needed that have low leakage and keep a stable voltage under a constant charge. Some dielectrics show time changes that depend on the previous charge history.

Other SH circuits are used. In the circuit of figure 9.2(b), overall feedback reduces the effects due to large switch-on transients and reduces the effect of switch on-resistance. The circuit of figure 9.2(c) uses the capacitor in the feedback, integrator or Miller effect configuration. The output voltage is equal to the input voltage but inverted. During the track period the output responds with an RC time constant. The hold properties are similar to those of the other circuits. For most applications this RC response is kept short, as it limits the tracking rate, but if it is made large we have the *integrating sample-and-hold* circuit, which will be used later in this chapter when the boxcar integrator is described.

SAMPLING THEOREM AND ALIASING

The *sampling* of a time-varying signal, which is the conversion of a continuous analog signal into a series of discrete analog or digital values, has limitations. In chapter 8 the ADC was shown to have limits to its voltage resolution given by the number of discrete quantized levels. There are also practical limits to the resolution due to the analog circuits set by the drift and droop of the 'hold' signal in a sample-and-hold circuit. Similarly the rate at which sampling and analog-to-digital conversion can proceed is limited by the response speed of the SH circuit and the conversion time of the ADC.

A more fundamental limit to sampled systems is set by the *sampling theorem*, which states that:

> To reproduce a signal with a Fourier component at a frequency f, the sampling rate, f_s, must be at least $2f$ ($f_s \geq 2f$).

This is illustrated in figure 9.3. In figure 9.3(a) a signal is shown sampled frequently. The arrows represent the sampled values of the sine-wave signal. The signal can be reconstructed by joining neighboring points to restore the original signal accurately. In the limiting case, where the sampling frequency $f_s = 2f$, for a sine wave of frequency f, shown in figures 9.3(b) and (c), the reproduced waveform is not a unique pattern since the sampled values and the simplest reconstructed waveform will depend on the phase difference between the signal and the sample pulses. In figures 9.3(d) and (e) it is shown that the reconstructed signal (shown broken) will not be at the input frequency if the sampling rate is too slow.

This discussion illustrates a problem introduced by sampling called *aliasing*.

> A signal at frequency f, sampled at a rate f_s, will be reproduced as a signal at $f - f_s$ if $f_s < 2f$.

Since there is no frequency, or rapidly varying, information above $f_s/2$, a sampled signal must be reconstructed as a low-frequency signal. However, signals at many different high frequencies could be sampled to give the same data points. These high frequencies will be reconstructed, after sampling, as a lower-frequency signal. Two examples of such reconstructions are shown broken in figures 9.3(d) and (e). To avoid this ambiguity, it is essential that all signals, before sampling, have any high-frequency component removed by a

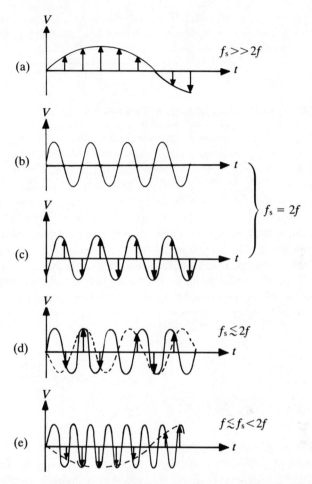

Fig. 9.3 Sampling of a sine wave at a frequency f. In (a) the sampling frequency f_s is much higher than $2f$ and the samples will reproduce the original waveform faithfully. If $f_s = 2f$ the reconstructed signal will be ambiguous and depend on the relative phases of the sample and input signals as shown in (b) and (c). If the sampling rate is slow so that $f_s < 2f$ then the signal can be reconstructed at a low frequency, shown in broken lines in (d) and (e).

low-pass, *anti-aliasing filter* so that there are no significant frequency components left above $f_s/2$. This filter has to have a very sharp cut-off so that there is a high attenuation above $f_s/2$ but the bandwidth of the frequencies that are passed unchanged is as large as possible.

Often the sampled signal is kept and stored in digital form. However, if the sampled signal is to be reconstructed as a low-frequency analog signal, for example for display on an oscilloscope, then various techniques may be used. A simple technique used in computer displays is to produce a straight line

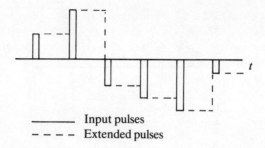

—————— Input pulses
– – – – Extended pulses

Fig. 9.4 A series of narrow input pulses can be converted into extended pulses, shown in broken lines, so that only a little filtering is necessary to reconstruct a smooth analog signal.

between adjacent points. A more sophisticated approach constructs a sine wave through the data points.

If the sampled values are analog voltage pulses such as produced by a DAC, then they should be passed through a low-pass filter with a sharp cut-off above $f = f_s/2$. To reduce the magnitude of the high harmonics, these sharp pulses can be converted into pulses with a width equal to the pulse separation time $1/f_s$ with a voltage holding circuit as in a sample-and-hold circuit. The resulting waveform is shown in figure 9.4.

SAMPLING INSTRUMENTS

For use in a particular application, a dedicated system of an SH circuit followed by an ADC and a memory is all that is required. In general experimental work a display of the signal is valuable so the *digital storage oscilloscope* (DSO) is used. This produces a conventional analog oscilloscope display by reconstruction from the memory. The amplifier gain can be altered and the sampling rate is adjusted automatically with the timebase setting. Facilities usually exist for linking the individual display points by a curve to reconstruct the original signal. For further manipulation of the digital signals the memory can be accessed. A significant feature of this instrument is that a signal can be stored indefinitely in the memory, or removed to a more permanent memory such as a magnetic disk, and perhaps later reintroduced via the oscilloscope memory for display. The memory also enables sections of the timebase to be enlarged for more detailed display although the time and amplitude resolution cannot be improved after acquisition.

A conventional, analog, storage oscilloscope continuously refreshes the analog signal displayed by using the special charge storage properties of the cathode ray tube. The start of a transient signal is difficult to investigate using this method since the signal has to be large enough to trigger the timebase before it can be displayed and hence stored. Although a signal delay can be placed between the trigger and the display, such delays can rarely be made long enough. The digital storage oscilloscope can overcome these problems by placing the acquired signal into a continuously circulating or temporary memory which acts as a delay. The trigger signal stops the circulation in the memory and the stored data can be displayed starting at a specified time, perhaps before the trigger. The signal before the obvious transient can therefore be investigated.

Not only does the digital storage oscilloscope have the advantage of a visual display and convenient controls, but also once the data have been acquired and stored in digital form all the signal processing techniques described later in this chapter and in appendices 2, 3, 4, and 5 can be performed.

In situations where fast transient, non-repetitive, signals are to be acquired, and the convenience of the display and simplified controls is not needed, the instrument for sampling and storage is called a *transient recorder*. In general these instruments are optimized for the rapid digitization of signals over a short period of time and their transfer into a memory. During the long period between successive signals, the contents of the memory can be transferred for further processing and storage. There are inevitable compromises between speed, resolution in time and amplitude, and the number of samples that can be stored.

A typical instrument might have a 20 MHz sampling rate to give a 5 MHz signal bandwidth and eight-bit resolution with 4096 samples in the memory.

Very fast, *repetitive* signals can be acquired and displayed using a *sampling oscilloscope*. The acquisition time of an SH circuit can be made to be much shorter than the time for the analog–digital conversion and storage in the memory. The principle is shown in figure 9.5. On each repetition the SH operates and the system acquires the signal at one point on the waveform at time nt_s after a trigger time. On each repetition the time is increased by equal increments, t_s. The DAC has a repetition time for the conversion. The signal is thus slowly scanned and is recorded to a memory or displayed. The time resolution and scan time are inversely related until the minimum acquisition time of the SH circuit is reached. The process is like the operation of a stroboscope.

Since the signals are at high frequencies, the sampling unit is usually placed very close to the circuit in a 'sampling head' so that the signals are not disturbed by large input capacitances or lead lengths (see chapter 11). The output of the SH circuit is of low frequency, the repetition rate, so that a long lead here is less important. The sampling switch has to be very fast and the diode bridge arrangement shown in figure 9.6 is often used. When the two pulsed bias signals are at zero, the diodes have high impedance since they are either near zero bias if the signal is small or one diode of each pair in series

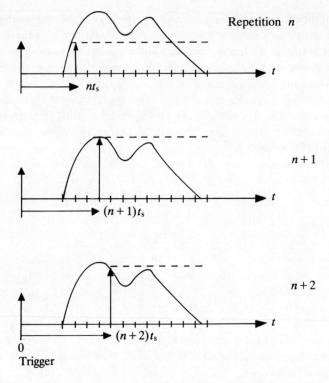

Fig. 9.5 On successive repetitions a sampling oscilloscope samples and holds the value of the waveform at successive increments of time, t_s. The sampled value, shown in broken lines, is held between repetitions for recording.

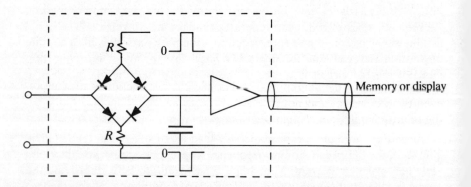

Fig. 9.6 The circuit of a typical sampling switch of a sampling oscilloscope.

with the signal is reverse-biased by the signal. The switch is closed by applying equal and opposite large pulses through resistors R. Provided the signal is not large, the diodes are forward-biased and hence have a low slope, or incremental resistance. With a moderate-sized signal, one pair of the diodes will always conduct.

TIME-SERIES ANALYSIS

Once a signal has been sampled and digitized into a series of data points in time, the information that it contains can be presented, processed, and modified in many different ways. The basic mathematical technique for doing this is *time-series analysis*, which is described in more detail in appendix 5. Here some of the important results are given.

For any signal an *amplitude probability density*, $p(V)\mathrm{d}V$, can be calculated. This is the fraction of the time that the signal exists between values V and $V+\mathrm{d}V$. The *amplitude cumulative probability distribution* $P(V)$ is the normalized integral form

$$P(V) = \int_{-\infty}^{V} p(V)\,\mathrm{d}V \bigg/ \int_{-\infty}^{\infty} p(V)\,\mathrm{d}V$$

which goes from 0 to 1 and gives a measure of the fraction of the time that the signal spends below a voltage V. Examples of common waveforms are given in figure 9.7.

In each case the signal has maximum and minimum values $+A$ and $-A$, except for the Gaussian noise which has r.m.s. values $\pm A$. Many noise signals have this Gaussian distribution. It can be seen that these distributions can give some information but the results are not unique to the waveform. Amplitude probability analysis involves a simple measurement and can be used for the investigation of processes involving probabilities. However, caution should be exercised in the analysis since even a linear system can alter the shape as well as the size of the amplitude distribution. The distribution of the sum of even two sine waves may not be easy to analyze and the shape will change if the relative amplitudes change after filtering.

More complex calculations are possible. For a repetitive signal the average of successive repetitions of the signal and its noise will result in an enhanced signal-to-noise ratio. This process is called *signal averaging*.

The spectrum of the digitized signal can be computed in a *spectrum analyzer* and this leads to the construction of *digital filters*. These will be discussed later in this chapter and in appendices 3 and 5.

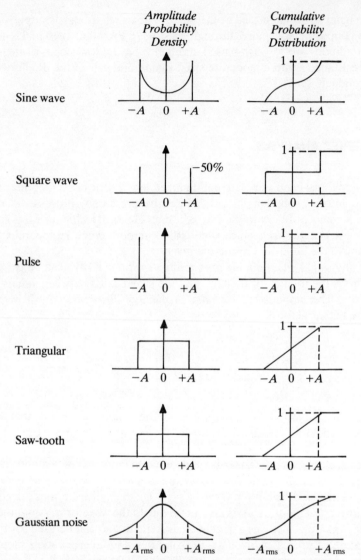

Fig. 9.7   The amplitude probability density and cumulative probability distribution for common waveforms with peak amplitude $\perp A$.

A function related to the spectrum is the *correlation function*, which is displayed against a time variable. It is discussed later and in appendix 4. The similar *convolution function* is also introduced in appendix 3.

Since all these computations, or combinations of them, can be made on the same basic sampled data, instruments can be constructed for performing several operations, although a given instrument may be optimized for only a selection of the functions.

SIGNAL AVERAGING

For a repetitive signal, the signal-to-noise ratio (S/N) can be increased by *signal averaging*. Consider a signal v_s with added noise v_n. The successive repetitions produce a recorded signal of size $v_s + v_{n1}$, $v_s + v_{n2}$, $v_s + v_{n3}$, etc. The average of M repetitions is thus

$$\frac{1}{M} \left(M v_s + \sum_{i=1}^{M} v_{ni} \right) = v_s + \frac{1}{M} \sum_{i=1}^{M} v_{ni} \tag{9.1}$$

If the noise is truly random, it will have a mean of zero, so that it will be of less significance to the averaged signal than in each measurement. For a finite number of repetitions, the statistical uncertain nature of the noise will ensure that the mean will not necessarily be zero and its standard deviation needs to be considered.

Since the noise signal can be assumed to be random, the noise intensities will add. Thus the average after M repetitions will be

$$v_s + \left(\frac{1}{M} \overline{v_n^2} \right)^{1/2}$$

where $\overline{v_n^2}$ is the mean-square value of the noise averaged over all samples, which are assumed to have similar characteristics. The signal amplitude and total noise intensity both increase by M so that the standard deviation of the noise increases as $M^{1/2}$. The S/N power ratio thus improves by a factor of M and the amplitude ratio by $M^{1/2}$. This improvement is the same as that found in random error theory, which gives an $M^{1/2}$ improvement in the accuracy of a measured quantity if M independent measurements are averaged.

Since the noise signals are assumed to be independent, this result is the best that can be achieved since in practice there may be some noise common to some or all repetitions. This may be a power line frequency signal at a constant phase with the repetition frequency or some slowly varying signal overlapping several repetitions.

The *digital signal averager* is based on the *multichannel analyzer* (MCA). The repetitive signal is sampled at regular discrete times, $n t_s$, $(n+1) t_s$, etc., which are integral multiples of the sampling period t_s, and measured relative to a trigger signal derived from or in fixed phase relation with the input signal. The samples are fed into separate locations, or channels, of a memory. On each repetition the new samples are taken and added in some way to the numbers in each location of the memory. The display is taken from the memory via a DAC. A schematic diagram is shown in figure 9.8.

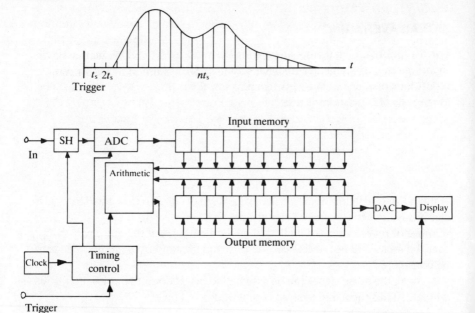

Fig. 9.8 The waveform and schematic circuit of a digital signal averager of repetitive waveforms.

The set of samples from each repetition can be added to the numbers in the memory in several ways. In the simplest form the new value for each time element is simply added to that already in the corresponding memory location. The signals are thus totalized and continually increase, and the S/N will improve. To obtain a calibrated, normalized display, the signals should be divided by the number of averages taken. The disadvantage of this method is that the total signal may become larger than the capacity of a particular memory location. A more convenient method is to store in the memory the average of the previous repetitions and add the new data with a suitable weighting to give a new average. A suitable algorithm is, for the nth repetition

$$V(n) = \frac{n-1}{n} V(n-1) + \frac{1}{n} V_{in}$$

$$= V(n-1) + \frac{1}{n}[V_{in} - V(n-1)] \tag{9.2}$$

where $V(n-1)$ and $V(n)$ are the original and final values in the memory and V_{in} is the new signal. With this process the display remains the same size but the S/N ratio improves with successive repetitions. Alternately if the new and stored signals are always given the same relative weight on addition irrespective of the value of n, the display records a running average with the repetitions weighted exponentially backward in time. In this way a slowly changing signal can be observed with some improvement in the S/N ratio.

The same principle can be used to improve the signal-to-noise ratio of other types of signals if the memory location, or channel number, is defined by some variable other than time. For example, successive measurements of a spectrum can be averaged if the channels are assigned to frequencies or an average amplitude distribution function can be determined if the channels become amplitude locations and the number of times each amplitude is obtained during the sampling process is stored in each location. Averaging of a spectrum is usually r.m.s. averaging in which the phase and sign information is lost. This has the effect of providing a more accurate and smoother spectrum of all the received intensity, signal and noise.

If the signal waveform is already known, and only a measurement of the amplitude is required, simpler techniques can be used. Just one channel of the above scheme could be used since the relative amplitudes in all channels are known from the signal waveform. However, it is better to use all the information available rather than just the value at a single sample time. In this way the S/N ratio is further improved. For simple waveforms of known shape, analog methods are usually used since these have high resolution and dynamic range.

THE PHASE-SENSITIVE DETECTOR

The phase-sensitive detector (PSD) was described in chapter 6 as a mixer, demodulator or detector. Here it will be considered as a signal averager.

For an input signal of a sine wave at the same frequency and phase as the reference signal, the signal after the switching circuit is a full-wave rectified signal with a waveform and spectrum as shown in figure 9.9(a). The noise accompanying it will, in general, be white and since it is random it will be almost unchanged by inversion each half-cycle of the reference signal, as shown in figure 9.9(b). The signal is averaged by passing through a low-pass filter or integrator with a response shown in figure 9.9(c).

From the spectra it can be seen that the signal d.c. output will be unchanged by a reduction in the low-pass filter cut-off frequency, $f_0 < 2f$, but the bandwidth and hence the total noise intensity will be reduced proportionally. Alternately the filter can be considered as an integrator or averager with a characteristic time $\tau_0 = 1/2\pi f_0$. A signal applied at an instant of time will produce an output that decays exponentially with time. Thus the output is an average of the input signal weighted exponentially decreasing backward in

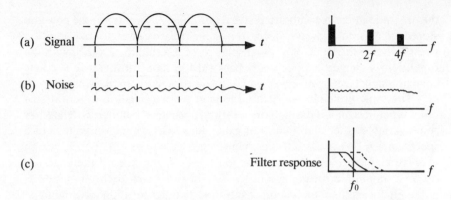

Fig. 9.9 The waveform and spectrum of an input sine wave after half-wave synchronous detection in a phase-sensitive detector (a). The accompanying noise is shown in (b). The effect of the final averaging filter with the response shown in (c) is to improve the signal-to-noise ratio.

time. Each repetition in time contributes a constant signal and a random noise. The time average of the signal is a constant while the noise is averaged to a small value.

THE BOXCAR DETECTOR

The *boxcar detector* is the equivalent analog detector for use with repetitive pulse signals occurring together with noise as the PSD is for sine- or square-wave signals with noise. It is especially useful for pulses with small on–off (mark–space) ratios such as occur in pulse–echo systems such as radar and sonar.

In chapter 4 the time window was introduced as a way of increasing the S/N ratio by allowing the input signal and noise to enter the receiver only when there was a signal present. This idea of time-domain signal processing is extended here for repetitive signals.

The arrangement is shown in figure 9.10. The input pulse shown in figure 9.19(a) occurs at a fixed time after a synchronizing trigger signal. A window or gate is opened for a period τ_2 at a time τ_1 after the trigger, as in figure 9.10(b). During this window period an integrating sample-and-hold circuit integrates this section of the input signal with a time constant comparable with τ_2 and holds the output signal until the next repetition. This output signal (figure 9.10(c)), which has a step change each repetition period, T, is averaged over a time much longer than T by a final averager, integrator or low-pass filter, as in figure 9.10(d). The integrating SH circuit shown in figure

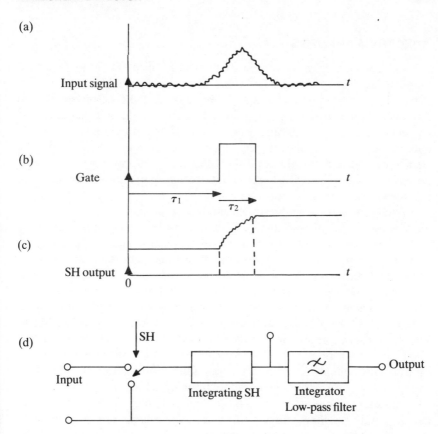

Fig. 9.10 The boxcar detector is designed to improve the signal-to-noise ratio of a pulse signal accompanied by noise as shown in (a). A gate signal shown in (b) admits the signal to an integrating sample-and-hold circuit only during the time interval τ_2, to produce the output shown in (c). The schematic circuit is shown in (d).

9.2(c) with a time constant RC may be used. In this way all the signal available during the whole pulse is used and averaged while successive repetitions are also averaged.

In the scan mode the delay time τ_1 is varied slowly compared with T and the output signal is recorded against τ_1 to give the waveform. This is a similar operation to that in the sampling oscilloscope described earlier. There the signal at each time point is acquired in one repetition and placed in a single channel of a digital signal averager. The use of the circuit in this mode gives rise to the name 'boxcar' because of the similarity of the waveform of figure 9.10(b) to a boxcar or railway wagon.

SPECTRUM ANALYSIS

An oscilloscope is a very useful instrument which displays the signal amplitude as a function of time. The principles of Fourier analysis, reviewed in appendix 3, indicate that the same information as the time display can be displayed in the form of a spectrum, that is amplitude and phase against frequency. For many applications the phase information is not very valuable and can be omitted. Although the same information is presented in both the frequency and the time displays, the latter has been more usual probably because of tradition but also because suitable, cheap spectrum analyzers have not been available.

Analog spectrum analyzers, which include all high-frequency and the early audiofrequency instruments, usually work by mixing the input signal with a constant-amplitude swept local oscillator at $f_L(t)$ and displaying the output which goes through a narrow band-pass filter. The schematic circuit is shown in figure 9.11. If, for example, the instrument is to detect signals between frequencies 0 and f_1 while the local oscillator is swept between $2f_1$ and f_1, then a narrow band-pass filter at $2f_1$ will only transmit the input signal component which produces an instantaneous sum frequency of $2f_1$. In this system there is a compromise between the sweep rate and the bandwidth and also no phase information is obtained. The system also only gives a reading of a particular frequency component if it is present at the appropriate time of the sweep. Thus time-varying signals cannot be analyzed easily.

Another technique is to apply the input signal simultaneously to separate narrow band-pass filters tuned to different frequencies. In this case the whole spectrum is obtained at the same time, but it becomes very expensive as the number of channels increases, so that it is usually used only for full-octave or half-octave bandwidth filters over a limited band of frequencies.

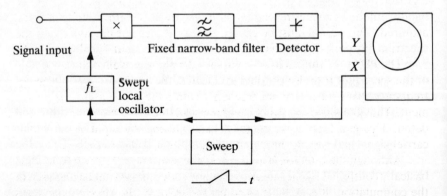

Fig. 9.11 An analog spectrum analyzer using a swept-frequency mixing technique.

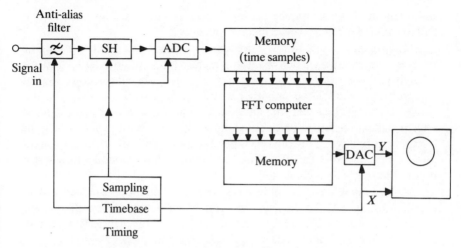

Fig. 9.12   A digital spectrum analyzer using the FFT technique.

For frequencies up to about 1 MHz, the time-varying signal during a time period can be sampled and digitized and the Fourier transform computed. The equations of Fourier analysis given in appendix 3 show that this is a slow process since each spectral line has to be calculated by an integral over all the sample points in the period. The *digital spectrum analyzer* can perform the computation more rapidly using an approximate method called the *fast Fourier transform* (FFT).

In this instrument, shown diagrammatically in figure 9.12, the input signal is passed through an anti-aliasing filter, sampled with an SH unit, and digitized at a rate and for a period determined by the frequency span selected. The data are then Fourier analyzed by a dedicated computer using the FFT algorithm and the spectrum placed in a display memory. The spectrum is thus digitized in typically 512 or 256 points along the frequency axis. The effective bandwidth, or frequency resolution, is limited by the length of the time signal acquired. This period must be chosen so that it does not introduce into the spectrum any periodicities that are not present in the input signal.

The FFT spectrum analyzer computes the phase as well as the amplitude of the spectrum. It is also possible to calculate the spectrum over a range of frequency spans starting at any frequency within the capability of the instrument. Thus the sideband structure of a modulated carrier can be studied in detail. This is achieved by, digitally, heterodyning the input signal with a carrier signal and passing the mixed signal through a narrow-span FFT.

Although the effective bandwidth of the instrument at any frequency is basically controlled by the length of the time series initially taken and used in the computation, it is possible to adjust the shape of the effective bandpass filter and to prevent the introduction of spurious components arising from the finite length of the sample by digital filtering techniques. This procedure is called 'windowing' and is described in appendix 5.

The signal-to-noise ratio, or precision, of the spectrum can be improved by averaging the spectra derived from several successive time-series records. Usually the spectra themselves are r.m.s. averaged. Then the average spectra of several records will be smoother with frequency than the spectrum of a single record. If, however, the input signal contains a periodicity and some trigger signal to define its phase, then the signal-to-noise ratio of this periodic component relative to the other components, non-periodic or at a phase that alters on each record, can be enhanced by performing an initial time average before the spectrum is computed.

A two-input sampled time-series spectrum analyzer can have extra capabilities beyond the display and comparison of the spectra of the two signals. The *transfer function* is a measure of the signal at channel B relative to that at channel A in amplitude and phase at every frequency.

If a random signal is applied to the input of a circuit or system and also connected to V_A and if the output signal of the circuit is made V_B, then the instrument will compute the circuit transfer function. This is particularly useful to measure the amplitude and phase response of filters. It is actually the ratio

$$H(f) = \frac{V_B}{V_A} = \frac{\overline{G_{AB}(f)}}{\overline{G_{AA}(f)}} \qquad (9.3)$$

where $\overline{G_{AB}(f)}$ is the r.m.s. averaged (over many records) cross-power spectrum $G_{AB}(f) = G_A(f)G_B^*(f)$, the product of the spectrum of V_A and the complex conjugate of the spectrum of V_B. The autopower spectrum is similarly $G_{AA}(f) = G_A(f)G_A^*(f)$.

The *coherence function*, γ, is a related quantity given by

$$\gamma^2 = \frac{\overline{G_{BA}(f)}\,\overline{G_{AB}^*(f)}}{\overline{G_{AA}(f)}\,\overline{G_{BB}(f)}} \qquad (9.4)$$

It represents the proportion of the signal in channel B that is derived directly from channel A. If it is near 1, then the transfer function measurement is valid. It will drop below 1 if there are signals that appear at the output but not at the input. This can happen if the system is non-linear, so that harmonics are generated, or if noise or other extra signals have been introduced into the system. The coherence function can be used as a measure of the quality of the system.

DIGITAL AND ANALOG SAMPLED FILTERS

Signal filtering can be readily performed in the frequency domain by modification of the spectrum. For example, consider a signal which includes an unwanted interfering signal at 100 Hz. The spectrum can be calculated by a Fourier transform, the amplitude in the 100 Hz channel reduced to zero, or an average of adjacent channels, and then the signal reformed into the time domain by another Fourier transformation. This general principle is used for filtering in other systems. If a two-dimensional picture has a regular grid of lines on it which need to be removed, then the spatial Fourier transform is computed, the spectral components due to the grid removed and the picture reformed with another Fourier transform. Similarly high or low spatial Fourier components can be enhanced or reduced to change the definition.

From these examples it is apparent that more complex filter functions may be achieved by the appropriate weighting of the amplitude and phase of each component of the frequency-domain signal. An initial anti-aliasing filter is needed before the sampling and a final low-pass filter is needed to smooth the sampling steps from the output signal.

Since the spectrum data have been derived from the original time-series data, it should be unnecessary to go through all these steps with two Fourier transforms. For example, a low-pass filter is essentially the same as a running average, and this can be computed by calculating each output data point corresponding to time t from a suitable weighted average of the three or five data points at and surrounding the input data point corresponding to time t. More details of digital filtering can be found in appendix 5.

The previous brief description showed that the basic operation of a digital filter is to produce each output pulse from a suitably weighted sum of input, and perhaps output, pulses. These pulses are samples taken at regular intervals or time delays. The process can be performed in analog form if devices exist that can produce a delay equal to the required sample period and also a summation.

The *charge-coupled device* (CCD) and the *bucket-brigade device* (BBD) are integrated circuits in which the signal is converted into analog samples in the form of charge packets which are then moved down a sequence of locations by a clock pulse to form an analog delay line. At each location the signal can be detected and passed by a weighting network to a summer. Clock frequencies up to about 100 MHz are possible.

At higher frequencies, about 1000 MHz, another analog delay line can be formed from the propagation time of sound waves. In the *surface acoustic wave* (SAW) *device* the analog signal is in the form of a continuous sound wave that propagates along the surface of a solid. It is generated by the piezoelectric effect in which a strain or displacement is produced in some solids by an applied electric field. Similarly a field is produced by a strain. The sound wave signal is transmitted from a pair of parallel metal electrodes on the surface to which the electrical signal is applied. The sound signal is converted back to an electrical signal by a similar pair of electrodes some distance, and hence time delay, away. Although the signal is continuous rather than sampled, discrete time delays are introduced by placing an array of parallel launching and receiving electrodes so that different distances and delays occur between individual pairs. The weighting of the delayed signals is achieved by differences in the widths of the electrodes. Since the velocity of sound and the weighting are fixed in this type of filter, each design will have fixed characteristics. On the other hand, digital, CCD, and BBD filters have characteristics in which the characteristic frequency is proportional to the sampling, or clock, frequency and are hence easily tunable.

SWITCHED CAPACITANCE AND N-PATH FILTERS

Analog, switched filters can be constructed to perform simple filter operations. These designs are particularly useful in the construction of integrated circuits since only small capacitors and few resistances and no inductances are used. Also the characteristic frequency of the filter can be altered by a change in the clock frequency. Since they are switched or sampled devices, preliminary anti-aliasing and final smoothing filters are required. In many cases they respond to harmonics.

The basic *switched capacitor filter* is shown in figure 9.13(a). A capacitor C_0 is switched at a frequency f_0 between the input and output terminals. The

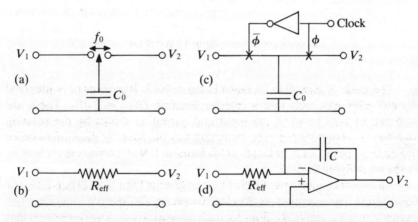

Fig. 9.13   The simple switch–capacitor circuit shown in (a) behaves electrically like the resistor shown in (b). The circuit can be constructed as shown in (c) and can be used as part of an integrating circuit as shown in (d).

charge transferred per cycle is $C_0(V_1 - V_2)$ so that the average current is $f_0C_0(V_1 - V_2)$ and the circuit represents an effective resistance $R_{eff} = 1/f_0C_0$ as shown in figure 9.13(b). The circuit is made using a pair of switches operated in opposite phase, as in figure 9.13(c). If it is used as an active integrator (figure 9.13(d)) the transfer function of the circuit is

$$\frac{V_2}{V_1} = -\frac{1}{j\omega} f_0 \frac{C_0}{C}$$

which depends on a simple ratio of capacitances and the clock frequency f_0, which is easily tunable.

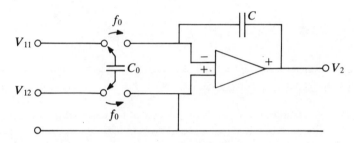

Fig. 9.14 A differential input switched capacitor integrator.

A similar differential integrator is shown in figure 9.14 and this has a transfer function

$$V_2 = -\frac{1}{j\omega} f_0 \frac{C_0}{C} (V_{11} - V_{12})$$

The basic *N-path filter* is shown in figure 9.15. It consists of N identical parallel networks each with a transfer function $H(\omega) \equiv V_2/V_1$. These are switched in turn between the input and output as shown by the rotating switches or commutators. The switching can be done by pairs of switches driven by N pulses each of length $1/Nf_0$ forming $1/N$ of a complete cycle at f_0, as shown in figure 9.16(a).

The most common use for this type of filter is for a high-Q band-pass or band-reject filter centered on the clock frequency f_0. Figure 9.16(a) shows an example using a simple RC filter for each network $H(\omega)$. The response is that of a band-pass filter, centered at f_0 with a bandwidth $2/2\pi NRC = 1/\pi NRC$.

The analysis is similar to that of the PSD (chapter 6). The capacitor on each path sees a pulse every cycle and eventually charges up to some average

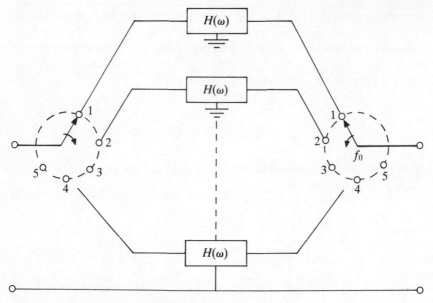

Fig. 9.15 The basic N-path filter circuit.

value. If, for example, the signal is a sine wave at the clock frequency, then the capacitor voltages will reach the values shown in figure 9.16(c). For signals at frequencies slightly away from this, the signals in each path will be changing slowly in phase at a rate depending on the frequency difference. For large frequency differences, each capacitor voltage will average to zero. It should be noted that the filter passes signals in narrow bands centered at frequencies 0 and all nf_0 except Nf_0, so that a preliminary filter may be needed. Since $Q = f_0 \pi NRC$, very high values can be obtained and the bandwidth is kept constant as the center frequency is moved by changing the clock frequency. This circuit is sometimes called a *coherent filter* since it tracks a reference signal. Notch filters can also be made.

If $H(\omega)$ is only a simple RC filter as shown in this example, the circuit can be simplified with the design shown in figure 9.16(b). As in figure 9.16(a) each capacitor is connected only for a part of each cycle.

CORRELATION

Another useful function that can be readily calculated from a time series of sampled data points is the *correlation function*. If one signal $V_A(t)$ is involved, then the *autocorrelation function* (ACF) is defined as

$$C_{AA}(\tau) = \frac{1}{t_1} \int_0^{t_1} V_A(t) V_A(t-\tau) \, dt \qquad (9.5)$$

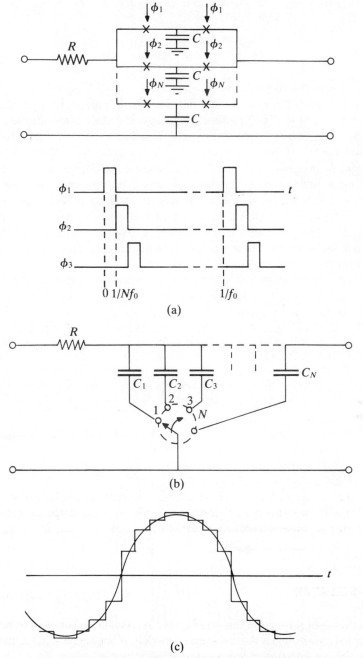

Fig. 9.16 A simple band-pass N-path filter with the ideal circuit and switching wave-forms shown in (a), a practical realization in (b), and the output waveform for a sine wave at the pass frequency shown in (c).

and for two signals $V_A(t)$ and $V_B(t)$ the *cross-correlation function* (CCF) is

$$C_{AB}(\tau) = \frac{1}{t_1} \int_0^{t_1} V_A(t) V_B(t - \tau) \, dt \qquad (9.6)$$

Here τ is a time-delay variable and t_1 is a time period that is long compared with any significant signal period. For some signals one may have to calculate the limit as $t_1 \rightarrow \infty$. The first function, equation (9.5), represents the multiplication at all t of a signal by the same signal delayed by a time τ and the product averaged over a long time t_1 to give a single value. This is shown in figure 9.17. This computation is then carried out for all values of the delay τ to build up a function of τ. In the cross-correlation process there are two separate signals $V_A(t)$ and $V_B(t)$. The schematic circuit for both functions is shown in figure 9.18. If the signal consists of a series of regularly spaced digital values, the computation is straightforward. The result can be displayed on a screen in the same way as the time or frequency function of an oscilloscope or spectrum analyzer.

Some examples of autocorrelation functions for common signals are shown in figure A4.3. A fuller mathematical description of the correlation process is given in appendix 4.

The ACF of a sine wave indicates general features of the function. The ACF has a maximum at $\tau = 0$ since then the curve is superimposed on itself.

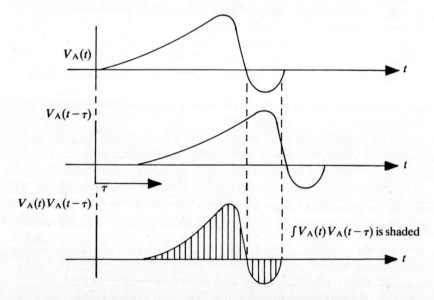

Fig. 9.17 The evaluation of the autocorrelation function is shown for the waveform $V_A(t)$. The shaded area is the correlation integral.

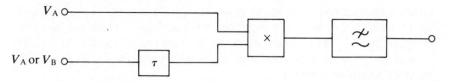

Fig. 9.18 The block diagram of a circuit to evaluate the auto- or cross-correlation functions.

The magnitude is then the total average signal intensity. The ACF is also symmetrical about $\tau = 0$. It has the same periodicity, if any, of the original time-dependent signal but, since no absolute time is involved, all phase information is lost.

Although the spectrum $G(\omega)$ of the signal amplitude contains information on the amplitude and phase, the Fourier transform $c_{AA}(\omega)$ of the ACF $C_{AA}(\tau)$ is the intensity spectrum or the *power spectral density* of the signal. This is formally expressed by the *Wiener–Khintchine relation*

$$c_{AA}(\omega) = G(\omega)\,G^*(\omega) = |G(\omega)|^2$$

(This is enlarged upon in appendix 4.)

The valuable feature of the ACF is that it shows up any periodicities within the signal, since each sine-wave Fourier component is processed in the same way as that just described. This is useful to reveal signals that are very indistinct. A signal with a periodic component that cannot easily be observed and then used to generate a trigger pulse at a constant phase, or with no external trigger signal, cannot be enhanced by a signal averager since successive repetitions of the signal will not place the periodic component in the same register. However, the ACF will reveal the periodicity with larger S/N and this extra information may enable this component to be enhanced by other methods such as filtering. The ACF cannot supply unknown phase information.

Wide-band Gaussian noise is a random signal in which the value of the signal at each instant of time is not related to, or correlated with, the value at the preceding part of the signal. The ACF is therefore zero except at $\tau = 0$. (This is seen in figure A4.3.) If the noise has a finite high-frequency cut-off at a frequency f_0 corresponding to noise passed through a single RC low-pass filter with $f_0 = 1/2\pi RC$, then the ACF decays exponentially as $\exp(-\tau 2\pi f_0)$. The noise is thus concentrated near $\tau = 0$ in the ACF. For linear systems the ACFs of added signals also add. The ACF of a periodic signal plus noise is thus separated into noise at $\tau = 0$ and signal at values of τ corresponding to multiples of the period. Signal-to-noise ratios can therefore be enhanced.

The cross-correlation function (CCF) gives a measure of the connection between the two signals involved. (Examples are shown in figure A4.4.) This connection may be a time delay, in which case a maximum in the CCF will occur at this delay, or it may be a common periodicity, which will produce peaks in the CCF at these periods and their multiples. All signal components that are not common or have no relationship between the two signals will produce no effect on the CCF.

It should be noted that the CCF is of value in detecting mutual periodicities between two signals if they are linearly related. This can be seen by calculating the CCF between a sine wave and a square wave of the same period as shown in figure A4.4.

The phase-sensitive detector (PSD) described in chapter 6 and in this chapter and the boxcar integrator described earlier are both simple analog cross-correlators. The reference signal is chosen to be noise-free and to have a waveform close to that of the component of the input that is being detected. The phase difference between the two signals, or the time delay τ, is adjusted so that the output is on a peak of the CCF. The output thus has an enhanced signal-to-noise ratio.

The cross-correlator can be used in many situations. If a signal is observed at two places, the peak in the CCF gives the time delay between these two signals. If the distance between the two detectors is known, this gives the transmission speed, or if the speed is known, the path difference can be calculated.

Consider the problem illustrated in figure 9.19 in which sound from a particular source, such as a piece of machinery, is reaching some place where it is not wanted. Before the problem can be controlled, it is necessary to know whether the sound is traveling through the air or the solid floor. Since the speed of sound is very different in these two media, the time delay of the peak in the CCF between signals derived from near the source and from the location will give an indication of the dominant route. The CCF is most pronounced if the source signal has as few periodicities as possible.

A flow meter can be constructed for most fluids, liquids or gases. This is shown in figure 9.20. The flow at an average velocity v is rarely completely uniform and there is turbulence, impurities, pressure fluctuations, etc., moving with the current. Two detectors are located a fixed distance, d, apart and their outputs correlated. The delay (d/v) represented by the peak in the CCF gives the flow speed. The detectors need to be chosen to be sensitive to some variation in the flow. In some cases special inhomogeneities such as solid impurity particles or turbulence may have to be added to the flow.

The signal-to-noise ratio of a signal can be improved by correlation. For example, a radar system normally measures the range of a target by transmitting a pulse and observing the time delay of the returned, reflected pulse. A limit on the range is the peak power that the system can transmit. To lengthen the pulse would reduce the range resolution. The total transmitted energy can, however, be increased by lengthening the pulse while keeping each part of the pulse identifiable separately. The pulse could be a specific

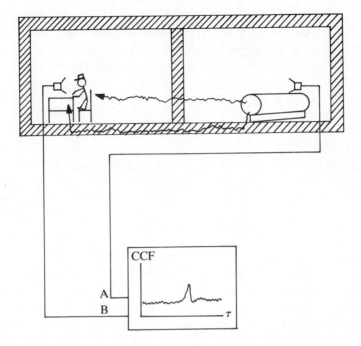

Fig. 9.19 An example of the use of the cross-correlation function to determine the time of flight of a sound signal and hence the probable signal path.

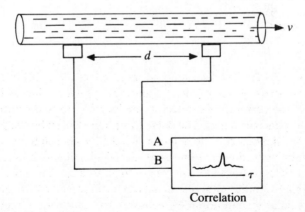

Correlation

Fig. 9.20 An example of the use of the cross-correlation function to determine the time of flight of turbulence or other inhomogeneities in a fluid in order to measure the flow rate.

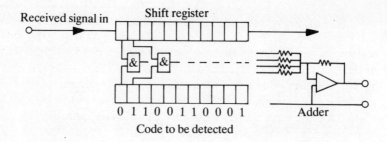

Fig. 9.21   A simple cross-correlation detector for a multi-bit binary signal.

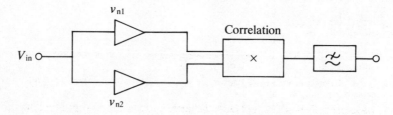

Fig. 9.22   An example of the use of autocorrelation to reduce the noise introduced by amplifiers. The signal common to both amplifiers will correlate and produce an output but the noise of each amplifier, v_{n1} and v_{n2}, is uncorrelated and produces no output.

random, or pseudo-random, signal. The CCF of the returned signal and the transmitted signal gives the delay and hence the range. Since the whole of the energy of the pulse over its total length is used, the range can be extended even with the same peak power. If the signal is in binary form as a coded series of 0s and 1s, a simple digital correlator can be used as shown in figure 9.21. The circuit is a detector of a particular sequence in a stream of bits and can be used for any signal recognition. A maximum in the output signal is expected.

The signal-to-noise performance of an amplifier can be improved by correlation. Normally the S/N is limited in a simple system by the noise in the preamplifier. This can be effectively reduced by feeding the signal into two parallel amplifying chains and correlating the output signals. The signal itself will correlate with itself but the noise in the two amplifiers will be independent and will average to nearly zero in the correlator. Such a system is shown in figure 9.22. It should be noted that the output signal is the input signal squared, so that there is some loss of information.

The signal out is $\overline{(V_{in} + v_{n1})(V_{in} + v_{n2})}$, where the bar represents the time average. This equals $\overline{V_{in}^2}$ since v_{n1} and v_{n2} are uncorrelated. However, there is still some uncertainty in the averaged noise. The S/N is improved by $(4\Delta f \tau)^{1/2}$, where Δf is the bandwidth of each amplifier and τ is the averaging time constant.

Correlation is used in its most general form as a way of increasing the confidence in the observation of a rare event. A given detector will respond to both real events and spurious signals generated locally and within the system. Two or more detectors can be arranged so that they are as independent as possible but will respond to a real event. The outputs of detectors of gravity waves located very far apart are checked for simultaneous recordings of events since a large wave might be detected nearly simultaneously by such detectors but spurious signals are unlikely to occur at the same time in each detector.

FURTHER READING

K. G. Beauchamp and C. K. Yuen, *Data Acquisitions for Signal Analysis*, Allen and Unwin (1980).

M. S. Beck, 'Correlation in instruments: cross correlation flowmeters', *J. Phys. E* **14** (1981) 7–19.

R. W. Brodersen, P. R. Gray, and D. A. Hedges, 'MOS switched-capacitor filters and their applications', *Proc. IEEE* **67** (1979) 61–7.

——— *Analog Switches and Their Applications*, Siliconix Inc. (1976), chap. 5.

R. W. Henry, *Electronic Systems and Instrumentation*, Wiley (1978).

P. A. Lynn, *The Analysis and Processing of Signals*, Macmillan (1982).

E. B. Magrab and D. S. Blomquist, *The Measurement of Time-Varying Phenomena*, Wiley (1971).

M. L. Meade, *Lock-in Amplifiers: Principles and Applications*, Peter Peregrinus (1983).

T. H. Wilmshurst, *Signal Recovery from Noise in Electronic Instrumentation*, Adam Hilger (1985).

10 INSTRUMENT CONTROL BY COMPUTER

INTRODUCTION

In some experiments the measurements can be performed with simple instruments, the data recorded by hand, and the results calculated simply from the data. However, many experiments and experimental arrangements require a considerable number of different measurements to be made with several different parameters, and complicated manipulations may have to be made on the raw data to reduce them to the final form. A computer can carry out the repetitive, tedious operations rapidly, accurately, and without error. With this help, an experiment can be done in a reasonable time, more data points can perhaps be taken, and the results can be reduced in different ways. Experiments that were otherwise not practicable become possible. As well as manipulating numbers, computers can be used to change variables, to alter instrument scale or operation mode settings, to stabilize systems, to sound warnings, etc.

Computer control of experiments, data acquisition systems, and large systems such as chemical process plant has been carried out for a long time, but in the early examples the computer system was dedicated to the particular experiment and considerable changes in the wiring and in the programming were needed to change the experiment. For many applications where the system does not change substantially for many years, this is adequate, but such changes can be very expensive and time-consuming. Many laboratories perform experiments that may require frequent changes in the actual measurements done although the same basic instruments, voltmeters, signal generators, etc., are involved. To arrange computer control in such cases may entail more time and effort than the experiment itself unless the computer and instruments are designed specifically for computer operation and the mechanical, electrical, and programming specifications are made easy for use and for compatibility between the models from different manufacturers. This chapter describes an international standard for instrument–computer interface systems. The system with a computer dedicated for use with it may still be required if very fast operation is needed and may be more economical if many such systems are needed so that the design cost per system will be low.

If digital information is to be passed between several instruments, devices or subsystems, and the signals are intermittent or slower than the maximum speed of the system, then it is most economical to have the same bundle of cables connecting all the instruments and to use this *bus* or *data highway* to pass all the messages in different directions and between different combinations of instruments. The same bus can then also be used to control the instruments. This is particularly suitable for scientific instruments, since the measuring processes are usually slow.

THE GENERAL-PURPOSE INTERFACE BUS

Although standard buses exist for other purposes, such as data flow within a computer, the accepted standard for digital data flow between instruments is that produced by the Institute of Electrical and Electronic Engineers, namely IEEE 488-1978, or ANSI MC1-1, which is a more tightly specified version of the original IEEE 488-1975. The same specification is also used by Hewlett-Packard in its HPIB and by other manufacturers in GPIB (general-purpose interface bus). The European standard is IEC TC66 WG3 (Publication 624-1). All these standards are basically the same except for the connectors.

The IEEE 488 standard uses a Microribbon (Amphenol or Cinch series 57) or CHAMP(AMP) connector wth 24 pins (figure 10.1), while the IEC standard uses a 25-pin Cannon type-D connector. However, many European manufacturers use the IEEE 488 connector. Another mechanical problem is that the fasteners on some connectors have US threads (nickel-plated) while most are metric (black).

The instruments in the system are interconnected by a multi-way screened cable. Provided that there is only one signal path, that is there is no complete loop, the connections may be made in any way topologically equivalent to a star or 'daisy-chain' as shown in figure 10.2

Most connectors are stackable, with both a plug and a socket at each end. The specified input and output impedances of the instruments at their connection to the bus cables limit the number of devices interconnected to 15 and the total length of cable to the smaller of 20 m or an average of 2 m for each device connected. These limitations can often be overcome with some buffer, expander, translator or extender.

The transmission rate is specified up to a maximum of 1 Mbyte/s but this may not actually be achieved. It will depend on the exact electrical characteristics of the line drivers at the output of the instrument onto the bus and the

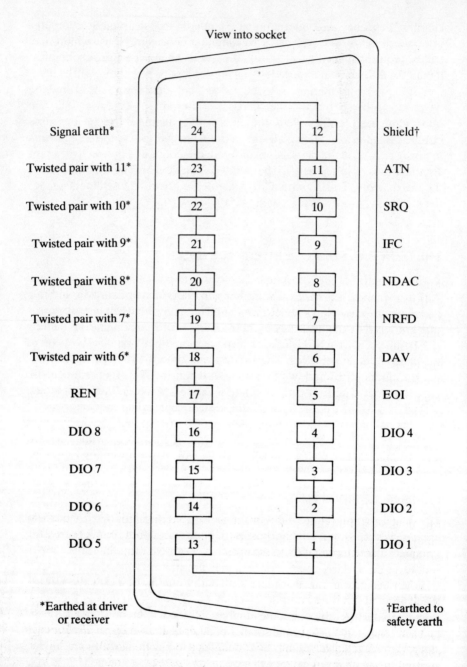

Fig. 10.1 The pin connections for the IEEE 488 bus cable.

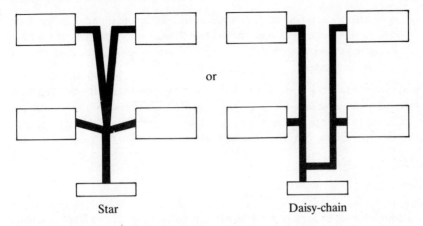

Star   Daisy-chain

Fig. 10.2 The bus may connect the controller and instruments in a star or 'daisy-chain'.

input impedance of the instrument seen by the bus. Open collector or three-state drivers are used. In practice, the control of the bus can be slower than its actual operation, so that the actual speed of use is governed by the complexity of the operations and the speed of the slowest device in that operation.

It should be noted that the bus cannot transmit analog signals and it is unsuitable if data need to be transmitted very quickly or if one instrument needs continuous connection. These problems may be overcome by the use of 'smart' instruments that partially process, condense or store the information before transmission along the bus. This will be expanded upon later.

The bus uses negative true logic, so that if the line is true (1) it will have its low voltage level. This design reduces malfunction due to bad contacts on any line. The logic levels on the bus are 0, +5 V, TTL. The threshold levels are:

Output,   high ≥ 2.4 V,   low ≤ 0.4 V.
Input,   high ≥ 2.0 V,   low ≤ 0.8 V.

The devices outputting into the bus must be able to supply 48 mA and the input devices must not load the bus. Both input and output connections must provide suitable termination to the bus.

Devices

Devices connected to the bus can be described as *talkers*, *listeners* or *controllers*. A given device may be commanded to function in different modes at different times. Each device will have its own *address* or 'name'.

A *talker* is a device that is transmitting data into the bus.

A *listener* is a device receiving data or commands.

A *controller* can transmit and receive bus commands, and can designate one device to be the talker and several devices to be listeners. As well as initiating data transfer, it can control the operation of a device such as a 'smart' instrument.

Normally there is only one controller, and at any one instant the bus can have only one active talker but may have several listeners. A device can be connected to the bus but not switched on and a device will not participate, even it is turned on, if it has not been addressed.

Operation

Although the operation of the bus will normally be by a high-level language such as BASIC through a controller such as a personal computer, an understanding of the detailed operation is valuable. Fast operation can be achieved by using machine code and this requires a detailed knowledge of the bus operation and also the operation of the particular computer.

To show the operations that are needed on the bus, consider a simple system in which an instrument T such as a voltmeter is set internally as a talker and instruments L1 and L2 such as printers have been set as listeners. When connected, data will flow without the need for a controller. In a more complicated system, each instrument may be both a talker and a listener, equipment may be connected but not used, and the voltmeter functions may be controllable. The sequence, in this case, is that the system must be set to some initial quiescent state. The controller, C, then addresses the instruments L1 and L2 as listeners and instrument T as the single talker. The range or mode of T must be specified, the measurement triggered off, and later the data transfer initiated. The talker T must indicate the end of the message. Each of the instructions between C and T, L1 or L2 and the data transfers between T and L1 or L2 take place over the *data lines* of the bus, and it is essential that each transaction is accomplished accurately even though the devices C, T, L1, and L2 may operate at very different speeds. This is done by a *handshake* procedure.

Bus wires

The sixteen active lines of the bus are divided into three groups as shown in figure 10.3

Data (this also includes some bus instructions) are carried on eight wires.
Validation of information transfer (or *handshake*) on the data wires uses three wires and ensures safe asynchronous transfer of the information.
Management of the system uses five wires.

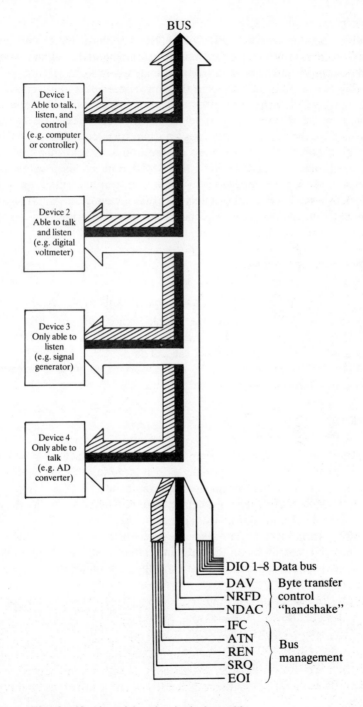

Fig. 10.3 The classification of the wires in the bus cable.

Data wires

The eight data lines are called DIO 1 to DIO 8, with the least significant bit (l.s.b.) placed on DIO 1. The data may be measurement data, that is numbers and a description of the meaning of the numbers (e.g. voltage), address data to specify the device that is to act as the source or receiver of information, or programming data such as the setting of instrument ranges or the setting of the response of an instrument to other bus commands. The data routing is controlled by the management wires and safe transfer is ensured by hand-shake (see later). The information on these lines is sent in a bit-parallel byte-serial form. A standard ISO-7 bit, ASCII, code (as used in teletype or telex) is used. A given message may require several sequential bytes. Each byte can thus be described alternately by its bus meaning, its ASCII meaning, its binary sequence or that sequence expressed to another base such as decimal, hexadecimal, etc. as shown in Table 10-1.

Validation (handshake) wires

The three wires are:

> DAV (Data Valid), which is signaled by the talker when data have been placed on the data lines and are suitable for acceptance.
> NRFD (Not Ready for Data), which is signaled by a listener instrument that is active but not available to accept data.
> NDAC (Not Data Accepted), which is signaled until a listener has received information from the data lines.

Management wires

The five wires are as follows:

> IFC (Interface Clear) is a system controller signal. It sets all interfaces to an initial condition. It is normally used at turn-on, at checks, and to clear a bus that has been given an incorrect command.
> REN (Remote Enable) is a system controller signal which sets a device to remote (bus) control from front panel (local) control.
> ATN (Attention) is a controller command which indicates that there is an address or command on the data lines rather than data from an instrument. If energized during a data transfer, the talker is set into a wait state.
> EOI (End or Identify) is a talker device signal which indicates the end of a multi-byte message. It is also used by a controller in polling (see later).
> SRQ (Service Request) is a signal from a device indicating to a controller that it needs attention (see also polling later). It is also energized when a device receives an incorrect signal.

Table 10.1 Commands and Addresses on Data Lines DIO 1-7 with bus meanings and their associated ISO-7 Bit Code (shaded). DIO 8 is always 0. These commands and addresses exert control only when ATN is true (1). If ATN is false (0) Data is being transmitted in ISO-7 code.

b7 b6 b5 →		0 0 0	0 0 1	0 1 0	0 1 1	1 0 0	1 0 1	1 1 0	1 1 1
b4 b3 b2 b1	**ROW / COLUMN**	**0**	**1**	**2**	**3**	**4**	**5**	**6**	**7**
0 0 0 0	0	NUL	DLE	SP	0	@	P	`	p
0 0 0 1	1	SOH GTL	DC1 LLO	!	1	A	Q	a	q
0 0 1 0	2	STX	DC2	"	2	B	R	b	r
0 0 1 1	3	ETX	DC3	#	3	C	S	c	s
0 1 0 0	4	EOT SDC	DC4 DCL	$	4	D	T	d	t
0 1 0 1	5	ENQ PPC	NAK PPU	%	5	E	U	e	u
0 1 1 0	6	ACK	SYN	&	6	F	V	f	v
0 1 1 1	7	BEL	ETB	'	7	G	W	g	w
1 0 0 0	8	BS GET	CAN SPE	(	8	H	X	h	x
1 0 0 1	9	HT TCT	EM SPD	)	9	I	Y	i	y
1 0 1 0	10	LF	SUB	*	:	J	Z	j	z
1 0 1 1	11	VT	ESC	+	;	K	[	k	{
1 1 0 0	12	FF	FS	,	<	L	\	l	|
1 1 0 1	13	CR	GS	-	=	M	]	m	}
1 1 1 0	14	SO	RS	.	>	N	^	n	~
1 1 1 1	15	SI	US	/	? UNL	O	_ UNT	o	DEL

Column group meanings (bottom of table):

Column	Group
0	ADDRESSED COMMAND GROUP (ACG)
1	UNIVERSAL COMMAND GROUP (UCG)
2, 3	LISTEN ADDRESS GROUP (LAG) — DEVICE LISTEN ADDRESS → UNL
4, 5	TALK ADDRESS GROUP (TAG) — DEVICE TALK ADDRESS → UNT
6, 7	SECONDARY COMMAND GROUP (SCG) — MEANING DETERMINED BY PCG

Columns 0–5 constitute the PRIMARY COMMAND GROUP (PCG). Columns 6–7 constitute the SECONDARY COMMAND GROUP (SCG). Columns 0–7, rows 0–15 give the STANDARD ISO 7 CHARACTERS.

ISO BIT & DIO LINE NUMBER: 8 7 6 5 4 3 2 1

Handshake implementation

This is used (figure 10.4) for all data line transfers (data and multi-line messages) except parallel poll (see later). A talker places data on the eight data lines (DIO 1–8) and energizes (1) Data Valid (DAV). All listener devices will then energize both Not Ready for Data (NRFD) and Not Data Accepted (NDAC).

As each listener completes its read cycle, it releases (0) its NDAC. When the last listener has read the information, the NDAC line will be released (0). The system is connected as 'wired OR' so that NDAC will remain low (1) as long as any interface has not accepted data (i.e. this line will go high only when all interfaces A and B and C and . . . have gone high).

At this stage the transfer is complete and the talker may release the DAV line and change the data.

The listener instruments may need to process the data just received or make a measurement as a consequence of these data, and until it is free to proceed each listener will maintain NRFD until it has completed its own internal cycle. When all listeners are free, NRFD (which is also 'wired OR') will be released to (0) and the next read-in cycle will commence when DAV is energized.

The bus in use

To illustrate the use of the bus, a typical sequence of events leading to the transfer of information between a talker and a listener will be described. It is assumed that a controller is in command of the system.

The sequence of messages will normally be commenced by the IFC

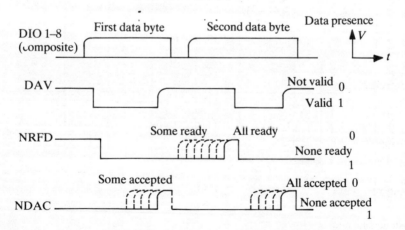

Fig. 10.4 The handshake timing diagram.

(Interface Clear) command, which will set all interfaces to their initial condition.

Following this the ATN (Attention) command is made (1) to signify that there is address or command information available on the eight data lines; this transfer of information is then controlled by means of the handshake routine. The information transferred during the interval defined by ATN will set up the message route; the initial information will give the addresses of listener instruments followed by the address of the talker instrument (a preferred, but not necessary, order).

On release of the ATN command (i.e. $\overline{\text{ATN}}$ or 0) the talker may then place data on the data lines (DIO 1 to DIO 8). This data transfer is controlled by the handshake routine and is received by all addressed listeners. The last data byte should be accompanied by EOI (End or Identify) to indicate that the talker has finished and the controller should resume control.

Before commencing another message sequence, the controller may switch all listeners off by the command Unlisten (UNL), and switch the talker off by the command Untalk (UNT), which will be issued in conjunction with ATN (Attention). The commands UNL and UNT are coded commands appearing on data lines (DIO 1–8).

Should a controller wish to interrupt during a data message sequence, it does so by energizing ATN; the talker then enters a wait state. In order to avoid losing information, ATN should be asserted synchronously with the handshake routine; when NRFD is energized NDAC released.

Example

A talker, T, is instructed to send a message, 987, to listeners L1 and L2, as shown in table 10.2.

Table 10.2 An example of the bus in use.

	Management lines	Data lines DIO 1–8	Validation lines
Controller sends	IFC	–	–
	ATN	Listen address of L1	Handshake
	ATN	Listen address of L2	Handshake
	ATN	Talk address of T	Handshake
T sends	$\overline{\text{ATN}}$	9	Handshake
	$\overline{\text{ATN}}$	8	Handshake
	$\overline{\text{ATN}}$ EOI	7	Handshake
Controller sends	ATN	UNL	Handshake
	ATN	UNT	Handshake
Listeners L1 and L2 receive	Message	987	

Instrument–bus interface controls

It is useful to consider each device to be connected to the bus by an interface circuit. The interface takes care of all the bus management functions and decides whether its instrument has been addressed, etc. When appropriate, the interface opens up a communication channel for data or control information to go between the instrument itself and the bus. The messages to the interface are standardized but those to the instrument will depend on the particular instrument.

In a previous section we have mentioned the commands UNL and UNT, which are messages sent over the data lines to control how the instrument interface should respond to the bus. There are other single- and multi-wire messages that signal information to the interface. These are given in table 10.3 together with the groupings of the commands. Reference should also be made to table 10.1.

Addresses

In order to route signals properly, each instrument on the bus must have an address or name. This is specified by the settings on a multi-bit binary switch on the instrument. Naturally each instrument must have a different address, which is restricted to between 0 and 30. The address is set by a five-bit word. Bits 6 and 7, measured from the l.s.b., are 10 for a listener only and 01 for a talker only. These settings enable an instrument set as a talker to send data to instruments set as listeners without the presence of a controller. The addresses can be seen from table 10.1 where columns 2 and 3 correspond to listener addresses (LAG) and columns 4 and 5 to talker addresses (TAG): For a talker/listener instrument, the mode is set by the controller by sending the full seven-bit address (e.g. a device with address 12 (11100) will have listen address (0111100) and talk address (1011100) in ISO-7 notation).

A controller has separate controller and talker/listener addresses. A common convention is that the controller address is 7 (00111) and for example the HP-85 computer interface is preset at 21 (10101) for its talker/listener address.

Service request

Service Request (SRQ) is a single, management line signal sent by an instrument to alert the controller that the instrument is in some state that needs controller action, for example it is incorrectly working or has been patiently making measurements and processing data while the bus is in use and it is now ready to release the data. Since this is only a single-line signal, the controller has to respond by conducting a *poll* to determine which instrument needs help.

The poll can be a *serial poll* or a *parallel poll*.

Table 10.3 Multi-line messages and mnemonics.

Mnemonic	Message name	Response
Commands		
GTL	Go to Local	Causes addressed devices to switch to local (front panel) control
UNL	Unlisten	Device is instructed to cease to be a listener
UNT	Untalk	Device is instructed to cease to be a talker
LLO	Local Lockout	Prevents local (front panel) control of device functions
DCL	Device Clear	Instructs all devices to be set to a predefined or power-up state
SDC	Selected Device Clear	Instructs an addressed device to be set to a predefined or power-up state
SPD	Serial Poll Disable	Devices leave the serial poll mode and are not allowed to send their status byte
SPE	Serial Poll Enable	Devices enter the serial poll mode and are allowed to send their status byte when addressed to talk
GET	Group Execute Trigger	Signals one or more devices to initiate simultaneously a set of device-dependent actions
TCT	Take Control	Passes bus controller responsibilities from the current controller to a device that can assume the bus supervisory role
PPC	Parallel Pole Configure	Controller allocates a specific data line to a device for parallel polling
PPU	Parallel Pole Unconfigure	Controller removes the previously allocated data line allocation
Descriptions		
PCG	Primary Command Group	Includes ACG, UCG, LAG, TAG
SCG	Secondary Command Group	A group of 32 commands that are valid only if they immediately follow a talker or listener address
ACG	Addressed Command Group	Commands that apply only to the addressed instruments
UCG	Universal Command Group	Commands to all instruments not in local control
LAG	Listen Address Group	A group of 31 listener addresses
TAG	Talk Address Group	A group of 31 talker addresses

Serial poll

In this slower poll method, each instrument is addressed separately. The controller sends an Unlisten (UNL) command followed by a Serial Poll Enable (SPE) multi-wire command. This sets all the talkers to an idle state. Then each instrument is sent its talk address in turn. If the instrument has sent the SRQ (Service Request), it energizes the DIO 7 line when the address message is completed at the release of ATN. The bus is returned to use after a serial poll with the Serial Poll Disable (SPD) command. The instrument may also use the other DIO lines to indicate why it sent an SRQ signal. For example, the line DIO 5 may be 1 if the device is overloaded. Since SRQ is a 'wired OR' function, the bus will not resume until all service requests have been satisfied.

Parallel poll

In this fast poll method, all instruments are addressed simultaneously and those with an SRQ indicate it by a signal on the one particular data line assigned to it for this purpose. (If there are more than eight instruments then extra subtlety is needed). This data line is assigned either by hard wiring on installation or is defined by the controller by means of a configuring process. This consists of the instrument listen address followed by the Parallel Poll Configure (PPC) command followed by a command that defines the data line number which will indicate that instrument's parallel poll SRQ indicator. An UNL command ends the configuring of that instrument. All are configured in this way. The instrument with the SRQ is then determined by sending EOI. The configuration as set will continue in force until Parallel Poll Unconfigure (PPU) message is sent. The parallel poll operation is often not easy to implement and all instruments do not allow it.

Front panel commands

The range, mode, gain, frequency, and other settings of an instrument are normally set by manual operation of the switches on the front panel (*local* operation). 'Smart' instruments can have these settings operated by the controller through the bus (*remote* operation).

> *REN (Remote Enable)* is a single-wire command that switches the instrument identified by its address from local to remote operation. It requires that the instrument remote/local front panel switch be at remote.
> *GTL (Go to Local)* is the multi-wire command, sent with the address, that sets the instrument in local operation. This can also be done by setting the front panel switch to local.
> *LLO (Local Lockout)* is the multi-wire command, sent with the address, that inhibits the front panel local/remote switch so that only remote operation is possible. It is reversed by the $\overline{REN}$ command.

In either local or remote states, the instruments can receive and store instructions in anticipation of the change of control state.

Instrument control

Under remote control the control of the front panel switches must be fed in as a message string from the bus.

Although the *general form* of instrument messages is agreed internationally, the precise format is decided by the designer of the instrument. Obviously the commands given to a voltmeter and to a frequency response analyzer will be different. What is agreed is that each control function (e.g. range) is given a letter (e.g. R), while subdivisions of a function are given numbers (e.g. R3 for range 3). As an example table 10.4 shows the control characters for a typical digital voltmeter.

Prior to the control string, the voltmeter and its interface must be put in a state to receive the control message. Frequently this will commence by Unlisten (UNL) to ensure that no other device will receive the control message should one have been left in the listen state. This is followed by the voltmeter's listen address and the controller's talk address. Table 10.5 shows an example.

The delimiter may have to be a character other than CR LF depending on the system in which the instrument is used.

Table 10.4 The control characters for a typical digital voltmeter.

Control function	Character	Subdivision of function	Character
Measurement type	M	V d.c.	0
		V a.c.	1
Range	R	Autorange	0
		100 V	1
		10 V	2
		1 V	3
		0.1 V	4
Integration time	I	0.01 s	0
		0.1 s	1
		1 s	2
Send Service Request on completion of each measurement	Q	No	0
		Yes	1
Trigger	T	Single	0
		Repetitive	1

Table 10.5 Example of message to digital voltmeter.

	Management lines	Data lines (in ISO-7 notation)	
Interface address to listener	ATN	?	Unlisten
	ATN	9	Voltmeter listen address
	ATN	W	Controller talk address
Interface made transparent to message	$\overline{\text{ATN}}$	M	d.c. measurement ⎫
	$\overline{\text{ATN}}$	O	
	$\overline{\text{ATN}}$	R	10 V range
	$\overline{\text{ATN}}$	2	
	$\overline{\text{ATN}}$	I	1 s integration time
	$\overline{\text{ATN}}$	2	Control
	$\overline{\text{ATN}}$	Q	No service request message
	$\overline{\text{ATN}}$	0	string
	$\overline{\text{ATN}}$	T	Repetitive sample
	$\overline{\text{ATN}}$	1	
	$\overline{\text{ATN}}$	CR	message delimiters ⎭
	$\overline{\text{ATN}}$	LF	

Data output

Devices that make measurements will have to put results onto the bus for transmission to recorders, or onto the controller where the results may be processed before transmission to a recorder.

Table 10.6 Example of output from digital voltmeter.

Management lines	Data lines (in ISO-7 notation)	
ATN	?	Unlisten
ATN	3	Recorder listen address
ATN	Y	Voltmeter talk address
$\overline{\text{ATN}}$	V	
$\overline{\text{ATN}}$	D	mode
$\overline{\text{ATN}}$	C	
$\overline{\text{ATN}}$	+	sign
$\overline{\text{ATN}}$	9	
$\overline{\text{ATN}}$	8	number
$\overline{\text{ATN}}$	7	
$\overline{\text{ATN}}$	CR	delimiter
$\overline{\text{ATN}}$	LF	

When a voltmeter has made a measurement, it usually will have to tell the controller that the data are ready for transmission. It may do this by sending SRQ (Service Request). If there are several devices, the controller has no means of immediately knowing which has sent SRQ; hence the controller conducts a poll to establish which device has requested service. With simple systems a poll will not be necessary.

All interface addresses can be cleared by the controller sending ?(Unlisten,UNL) followed by the new listen address (of the recorder) and the new talk address (of the voltmeter). The voltmeter knows what it is measuring (e.g. V d.c.) so it may send this as a header to the measured value (see table 10.6).

The delimiter may have to be a character other than CR LF depending on the system in which the instrument is used.

Multiple controllers

Although only one controller may be active on the bus at any one time, it is possible to have more than one instrument that can function as a controller connected to the bus. In this case the current controller can pass control to another device by using the TCT (Take Control) command. The normal sequence is the new controller's talk address followed by TCT. The controller then releases ATN and the new device takes over. The new controller then has command and has to implement any return to the original controller.

Programming

Programming cannot be discussed in general since each system will require different instructions. This is especially true of low-level languages where each bus operation will require a separate instruction. Machine language is needed in the construction of individual instruments and for dedicated use, but most bus systems will be operated by some high-level language such as BASIC or a bus controller language.

In these high-level languages, the individual statements will automatically make the controller perform all the necessary bus interface operations such as the handshake, IFC, UNL, UNT, and ATN commands.

Examples of bus control statements for the HP-85 computer are the following:

'PRINTER IS' followed by a listener address changes the destination for all 'PRINT' and 'PLIST' statements to the bus listener addressed rather than the computer's own printer.

'CRT IS' does the same for 'DISP', 'LIST', and 'CAT' statements, which normally output onto the computer's own display.

'OUTPUT' followed by destination address and a list of items to be output is the basic controller output statement, e.g. OUTPUT 703, 725; A$. The HP-85 interface has code 7 to precede all address of instruments, in this case listeners 3 and 25 will receive the string A.

'ENTER' followed by the source address and a list of items to be received is the basic controller input statement, e.g. ENTER 705; B$. In this case talker 5 will send the string B.

'TRIGGER' between 'OUTPUT' and 'ENTER' enables simultaneous measurements to be made by several instruments.

'REMOTE', *'LOCAL'*, and *'LOCAL LOCKOUT'* perform the local/ remote operations when followed by the controller address (7) and the instrument address if required.

Thus a typical program might be:

```
10   DIM A$[10]
20   OUTPUT 705; "MOR2I2QOT1"
30   ENTER 705; A$
40   END
```

In some instruments the front panel settings may be needed by the controller. If this is possible, the experiment can be set up manually and, when everything is working correctly, the controller can be made to read and record the settings and then use these for further measurements.

BUS SYSTEMS

The advantages of bus systems are their speed of assembly and their flexibility, and the principal disadvantage is the high initial cost. They are an advantage where there is a considerable amount of data to be collected and processed or where several different circuit interconnections need to be made in rapid succession. Time should be spent in the planning of a system.

The amount of data to be collected should be calculated in bytes. Each instrument reading may involve many bytes. In a given data measuring sequence, there must be sufficient storage available which can be accessed rapidly enough. Usually this is within the computer's RAM. During quiet periods the data can be moved into a more permanent store. The data, or reduced results, may be displayed on a VDU, printed or plotted. If the results are to be stored in a memory such as magnetic tape or disk, then calculations of the required capacity must be made at an initial stage. Often it is more economical only to store either the raw data or the final results after full data reduction.

The speed of the system also needs to be calculated during the planning stage. Important quantities are the maximum required transfer rate and the average data rate. If fast high-resolution data are to be taken, as with a transient recorder, the maximum speed of the bus can easily be exceeded. Then the measuring instrument has to be made 'smart' with an internal data store to record each transient for transmission along the bus during the quiet part of the measurement period when no signal is being received. It may be that the 'smart' device has its own internal computer to perform a time

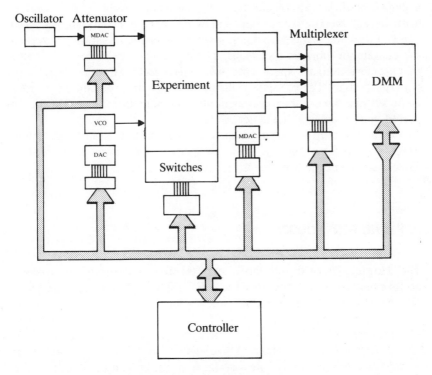

Fig. 10.5 An example of an IEEE 488 experimental system.

average over many transients and hence reduce the data before transmission along the bus. Such buffers and distributed data reduction can reduce the total data flow along the bus and hence reduce the speed necessary.

The cost of a bus system can be kept low with careful planning. One good-quality measuring instrument such as a digital multimeter (DMM) can be used for many measurements in a single system if simple listen-only interface devices are used. A simple interface can be commanded to output an eight-bit or a sixteen-bit byte. Such a device and its digital output signal can be used to drive a multiplexer (so that the DMM receives different signals), to operate switches, and to drive a DAC (to give a controlled voltage source) or a multiplying DAC (MDAC) (to give a controlled attenuator). The controlled voltage source can also be used to drive other instruments such as a VCO, to give a controlled frequency oscillator. Such a system is shown schematically in figure 10.5.

The actual operation of instruments and taking of data over a bus through a controller is very remote from the connection of individual instruments and manually recording individual data points. With less personal supervision of the experiment itself, there is more possibility of unforeseen error or malfunction to be present and to remain undetected. For this reason extra care should be taken in doing simple tests on the system with simulated or separately calibrated specimens. There are many experimental changes that are obvious to an experimenter who will correct for them at once, almost without thought. The computer will not recognize the problem. An example is the settling time of the experiment after a parameter change. During this period, measurements should not be made.

Similarly there is a strong tendency to believe that a fancy instrument, which costs a lot of money, works perfectly and is always in calibration. Checks should be made frequently on automatic systems.

HPIL AND RS232 BUSES

The Hewlett-Packard Interface Loop (HPIL) is designed as a lower-performance instrument bus than the IEEE 488 bus. The messages are sent in bit-serial form rather than bit-parallel. All the devices, controllers, talkers, and listeners are connected in a single loop of a balanced two-wire cable with $100 \, \Omega$ source and load impedances. The signals are three-level, 0 and ± 1.5 V, with a maximum speed of about 5 kbyte/s with an eleven-bit byte. The devices round the loop each receive the message from the previous device and either act on the instructions, if the message is addressed to itself, or retransmit the message to the next device in the loop. This serial system is naturally slow but simple and the transmitter in each device need feed the message into only one receiver.

The RS232 bus uses a 25-wire system and is designed for one transmitter to send signals to one of several receivers. The messages are usually ASCII coded. There is a handshake procedure. The signal is bit-serial at standard rates between 10000 and 20000 bits per second. The signal is bipolar with logic levels ± 6 V. The threshold level is 0 ± 0.2 V. Newer versions of this standard are the RS422 for bipolar signals on a balanced pair of cables and RS423 for unipolar signals on an unbalanced pair of cables.

FURTHER READING

IEEE, *IEEE Standard Digital Interface for Programmable Instrumentation*, ANSI/ IEEE Standard 488-1978, IEEE (1978).

R. D. Quick and S. L. Harper, 'A low-cost digital interface for portable applications', *Hewlett-Packard J.* **34** (1983) 3–10.

11 HIGH-FREQUENCY CIRCUITS

INTRODUCTION

The electronic circuits, components, and techniques described in the preceding chapters can generally be used for frequencies up to about 1 MHz. At much higher frequencies, above about 1 GHz (1000 MHz), special microwave techniques are needed in which the signals are best considered in the form of electromagnetic waves that are normally guided within the conducting boundaries of waveguides or cavities. Above about 100 GHz, optical techniques may be more appropriate. These very high-frequency effects will not be discussed here but we will consider the problems that arise, and the necessary solutions, as the circuits described in earlier chapters are extended for use at higher frequencies, especially in the range 1–100 MHz. An understanding of high-frequency circuits is necessary because the signal frequency itself, or its harmonics in the case of fast pulse or large circuits, may be high. If the active circuit components have a high-frequency response, then the circuit may be unstable at some high frequency and need correction.

In general, the effects that become important at high frequencies and modify the circuits described so far are due both to the non-ideal nature of the active and passive components and to wave effects. The former can largely be accommodated by suitable choice of components but the latter are inherent in the behavior of high-frequency signals and must be understood.

ACTIVE COMPONENTS

Every active component such as a transistor or integrated circuit will cease to operate above some high frequency. In some cases, this is because of some internal process that ceases to be effective, such as the signal period becoming

312

comparable to the transit time of the carriers. The details of this type of limitation can be found in suitable texts and will not be developed here. In other cases the limiting frequency is determined by some inherent circuit time constant associated with the construction of the device. Usually the high-frequency limit of operation will be described by the manufacturer by some characteristic frequency at which the gain has dropped by 3 dB.

A given device can usually be used with different components to give a range of overall gains but the achievable *gain–bandwidth product*, which is the wide-band gain multiplied by the high-frequency 3 dB point, is a constant. This has been seen already as the $1/\omega$ high-frequency response of the operational amplifier assumed in chapter 2. The practical frequency limitation is often because the full equivalent circuit is such that the signal is attenuated or filtered by combinations of impedances in the device and the circuit. There are thus some ways of using an active component which will produce a better high-frequency performance than others. The full equivalent circuit of the active and passive components, together with the interconnections, needs to be considered and this is done in the next section.

As a simple example, the high-frequency response of integrated circuit operational amplifiers is normally limited by the internal compensation provided by a small capacitor within the device. This gives the convenient $1/\omega$ response that makes the device easy to use. In some cases the same circuit is also manufactured without this capacitor. The high-frequency response is then higher but less clearly defined. In this case external compensation, in the form of particular feedback *RC* networks, has to be added for each application in order to stabilize the circuit and to give a good open-loop gain–frequency response. The compensating network can be designed to stabilize the whole circuit consisting of the amplifier together with the components added for that particular application.

HIGH-FREQUENCY EQUIVALENT CIRCUITS

At high frequencies, the presence of 'stray' circuit components has to be considered. These are components that exist owing to the physical construction of the circuit but have not been deliberately designed into it. In chapter 1 the effect of these stray components on passive devices was shown to make them non-ideal. Similar effects occur in active devices.

As the frequency is increased, the impedance of capacitors decreases and that of inductors increases. Signal filtering and attenuation are due to the ratio of impedances, as in simple attenuators and *RC* filters. Thus the stray components that reduce high-frequency signals the most are inductors in series with existing impedances and, particularly, capacitors in parallel with existing impedances such as shown in figure 11.1. These stray impedances exist because of the physical construction of the devices and the circuit. Any loop in a conductor or in the circuit has self-inductance and two adjacent conductors form a capacitor. The small impedances spread throughout the circuit are called *distributed* as opposed to localized, *lumped* conventional discrete components. There is also a small stray increase at high frequencies in the resistance of conductors due to the *skin effect* whereby high-frequency currents are concentrated near the surface. However, this effect is usually not so important as the reactive stray effects.

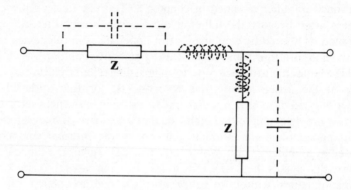

Fig. 11.1 At high frequencies, stray capacitances and inductances become significant.

The size of these stray impedances is generally fixed by physical considerations such as the dimensions of the circuit and the component size and separation. Little can be done to reduce the net effect by reducing the spacing between the conductors since a reduction in the dimension increases the shunt capacitance by about the same proportion as the series inductance decreases, so that the net loss of signal is approximately unchanged. A decrease in the conductor length has a proportionate effect. As the frequency of operation increases, lower lumped impedance values are used to reduce the shunting effect of the stray impedances. As a rough indication, typical circuit impedances at z.f. (d.c.) are 10^5 Ω, at 1 kHz are 10^3 Ω, and at 1 MHz are 100 Ω.

Thus, at high frequencies it becomes advantageous to lessen the use of lumped components and substitute distributed components. In this way the 'stray' impedances are incorporated as deliberate parts of the circuit. This change from lumped to distributed circuit elements requires the different conceptual approach that will be outlined later in this chapter.

The dominant stray components in active devices are the capacitances between the terminals. These are shown in figure 11.2 for a differential

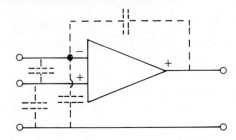

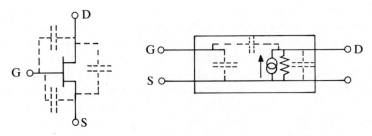

Fig. 11.2   The important stray capacitances of an amplifier and a field-effect
transistor shown on the symbol and the equivalent circuit.

amplifier and a field-effect transistor. These components are specified by the
manufacturer and should be added to the low-frequency equivalent circuit for
the full circuit analysis. The complete circuit will also include the stray
impedances of the wiring and the usual passive lumped components.

A quick look at the total circuit will indicate that many of these stray
components can either be amalgamated with existing components or
neglected since they are in parallel with much smaller impedances or in series
with much larger impedances.

The input and output capacitances are often important because there are
long connecting cables that have a typical capacitance of 50–100 pF/m. The
effect of a stray capacitance C between a voltage source and a load can be
discussed using the circuit shown in figure 11.3. The Thévenin equivalent
circuit analysis of the resistance circuit gives a voltage across the load of
$V_0 R_L/(R_S + R_L)$ from an equivalent impedance of $R_L \| R_S = R_S R_L/(R_S + R_L)$.
The effect of the capacitance is therefore to act with this output impedance to
form a low-pass filter with a characteristic frequency $(R_S + R_L)/CR_S R_L$. In the
design of high-frequency circuits, the input and output impedances must be
considered in relation both to the loading effects and to the high-frequency
attenuation due to strays. The different active device configurations (e.g.
common gate, common source, and common drain) described in chapter 1,

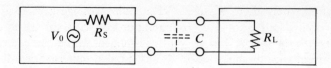

Fig. 11.3. The cable capacitance between circuits attenuates the signal at high frequencies.

provide possible ways of satisfying the requirements with a given device since the input and output impedances vary widely.

The most important stray capacitance for amplifying devices operating at high frequencies is the feedback capacitance between the output and any inverting input as shown in figure 11.4. Although it is comparable in size to other stray capacitances, this has a large influence because of its location as a feedback impedance. An analysis following that in chapter 2 shows that it can be replaced by an effective input capacitance equal to $C(A + 1)$ which might be very large. This is called the *Miller effect*. Physically it arises because if a voltage V is applied to the input, a voltage $-AV$ appears at the output, so that a voltage difference $(A + 1)V$ is imposed across the capacitor. This results in a large current flow and hence a low effective input impedance.

The Miller effect can be eliminated by using the device as a non-inverting voltage amplifier (e.g. as a common gate amplifier (chapter 1)) or in a

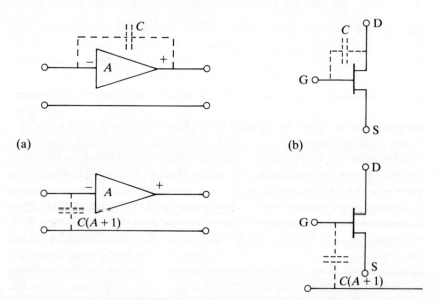

Fig. 11.4 The stray feedback capacitance C in an inverting amplifier (a) or a single device in an inverting configuration (b) produces a large effective input capacitance $C(A + 1)$ through the Miller effect.

configuration where there is current rather than voltage gain (e.g. in the common drain, source follower configuration) or as a voltage-to-current converter with the output voltage kept constant (as in the cascode circuit). The high-frequency modification to the long-tailed pair is shown in figure 11.5. The basic operation of this differential amplifier was described in chapter 1. The input transistor acts as a source follower and shows no Miller effect since the drain is at constant voltage and the source follows the gate so that no current flows through the gate-to-source capacitance. This transistor thus has a high input impedance and a low output impedance. The second transistor is in the common gate configuration which is non-inverting and hence shows no Miller effect. This stage has a small input impedance but little

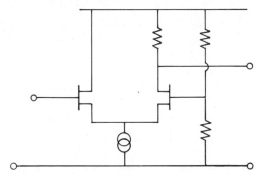

Fig. 11.5   A high-frequency modification to the differential amplifier which produces no Miller effect.

signal is lost in any mismatch between the stages since the output impedance of the first stage is very low. The symmetry and hence the differential balance properties of the circuit are, however, reduced.

The *cascode* circuit is shown in two forms in figure 11.6. In figure 11.6(a) the input transistor is represented by its equivalent circuit and the bias circuit is omitted. It can be considered as a voltage-to-current converter. The output current is fed into a feedback current-to-voltage converter with a very small input impedance. Hence the d.c. output voltage of the first stage (the signal current flowing through the small input impedance of the second stage gives negligible signal voltage) is constant so that there is no Miller effect. In the fully discrete device version in figure 11.6(b) the current-to-voltage converter is transistor T_2 in the common gate configuration. The two devices in series can be combined into one device with two gates in series. In the operational amplifier version, the input device is perhaps an FET with a large drain bias resistor and a transconductance g_m. The (a.c.) output current from this high-impedance source is fed into a feedback current-to-voltage converter

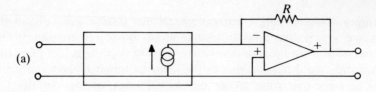

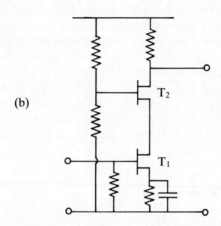

Fig. 11.6 The cascode circuit shows no Miller effect. In (a) the circuit is described by the equivalent circuit of the input transistor followed by a feedback current-to-voltage converter. The full two-device circuit is shown in (b).

with transresistance $(\equiv V_{out}/I_{in}) = R$ and low input impedance $R/(A+1)$. There is thus little lost due to mismatch between stages. The voltage gain is $g_m R$.

TRANSMISSION LINES

At low frequencies the wires connecting systems, circuits or components need not be considered in detail beyond their ability to conduct the current. However, the energy is actually passed between the circuit elements in the form of electric and magnetic fields. The fields obey Maxwell's equations so that the propagation of the signal is in the form of an electromagnetic wave at the signal frequency and with a wavelength corresponding to that in the medium in which the fields exist. If the length, l, of the connections or any part of the circuit is comparable with the wavelength (say $l \geq \lambda/8$), then the fields are in the space round the conductors rather than in the C and L components. and hence these wave properties must be considered. This condition is equivalent to the condition that the capacitive reactance of the conductor pair is comparable to the inductive reactance at the signal frequency. In this section we will consider the simple case where the signal can be considered as flowing along a pair of conductors, or *transmission line*, where the energy is carried in the form of a wave with the fields and hence the energy mainly concentrated between the conductors. The geometry of the conductors can take many forms; some are shown in figure 11.7. A dielectric material is used to locate the conductors relative to each other.

To see physically what is happening, consider the lumped circuit that most closely approximates to the distributed component transmission line. If there are no real lumped components but just a pair of conductors, the only effective impedances are the distributed series inductance and shunt capacitance as shown in figure 11.8. Any resistance will only cause dissipation of the signal and this can be added later as a correction. Each inverted L-shaped section taken separately has a resonant frequency $\omega_0 = 1/\sqrt{(LC)}$, so that a

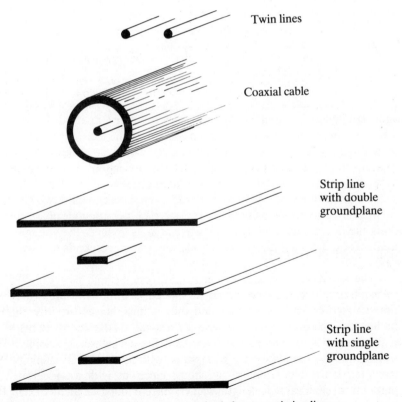

Twin lines

Coaxial cable

Strip line
with double
groundplane

Strip line
with single
groundplane

Fig. 11.7 Some possible construction methods for transmission lines.

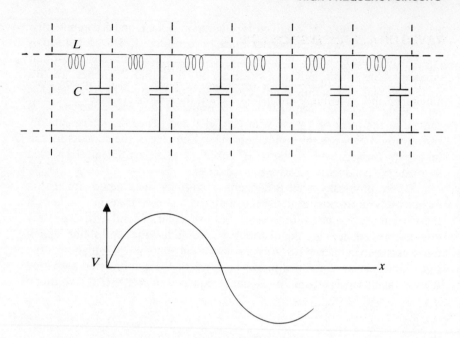

Fig. 11.8   A transmission line can be divided into sections that can each be represented by a lumped LC filter. A wave experiences a constant phase delay through each section.

signal applied to the input takes a time of about a quarter period, $1/(8\pi\omega_0)$, to reach its maximum. This is the signal passed on to the next stage. As there is no attenuation, the net result is that the signal is present along the line at constant amplitude but with a phase-shift between sections. In the limit as this lumped element circuit tends to a distributed element circuit, the number of sections per unit length can be considered as increased to infinity by making the individual components smaller. There is then a continuous phase change along the line at any time. If a sine wave at ω_0 is applied, the voltage at all points along the line has a frequency ω_0, and this corresponds to a traveling wave.

The situation is of course really more complicated, as the individual resonant circuits have been treated as independent units whereas they are joined together and their input and output impedances produce mutual loading. As with other systems of coupled resonators, the frequency response of the system is not sharp at the resonant frequency of each element but propagation is possible over a wide range of frequencies. By analogy, for example, in the band theory of metals, electrons with a wide range of quantum-mechanical wavelengths can propagate along an array of coupled atomic oscillators.

WAVES ON A TRANSMISSION LINE

For the most common transmission line configurations, a pair of coaxial cylinders and a pair of parallel wires shown in figure 11.9, the distributed inductance and capacitance are as follows. For the coaxial cylinders

$$C' = \frac{2\pi\epsilon\epsilon_0}{\ln(b/a)} \qquad \text{F/m}$$

$$L' = \frac{1}{2\pi}\mu\mu_0\ln(b/a) \qquad \text{H/m} \tag{11.1}$$

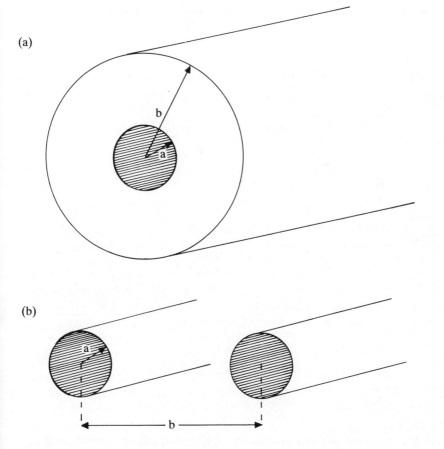

Fig. 11.9   The geometry of a coaxial cable (a) and a twin wire (b) transmission line.

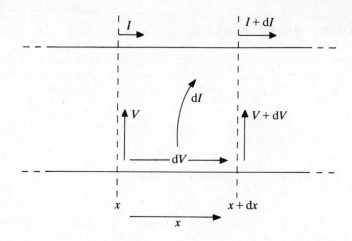

Fig. 11.10   The current and voltage sign convention on a transmission line.

and for a pair of parallel wires

$$C' = \frac{\pi \epsilon \epsilon_0}{\ln(b/a)} \qquad \text{F/m}$$

$$\tag{11.2}$$

$$L' = \frac{1}{\pi} \mu \mu_0 \ln(b/a) \qquad \text{H/m}$$

Where $\epsilon_0 = (1/36\pi) \times 10^{-9}$ F/m, $\mu_0 = 4\pi \times 10^7$ H/m, and the conductors are surrounded by a medium with relative dielectric constant ϵ and relative permeability μ. As the dimensions only occur as a logarithmic factor, the magnitudes of these impedances are much the same for all practical lines.

Consider the short section of an infinitely long conductor pair between points x and $x + dx$ as shown in figure 11.10. The voltage is measured relative to the lower conductor and both voltage and current are taken to increase with increasing x. The voltage and current are taken as sinusoidal at frequency ω, so that $V \sim e^{j\omega t}$ and $I \sim e^{j\omega t}$. The series impedance per unit length can be written in the complex form $\mathbf{Z}' = R' + j\omega L'$ and the shunt admittance $\mathbf{Y}' = G' + j\omega C'$, where the primes indicate that these are impedances per unit length as shown in figure 11.11.

Kirchhoff's laws for the small length of line give:

$$\begin{aligned} dV &= -I\mathbf{Z}'\,dx = -I(R' + j\omega L')dx \\ dI &= -V\mathbf{Y}'\,dx = -V(G' + j\omega C')dx \end{aligned} \tag{11.3}$$

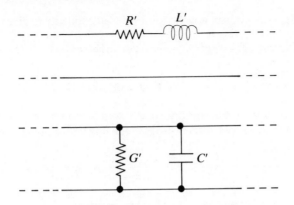

Fig. 11.11 The series impedance per unit length, $R' + j\omega L'$, and the shunt admittance per unit length, $G' + j\omega C$, for a transmission line.

for the current flow along the line and across the line. Because of the sign convention, the voltage and current decrease with increasing distance:

$$\frac{dV}{dx} = -\mathbf{Z}'I \qquad \frac{dI}{dx} = -\mathbf{Y}'V \qquad (11.4)$$

Differentiating and rearranging these:

$$\frac{d^2V}{dx^2} = \mathbf{Z}'\mathbf{Y}'V \qquad \frac{d^2I}{dx^2} = \mathbf{Z}'\mathbf{Y}'I \qquad (11.5)$$

The general solutions to these equations are:

$$V = V_1\exp[-\sqrt{(\mathbf{Z}'\mathbf{Y}')}x] + V_2\exp[+\sqrt{(\mathbf{Z}'\mathbf{Y}')}x]$$
$$I = I_1\exp[-\sqrt{(\mathbf{Z}'\mathbf{Y}')}x] + I_2\exp[+\sqrt{(\mathbf{Z}'\mathbf{Y}')}x] \qquad (11.6)$$

where the amplitudes are constants of integration with magnitudes depending on the boundary conditions.

In the simplifying limit of negligible series resistance and shunt admittance ($R' \ll \omega L'$, $G' \ll \omega C'$; the low-loss or high-frequency limit):

$$\sqrt{(\mathbf{Z}'\mathbf{Y}')} = \sqrt{(j\omega L' \times j\omega C')} = j\omega\sqrt{(L'C')}$$

The effect of resistive conductors ($R' \neq 0$) and leaky or lossy dielectric ($G' \neq 0$) can be considered later.

The time dependence can now be reintroduced explicitly to give:

$$V = V_1 \exp\{j\omega[t - \sqrt{(L'C')}x]\} + V_2 \exp\{j\omega[t + \sqrt{(L'C')}x]\}$$

$$I = I_1 \exp\{j\omega[t - \sqrt{(L'C')}x]\} + I_2 \exp\{j\omega[t + \sqrt{(L'C')}x]\} \tag{11.7}$$

The voltage and the current are each composed of two independent waves, one traveling in each direction along the line with a phase velocity:

$$v = \frac{1}{\sqrt{(L'C')}} = \frac{1}{\sqrt{(\mu\mu_0\epsilon\epsilon_0)}} = \frac{c}{\sqrt{(\epsilon\mu)}}$$

where $c = 1/\sqrt{(\mu_0\epsilon_0)}$ is the velocity of light in free space. This velocity v is the same velocity as that of electromagnetic waves propagating freely in the medium surrounding the conductors. Thus the signal is in the form of electromagnetic waves at a frequency ω, velocity $c/\sqrt{(\epsilon\mu)}$, and wavelength $\lambda = 2\pi c/\omega\sqrt{(\epsilon\mu)}$ propagating along the line.

If R' and G' are non-zero so that

$$\sqrt{(\mathbf{Z}'\mathbf{Y}')} = \sqrt{[(R' + j\omega L') \times (G' + j\omega C')]} = \alpha + j\omega\beta,$$

where α and β are functions of R', G', L', and C', the waves become:

$$V = V_1 e^{-\alpha x} e^{j\omega(t - \beta x)} + V_2 e^{\alpha x} e^{j\omega(t + \beta x)}$$

$$I = I_1 e^{-\alpha x} e^{j\omega(t - \beta x)} + I_2 e^{\alpha x} e^{j\omega(t + \beta x)} \tag{11.8}$$

The coefficient α is the attenuation, which is a measure of the decrease in the wave amplitudes along the line as the energy is dissipated, and $1/\beta = v$ is the phase velocity.

The solution so far is for independent voltage and current waves. However, equations (11.4)

$$\frac{dV}{dx} = -\mathbf{Z}'I \qquad \frac{dI}{dx} = -\mathbf{Y}'V$$

provide a link between the voltage and current waves and can be simplified for the zero-loss conditions to give:

$$\frac{dV}{dx} = -j\omega L'I \qquad \frac{dI}{dx} = -j\omega C'V \tag{11.9}$$

For the waves propagating in the positive x direction (from equation (11.7)):

$$V = V_1 \exp\{j\omega[t - \sqrt{(L'C')}x]\} \qquad I = I_1 \exp\{j\omega[t - \sqrt{(L'C')}x]\}$$

these relations give:

$$\frac{V_1}{I_1} = +\sqrt{\left(\frac{L'}{C'}\right)} \equiv Z_0 \qquad (11.10)$$

Thus the ratio of the amplitudes of the voltage and current waves is given by Z_0, the *characteristic impedance*. For the coaxial cable (from equation (11.1))

$$Z_0 = \sqrt{\left(\frac{L'}{C'}\right)} = \frac{1}{2\pi}\left(\frac{\mu\mu_0}{\epsilon\epsilon_0}\right)^{1/2}\ln(b/a)$$

and for the parallel wire pair (from equation (11.2))

$$Z_0 = \sqrt{\left(\frac{L'}{C'}\right)} = \frac{1}{\pi}\left(\frac{\mu\mu_0}{\epsilon\epsilon_0}\right)^{1/2}\ln(b/a)$$

In this low-loss approximation, this quantity is real, so that the voltage and current waves are in phase. Typical values are 50–100 Ω.

For the waves propagating in the negative x direction (from equation (11.7)):

$$V = V_2\exp\{j\omega[t + \sqrt{(L'\,C')}x]\} \qquad I = I_2\exp\{j\omega[t + \sqrt{(L'\,C')}x]\}$$

So that (as $dV/dx = -j\omega L'\,I$, equation (11.9))

$$\frac{V_2}{I_2} = -\sqrt{\left(\frac{L'}{C'}\right)} = -Z_0 \qquad (11.11)$$

The negative sign arises from the current and voltage sign convention adopted and shown in figure 11.10, which is the same for the waves in both directions.

Thus on an infinitely long, uniform transmission line the signal propagates in the form of a wave. For the low-loss line, the velocity is that which the wave would have if propagating freely in the medium surrounding the conductors. The current and voltage in the wave are in phase and related by the characteristic impedance Z_0. Although, from continuity, equal currents flow in both conductors, voltage differences only appear in the one conductor because one conductor is taken as the reference, zero level of voltage. The situation is more complicated in practice where the currents flowing through the non-zero resistance of the reference conductor produce voltages along the line.

The characteristic impedance is a measure of the properties of the medium and the shape of the boundaries of the medium through which the wave propagates. For electromagnetic waves in unbounded free space, the characteristic impedance is $\mu_0/\epsilon_0 = 120\pi\,\Omega$ and relates the magnitudes of the electric and magnetic fields of the wave since voltages and currents then have no meaning.

For other types of waves there is also a characteristic quantity relating the amplitude of the variables of the wave. For example, for a sound wave in an infinite medium, the acoustic impedance ρv_s (ρ is the material density and v_s the sound velocity) is a measure of the ratio of the amplitudes of the sound pressure wave and the particle velocity wave. Alternately, this is the ratio between the elastic and kinetic energy parts of the wave.

Some transmission lines are specially made to have a low propagation velocity and are used as *delay lines*. The inductance is increased by making the linear conductor a helix, and materials of high permeability and high dielectric constant are used where possible. With a length of this line, a time delay can be inserted into a signal path. For a constant velocity of propagation and a single frequency, this also corresponds to a phase-shift between the output and input.

One boundary condition

The solution so far has been for the possible independent waves that can propagate on an infinite transmission line. If a change of variable is made from velocity to the wave-vector $k = 2\pi/\lambda = \omega/v$ the waves in the forward (subscript 1) and backward (subscript 2) directions become (from equations (11.7))

$$V = V_1 e^{j(\omega t - kx)} \qquad I = \frac{V_1}{Z_0} e^{j(\omega t - kx)} \qquad (11.12)$$

$$V = V_2 e^{j(\omega t + kx)} \qquad I = -\frac{V_2}{Z_0} e^{j(\omega t + kx)} \qquad (11.13)$$

At any point on the line, the total voltage and current are due to both waves:

$$V = V_1 e^{j(\omega t - kx)} + V_2 e^{j(\omega t + kx)}$$

$$I = \frac{V_1}{Z_0} e^{j(\omega t - kx)} - \frac{V_2}{Z_0} e^{j(\omega t + kx)} \qquad (11.14)$$

Two waves are no longer independent if a boundary condition, or constraint, which defines the relationship between V and I, is introduced at some point along the line. The amplitudes V_1 and V_2 will then be related in magnitude and phase.

Consider an impedance $\mathbf{Z}_L$ at $x = 0$ as shown in figure 11.12. Then for all time $(V/I)_{x=0} = \mathbf{Z}_L$ where V and I are the total voltage and currents due to both waves:

$$\mathbf{Z}_L = \left(\frac{V}{I}\right)_{x=0} = \frac{V_1 + V_2}{(V_1/Z_0) - (V_2/Z_0)} = Z_0 \frac{V_1 + V_2}{V_1 - V_2} \qquad (11.15)$$

Rearranging

$$\frac{V_2}{V_1} = -\frac{I_2}{I_1} \equiv \mathbf{R} = \frac{\mathbf{Z}_L - Z_0}{\mathbf{Z}_L + Z_0} \qquad (11.16)$$

where $\mathbf{R}$ is the amplitude *reflection coefficient*.

The reflection coefficient is, in general, a complex quantity since $\mathbf{Z}_L$ is complex, so that it represents the amplitude and phase of the reflected wave relative to the incoming wave. The choice of $x = 0$ has incidentally simplified the argument. For arbitrary x the expression becomes

$$\frac{V_2}{V_1} = \mathbf{R} = \mathbf{R}_0 e^{-2jkx}$$

so that V_2 and V_1 have the same time dependence but have a phase difference that depends on the position. The phase of $\mathbf{R}$ therefore depends on x and $x = 0$ is chosen for the reference of the phase.

The general behavior can be seen from a few special cases. For $\mathbf{Z}_L$ real or pure resistive, $\mathbf{R}$ is also pure real. For $\mathbf{Z}_L = \mathbf{Z}_0$, $\mathbf{R} \equiv V_2/V_1 = 0$, $V_2 = 0$, so that there is no reflected wave. Hence all the incoming power is absorbed into the load. The load acts as if it were a semi-infinite line, that is a line continuing

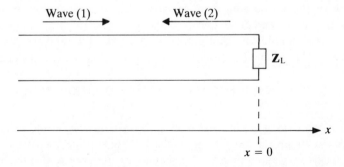

Fig. 11.12 The effect of a boundary condition, here a load impedance $\mathbf{Z}_L$, which defines the relation between the total voltage and current at that point.

to infinity in one direction from that point, of the same characteristic impedance as the line itself. The incoming wave comes from a semi-infinite line of impedance Z_0 and is totally absorbed into a load $\mathbf{Z}_L = Z_0$. This is just the condition for maximum power transfer from a source of internal resistance Z_0 to a load of equal resistance. A line terminated in this manner is said to be *matched* or, more loosely, *terminated*.

If $\mathbf{Z}_L$ is real and less than Z_0, the voltage wave is partially reflected with inversion ($-1 \leq \mathbf{R} < 0$) whereas there is reflection without inversion for $\mathbf{Z}_L$ real and greater than Z_0 ($0 < \mathbf{R} \leq 1$).

In the particular cases of $\mathbf{Z}_L = 0$ (short circuit) and $\mathbf{Z}_L = \infty$ (open circuit), there is total reflection as there is nowhere for the power to go by dissipation or transmission. A familiar example from another field is the reflection of a transverse displacement wave on a string at the end of the string when it is either free (no inversion, $\mathbf{Z}_L = \infty$) or fixed (inversion, $\mathbf{Z}_L = 0$).

If $\mathbf{Z}_L$ is complex, $\mathbf{R}$ is complex and the phase between V_2 and V_1 (and also I_2 and I_1) differs from zero or π. The results are more clearly seen if the total effect of the reflected wave is considered. The incoming and reflected waves interfere with each other to produce *standing waves*. At some points the wave amplitudes will add to produce a voltage maximum $|V_1| + |V_2|$ and at other places the waves will destructively interfere to produce a voltage minimum $|V_1| - |V_2|$. The ratio of the standing wave amplitudes is the *(voltage) standing wave ratio* (SWR or VSWR), S:

$$S = \frac{V_{\max}}{V_{\min}} = \frac{|V_1| + |V_2|}{|V_1| - |V_2|} = \frac{1 + |\mathbf{R}|}{1 - |\mathbf{R}|} \tag{11.17}$$

This is thus an alternate quantity that can be used to describe the reflection properties of the termination of a transmission line. The standing wave ratio is always positive and greater than or equal to unity with increasing magnitude corresponding to greater reflection. It, however, gives no information about the relative phases of the waves (the phase of $\mathbf{R}$) and hence about the exact nature of the terminating impedance or the distance of the maxima and minima from the end of the line.

For the simple case of $\mathbf{Z}_L = \infty$, $V_2 = V_1$ and the total voltage is (from equations (11.12) and (11.13))

$$V = V_1 e^{j(\omega t - kx)} + V_2 e^{j(\omega t + kx)} = 2V_1 \cos kx\, e^{j\omega t} \tag{11.18}$$

At any point along the line, the voltage has a frequency ω and an amplitude $2V_1 \cos kx$ (figure 11.13). The periodicity along the line is thus λ. However, the phase of the rapid time variation at ω can often not be distinguished and the signal amplitude $|V| = 2V_1|\cos kx|$, and the energy density, have a periodicity $\lambda/2$.

If $Z_L = 0$, ∞ or pure reactive, the reflection coefficient is unity and the VSWR infinite. For each of these loads, the standing wave is the same size and shape but displaced by different amounts along the line (as shown in figure 11.14). We see that, in general, for a given magnitude of reflection coefficient, the standing wave is the same but displaced by an amount depending on the phase of the reflection. To study the shape, we need only therefore consider real reflection coefficients.

For a perfect termination, $Z_L = Z_0$, $R = 0$, the VSWR = 1, and there is no standing wave as only the incoming traveling wave exists. For intermediate values of $|R|$, the voltage on the line is part standing wave and part traveling wave (the part that is not reflected but is absorbed by the load). In these cases,

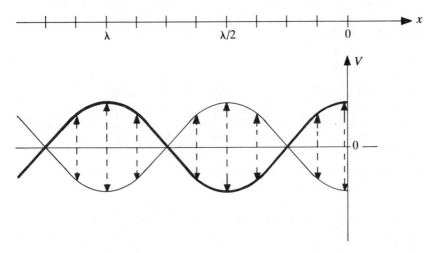

Fig. 11.13 The voltage standing wave on a transmission line with an open circuit, $Z_L = \infty$, at $x = 0$, and a wave incident in the positive x direction.

the minima do not form nodes with zero amplitude. This is shown in figure 11.15.

The standing wave ratio, or reflection coefficient, gives the relationship between the incoming and reflected voltage waves, or alternately the incoming and reflected current waves. For the wave in each direction, the voltage and current components are related by the characteristic impedance, $\pm Z_0$. At a boundary the voltage and current parts of the waves behave differently in that only one is inverted by reflection, the other being reflected without inversion. The voltage and current standing waves have the same form but are displaced relatively by $\lambda/4$. Thus the ratio between the total voltage and total current at any point in the standing wave is no longer the

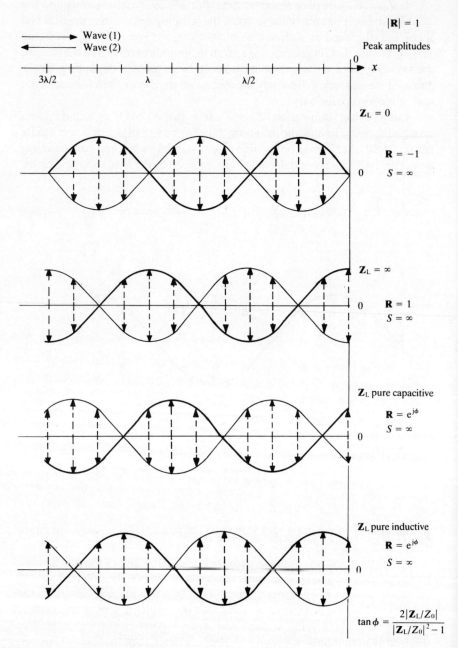

Fig. 11.14. The voltage standing waves on a transmission line with various non-dissipative impedances at $x = 0$.

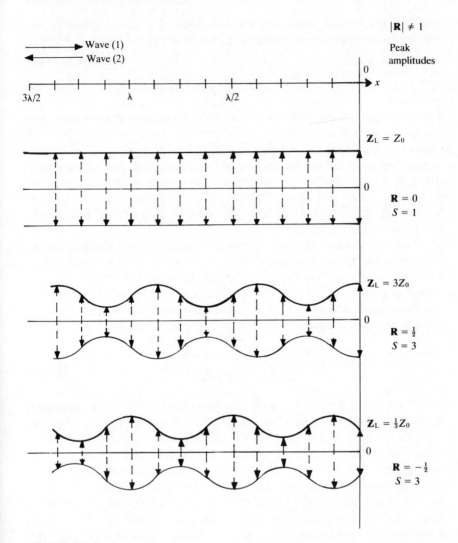

Fig. 11.15 The voltage standing waves on a transmission line with various values of resistive load at $x = 0$.

same everywhere and is no longer given by the characteristic impedance as for each wave, but by some local or *transmission line impedance*:

$$\mathbf{Z} = \frac{V}{I} = \frac{V_1 e^{j(\omega t - kx)} + \mathbf{R}V_1 e^{j(\omega t + kx)}}{(V_1/Z_0) e^{j(\omega t - kx)} - \mathbf{R}(V_1/Z_0) e^{j(\omega t + kx)}} = Z_0 \frac{1 + \mathbf{R} e^{2jkx}}{1 - \mathbf{R} e^{2jkx}} \qquad (11.19)$$

For $\mathbf{R} = 0$ ($\mathbf{Z}_L = Z_0$), a perfectly terminated line, $\mathbf{Z} = Z_0$ at all points along the line as only the incoming wave exists. For $\mathbf{R} = 1$ ($\mathbf{Z}_L = \infty$),

$$\mathbf{Z} = Z_0 \frac{e^{-jkx} + e^{jkx}}{e^{-jkx} - e^{jkx}} = -jZ_0 \cot kx \qquad (11.20)$$

Thus for a perfect mismatch ($\mathbf{R} = \pm 1$) the impedance is pure reactive and changes between 0 and ∞ with a $\lambda/2$ periodicity and the phase changes each $\lambda/4$ alternately inductive and capacitive (figure 11.16). An open-circuit line looks capacitive for the $\lambda/4$ nearest the load and then inductive. The behavior near the load is that expected by the geometry as it approximates to a lumped element, a coaxial pair capacitor for the open-circuit line, and a coaxial loop for the short-circuit line. Thus the impedance measured along a line is widely varying and has a $\lambda/2$ periodicity.

For intermediate real reflection coefficients, the impedance curve is smoothed. As the magnitude of the reflection coefficient is changed through zero, but the phase is fixed, the sharp peaks of impedance smooth out and reappear displaced by $\lambda/4$. For intermediate phases of the reflection coefficient, but a constant VSWR or mismatch $\mathbf{R} = |\mathbf{R}|e^{j\phi}$, the impedance pattern is translated since equation (11.19) may be rewritten as

$$\mathbf{Z} = Z_0 \frac{1 + |\mathbf{R}| e^{j(2kx + \phi)}}{1 - |\mathbf{R}| e^{j(2kx + \phi)}} \qquad (11.21)$$

The impedance that has been calculated here is that due to the interference of an incoming wave and its reflection from the load. It is thus the impedance of the section of the line and its terminating load that would be measured (or 'seen') if the line were cut and the measurement made on the pair of terminals produced. This assumes that the impedance of the source used for the measurement is equal to the characteristic impedance so that no secondary reflections are produced by the measuring apparatus. Alternately, the signal for the measurement comes from a semi-infinite line of the same characteristic impedance. Thus the combined impedance of the line (distributed) and its load (lumped) can be replaced by a single Thévenin equivalent input impedance in the form of either a single lumped impedance or a single semi-infinite line of the appropriate characteristic impedance. This equivalence only applies for waves of a single frequency, constant amplitude for all time, because the time taken for a reflection to return (*transit time*) is non-zero for a transmission line but zero for a lumped impedance. The interference is between the incoming wave and the reflection from a wave that was incoming some time previously. If the period of any amplitude modulation (chapter 6) is then about equal to or less than the transit time, the amplitude of the interfering waves will not be simply related by the reflection coefficient.

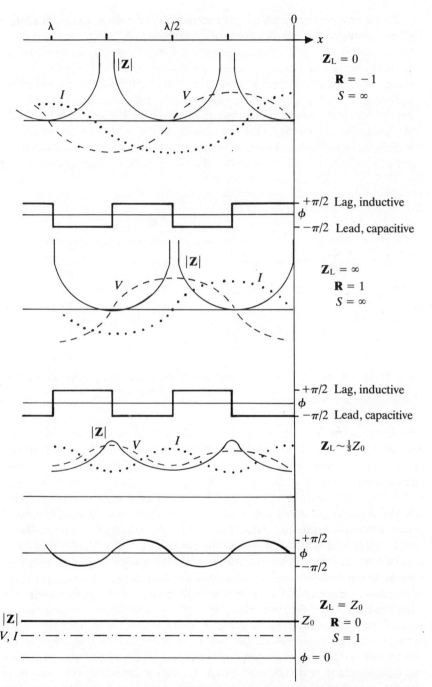

Fig. 11.16 The impedance seen at different points on a transmission line from a load. The individual voltage and current standing waves are also shown.

The replacement of lines by an equivalent lumped input impedance allows considerable simplification of calculations. A line terminated in its characteristic impedance, or a semi-infinite length line, looks at all points along the line like a lumped impedance of this value, so that the reflection of a wave at a junction between semi-infinite lines of different characteristic impedances can be simulated by replacing the 'receiving' line by a lumped impedance at the junction as shown in figure 11.17. If the 'receiving' line is terminated in some other impedance, then the line and the load impedance together can be replaced by a single lumped impedance equal to the input impedance of the line as measured at the junction. For example, a wave on a

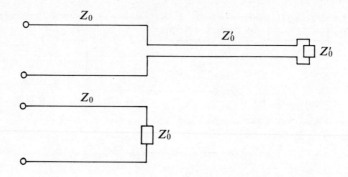

Fig. 11.17 A transmission line with characteristic impedance Z_0', terminated with Z_0', may be replaced by a single lumped impedance of value Z_0'.

50 Ω (characteristic impedance) line joined to a 100 Ω line, $3\lambda/4$ long, terminated in a short circuit is reflected at the junction as if the 100 Ω line was not there and the 50 Ω line was open circuit. The 100 Ω line has an input impedance of infinity.

The same arguments can be used for the reflection of other types of waves at the interface between media of different impedances. The reflection of sound waves depends on the acoustic impedance and that of light waves on the electromagnetic impedance (refractive index). In general there will be some reflection at a junction between media of different impedances. An object is invisible if it is immersed in a medium of the same refractive index (provided the losses in both media are the same), as there is no reflection at the interface.

There are many specific applications of transmission lines which use some of the particular properties that have been described. Because of the periodicity of the standing waves in a length of $\lambda/2$ (in a loss-free line), a line can be altered in length by multiples of $\lambda/2$ without affecting its transmission properties. Again, this is only true for the steady-state conditions using a constant-amplitude incoming wave.

Whereas the $\lambda/2$ line acts as a passive extender, a line with a length $l = \lambda/4$ (or $l = (2n + 1)\lambda/4$ with n integral) acts like a transformer, such that $\mathbf{Z}_{in}\mathbf{Z}_L = Z_0^2$ as shown in figure 11.18. To show this we have, from equations (11.19) and (11.16):

$$\mathbf{Z}_{in} = Z_0\frac{1 + \mathbf{R}\,e^{2jkx}}{1 - \mathbf{R}\,e^{2jkx}}$$

for $x = \lambda/4$, $e^{2jkx} = e^{j\pi} = -1$, so that $\mathbf{Z}_{in} = Z_0^2/\mathbf{Z}_L$.

For comparison, the input impedance of a lumped circuit transformer with a turns ratio n and a load $\mathbf{Z}_L$ across the secondary is $\mathbf{Z}_{in} = (1/n^2)\mathbf{Z}_L$. The *quarter-wavelength transformer* is a demonstration of the high $\rightarrow$ low, capacitive $\rightarrow$ inductive change in the impedance every $\lambda/4$ along the line. The

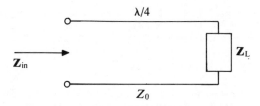

Fig. 11.18 A transmission line of length $\lambda/4$ acts as a transformer.

waves reflected from the two discontinuities interfere to produce this effect. With a quarter-wave transformer, a current source (high internal impedance) can be matched to a low impedance without loss of signal. Similarly, maximum power can pass from a semi-infinite line of characteristic impedance $\mathbf{Z}_{01}$ to a semi-infinite line of impedance $\mathbf{Z}_{02}$ if they are joined by a quarter-wavelength of line of impedance $(Z_{01}Z_{02})^{1/2}$. This is analogous to the 'blooming' of optical glass surfaces in which $\lambda/4$ thickness of transparent material with dielectric constant (impedance) $(n_1 n_2)^{1/2}$ is placed between the media of refractive indices n_1 and n_2 so that little light is lost by reflection at the interface.

Cavity modes and resonance

In the analysis so far, the wave has been assumed to have come from a semi-infinite line and any reflected wave has disappeared into the same line. This is a reasonable assumption because if the source has an internal impedance Z_0, the line behaves in all ways like a semi-infinite line. If the

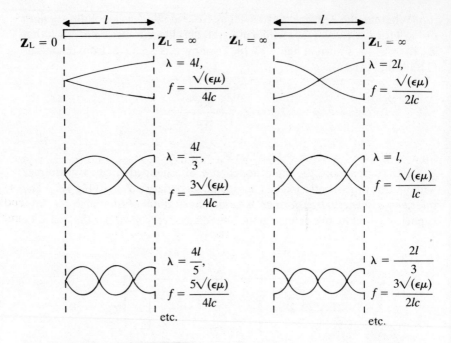

Fig. 11.19 Transmission lines with two boundaries can be excited by standing waves at certain allowed frequencies.

source has any other impedance, there will be reflected waves in both directions, multiple reflections, and two sets of boundary conditions. These produce cavity eigenmodes analogous to organ-pipe or violin-string resonances or the allowed modes or energies of quantum-mechanical waves in a potential well. For a line with one end open and the other closed, resonance occurs for $l = (2n + 1)\lambda/4$, $f = \sqrt{(\epsilon\mu)}(2n + 1)/4lc$ (n integral); and with both ends either open or closed for $l = (n + 1)\lambda/2$, $f = \sqrt{(\epsilon\mu)}(n + 1)/2lc$ (n integral) (figure 11.19). If the reflection coefficient is unity at each and there is no loss, these resonances correspond to the ideal LC lumped circuit resonant circuit, although for this there is only one resonant frequency.

The impedance measured at the end of the line at resonance will be either zero or infinity, corresponding to a series or a parallel tuned circuit. For example, the one-end-shorted element at resonance appears like a parallel tuned circuit seen from the open end but a series tuned circuit from the shorted end. In practice, the transmission line resonant circuit has significant advantages over lumped element circuits at high frequencies: losses are lower, so that higher Qs are possible, and also stray impedances are eliminated, so that unwanted resonances do not occur. As the Qs and hence VSWRs found in practice are large, care must be taken that the voltages at the

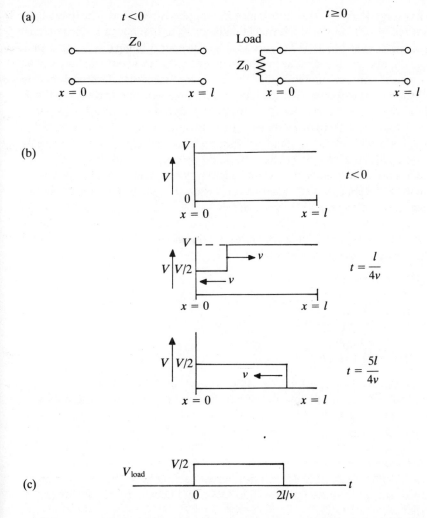

Fig. 11.20 If a transmission line with characteristic impedance Z_0 is charged to a constant voltage and then terminated at one end with a load Z_0 as in (a), then a voltage wave moves along the line as shown in (b) to produce a voltage pulse across the load as shown in (c).

voltage antinodes of the resonance do not become large enough to cause damage to the dielectric in the line.

The time taken for a wave, a pulse or a modulation to travel along the line has been mentioned before specifically as a means of introducing a time delay into a signal path. This property can also be used to produce or shape pulses. Consider a line of length l, characteristic impedance Z_0, along which waves can propagate at velocity v. Initially, the line is open at both ends and charged to a voltage V. At $t = 0$ an impedance Z_0 is applied to one end. The line acts as a source of voltage V and internal impedance Z_0 so that power is dissipated in the load Z_0 at a voltage $V/2$ (figure 11.20). The energy being dissipated comes from the energy stored in the line which propagates at velocity v in the form of a wave of constant amplitude $V/2$ and a steep back end. This back end is reflected by the open end of the line without inversion and leaves no voltage across the line. After a time $2l/v$ all the energy stored in the line has dissipated in the load in the form of a voltage pulse of magnitude $V/2$. This voltage pulse contains a wide range of Fourier component frequencies and the analysis assumes that each frequency has the same propagation velocity, that is the line has no dispersion. This is a convenient way of making voltage pulses with lengths less than about 10 μs. However, the switch that initiates the discharge must act in a time much shorter than this.

The velocity of light in free space (c) is about 3×10^8 m/s but is reduced by the dielectric material in the transmission line to $v \sim (1.0\text{--}1.5) \times 10^8$ m/s. Thus an approximate wavelength is:

1 km at 100 kHz
100 m at 1 MHz
10 m at 10 MHz
1 m at 100 MHz
0.1 m at 1 GHz
0.01 m at 10 GHz

The effects caused by the interference of reflected waves become significant for circuit dimensions larger than about $\lambda/8$. Thus the approaches to signal flows described in this chapter should be considered for commercial power transmission (50 or 60 Hz) over distances of several hundred miles, for telephone transmission ($\sim$1 kHz) over distances of several tens of miles, for interconnections between pieces of electronic apparatus (say 1 m) at frequencies above about 25 MHz, for interconnection between sub-assemblies (say 10 cm) at frequencies about 250 MHz, and between components (say 1 cm) at about 2.5 GHz.

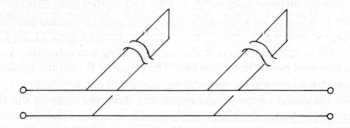

Fig. 11.21   Matching a load to a source can be achieved using stubs with a suitable spacing and length.

In the frequency region where these interference effects are important, the components must be designed carefully so that there is no impedance discontinuity or *mismatch* which could produce reflections or standing wave ratios greater than unity. Many components have the VSWR that they produce specified by the manufacturer. Reflections result in loss of power transfer, undesirable impedances, and the possibility of dielectric breakdown because of high standing wave electric fields. In general, all high-frequency apparatus should have correctly terminated input and output terminals, and transmission lines of standard characteristic impedance should be used. Optimum matching between impedances can often be obtained with a variable length line or with adjustable side arms or *stubs* (figure 11.21).

THE SMITH CHART

There are several convenient ways of displaying these transmission line effects graphically. The most familiar is the *Smith chart*. (The Blanchard chart is an inversion of the Smith chart.) A familiarity with this chart enables many calculations to be performed rapidly.

The Smith chart (figure 11.22) is a plot of the complex reflection co-efficient $\mathbf{R} = |\mathbf{R}|e^{j\theta} = u + jv$ on the complex plane. As $|\mathbf{R}| \leq 1$, only a section of the complex plane within a circle of radius 1 is actually used. Since (from equation (11.16)):

$$\mathbf{R} = \frac{(\mathbf{Z}_L/Z_0) - 1}{(\mathbf{Z}_L/Z_0) + 1}$$

each point within this section of the complex plane corresponds to a value of the normalized impedance $\mathbf{Z}_L/Z_0$. Thus the Smith chart is a plot of impedance on a distorted coordinate system, with the lines of constant normalized resistance R/Z_0 forming the non-concentric circles (figure 11.23(a)) and lines of constant normalized reactance jX/Z_0 forming circular arcs, so that the plane includes all impedances $\mathbf{Z}/Z_0 = (R + jX)/Z_0$ (figure 11.23(c)).

The coordinate system is such that lines of equal reflection coefficient $\mathbf{R}$ or voltage standing wave ratio S are concentric circles (figure 11.23(d)). The radial scale is thus calibrated in the corresponding quantities $|\mathbf{R}|$, S, power return loss, and power reflection loss. The phase of $\mathbf{R}$ (not the transmission line impedance) for a given terminating impedance can be obtained from the angle of the radial vector to that impedance using the scale on the circumference of the chart.

A loss-less line with a given load has a constant VSWR along its length. Progression along the transmission line away from the load corresponds to motion clockwise round the circle of constant radius such that one revolution

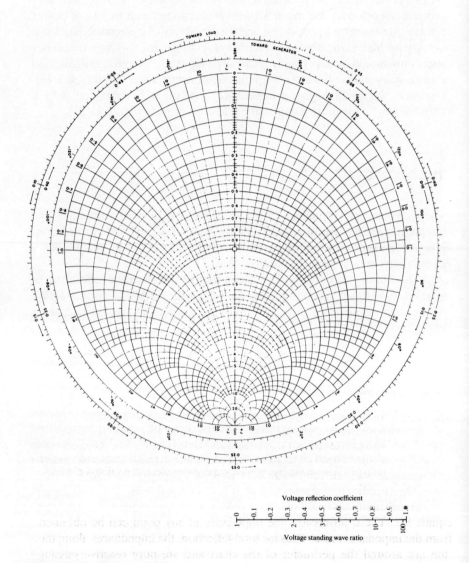

Fig. 11.22 The Smith chart.

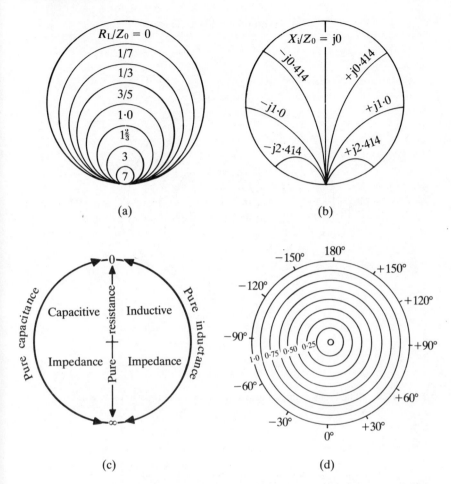

Fig. 11.23 The constituent features of the Smith chart are the circles of constant normalized resistance (a), the lines of constant normalized reactance (b), which divide the circle into regions of impedance (c), and the concentric circles of constant voltage reflection coefficient or voltage standing wave ratio (d). Also shown is the phase angle of the voltage reflection coefficient.

equals $\lambda/2$. The transmission line impedance at any point can be obtained from the impedance scale. Thus for total reflection, the impedances along the line are around the perimeter of the chart and are pure reactive passing through zero, pure inductive, infinity, and pure capacitive.

The effect of line attenuation can be obtained from another radial scale. The attenuation produces a decrease in the ratio of the reflected to the incoming wave amplitude (i.e. the effective reflection coefficient) along the line as the former decreases and the latter increases in size nearer the source.

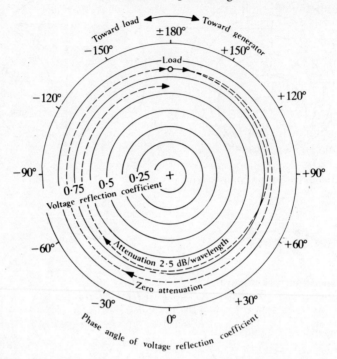

Fig. 11.24   The locus of impedance along a lossy transmission line is a spiral.

Fig. 11.25   The scattering or S matrix relates the incoming, outgoing, and reflected waves.

The locus of impedance along the lossy line is thus a spiral inward for a motion toward the source (figure 11.24).

In low-frequency circuit analysis, impedances are used. These are less useful at high frequencies because impedances cannot be measured easily. It is the wave amplitude or the VSWR that can be measured easily. The properties of a circuit can be described by a scattering matrix (S) in which the coefficients relate the outgoing waves to the ingoing waves and the transmitted waves in terms of the incident waves. The incoming waves are represented by V_1^+ and V_2^+ and the reflected waves by V_1^- and V_2^- (figure 11.25). The **S** coefficients are defined by the relations:

$$V_1^- = \mathbf{S}_{11} V_1^+ + \mathbf{S}_{12} V_2^+$$

$$V_2^- = \mathbf{S}_{21} V_1^+ + \mathbf{S}_{22} V_2^+$$

The construction techniques that should be used when there are high-frequency signals present in a circuit are described only briefly in appendix 2, but for precision circuits and for very high frequencies, say above 1 GHz, even more specialized techniques are necessary.

FURTHER READING

A. J. Baden Fuller, *Microwaves*, Pergamon (1969).
F. R. Connor, *Wave Transmission*, Edward Arnold (1972).
H. Mooijweer, *Microwave Techniques*, Macmillan (1971).
S. Ramo and J. R. Whinnery, *Fields and Waves in Communication Electronics*, Wiley (1984).

APPENDIX 1   DATA

DECIBEL

A power ratio P_2/P_1 can be expressed as $10\log_{10}(P_2/P_1)$ decibel (dB). If the powers, P_2 and P_1, are developed over the same impedances, then the voltage ratio $(V_2/V_1) = (P_2/P_1)^{1/2}$ can be expressed as $20\log_{10}(V_2/V_1)$ dB. For example:

Decibels	P_2/P_1	V_2V_1
+1	1.259	1.122
+3	1.995	1.413
+6	3.981	1.995
+10	10.00	3.162
+20	100.00	10.00

Voltage ratios are sometimes expressed in decibels without strict adherence to the requirement for a constant impedance.

Often the power levels of specific quantities such as sound or radio-frequency signals are expressed as decibels relative to some standard reference level of power. The absolute power level can be obtained only if this reference level is known.

COLOR CODES

There is a well established color code to represent numbers on components where the actual numerical values cannot easily be marked:

0 black
1 brown
2 red
3 orange
4 yellow
5 green
6 blue
7 violet
8 gray
9 white

For resistors the value is represented by colored bands, as shown in figure A1.1. The colors of the first two or three bands represent the numerical values of the first two or three digits of the resistance. The next band gives the

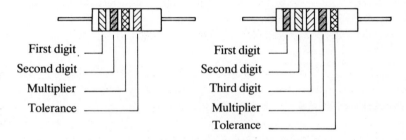

First digit
Second digit
Multiplier
Tolerance

First digit
Second digit
Third digit
Multiplier
Tolerance

Fig. A1.1 Two and three significant figure resistance color codes.

multiplier or the number of zeros to add to the first digits. The final band represents the tolerance or accuracy to which the value represents the true resistance. For two-digit accuracy, the tolerance is given by

±10%   silver
±5%   gold

and for three-figure accuracy by

±2%   red
±1%   brown

For example, green, blue, red, gold represents a resistor of magnitude $5600\,\Omega \pm 5\%$ and red, blue, brown, orange, brown represents $261000\,\Omega \pm 1\%$.

For capacitors the same scheme is used with the number expressed in picofarads (pF) and there may be extra bands to represent the temperature coefficient or the working voltage, as shown in figure A1.2.

EER–L*

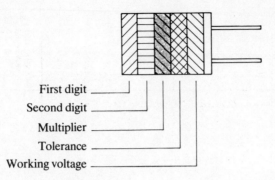

Fig. A1.2   Capacitor color code.

Not all resistance values are manufactured. Those that are produced are of 'preferred values' which are related in geometric progression so that the values are the same percentage apart. A series might be:

1.0, 1.2, 1.5, 1.8, 2.2, 2.7, 3.3, 3.9, 4.7, 5.6, 6.8, 8.2, etc.

NUMBER SYSTEMS

Binary	Octal	Hexadecimal	Decimal
0000	00	0	0
0001	01	1	1
0010	02	2	2
0011	03	3	3
0100	04	4	4
0101	05	5	5
0110	06	6	6
0111	07	7	7
1000	10	8	8
1001	11	9	9
1010	12	A	10
1011	13	B	11
1100	14	C	12
1101	15	D	13
1110	16	E	14
1111	17	F	15

Table A1.1   Commands and Addresses on Data Lines DIO 1-7 with bus meanings and their associated ISO-7 Bit Code (shaded). DIO 8 is always 0. These commands and addresses exert control only when ATN is true (1). If ATN is false (0) Data is being transmitted in ISO-7 code.

ISO BIT & DIO LINE NUMBER (7 6 5) →	0 0 0	0 0 1	0 1 0	0 1 1	1 0 0	1 0 1	1 1 0	1 1 1
COLUMN →	0	1	2	3	4	5	6	7
ROW (4 3 2 1) ↓								
0 (0 0 0 0)	NUL	DLE	SP	0	@	P	`	p
1 (0 0 0 1)	SOH GTL	DC1 LLO	!	1	A	Q	a	q
2 (0 0 1 0)	STX	DC2	"	2	B	R	b	r
3 (0 0 1 1)	ETX	DC3	#	3	C	S	c	s
4 (0 1 0 0)	EOT SDC	DC4 DCL	$	4	D	T	d	t
5 (0 1 0 1)	ENQ PPC	NAK PPU	%	5	E	U	e	u
6 (0 1 1 0)	ACK	SYN	&	6	F	V	f	v
7 (0 1 1 1)	BEL	ETB	'	7	G	W	g	w
8 (1 0 0 0)	BS GET	CAN SPE	(	8	H	X	h	x
9 (1 0 0 1)	HT TCT	EM SPD	)	9	I	Y	i	y
10 (1 0 1 0)	LF	SUB	*	:	J	Z	j	z
11 (1 0 1 1)	VT	ESC	+	;	K	[	k	{
12 (1 1 0 0)	FF	FS	,	<	L	\	l	|
13 (1 1 0 1)	CR	GS	-	=	M	]	m	}
14 (1 1 1 0)	SO	RS	.	>	N	^	n	~
15 (1 1 1 1)	SI	US	/	? UNL	O	_ UNT	o	DEL
	ADDRESSED COMMAND GROUP (ACG)	UNIVERSAL COMMAND GROUP (UCG)	LISTEN ADDRESS GROUP (LAG) ← DEVICE LISTEN ADDRESS	← DEVICE LISTEN ADDRESS → UNL	TALK ADDRESS GROUP (TAG) ← DEVICE TALK ADDRESS	← DEVICE TALK ADDRESS → UNT	SECONDARY COMMAND GROUP (SCG) ← MEANING DETERMINED BY PCG	← MEANING DETERMINED BY PCG →

PRIMARY COMMAND GROUP (PCG)

STANDARD ISO 7 CHARACTERS

TRANSISTOR NUMBERS

There are several systems for designating the type number of discrete devices such as diodes and transistors. A new device will have the number given to it by the manufacturer. This normally has a few letters, or numbers followed by letters, and then a few-digit serial number. Each manufacturer has his own system. However, once a particular device with a given set of characteristics has become established, a standard number is given to describe all devices with that specification from any manufacturer.

The US system consists of 1N followed by a serial number for diodes, 2N... for transistors with three terminals, and 3N... for four-terminal transistors.

The Pro-Electron code consists of two letters followed by a three-symbol serial number comprising a letter and a two-digit number. The principal letters used are:

First letter
A   germanium
B   silicon
C   gallium arsenide
R   compound semiconductor
Second letter
A   diode, low power
B   diode, varactor
C   transistor, low power, audiofrequency
D   transistor, high power, audiofrequency
E   diode, tunnel
F   transistor, low power, high frequency
G   multiple devices
H   diode, magnetic sensitive
L   transistor, high power, high frequency
N   opto-coupler
P   radiation detector
Q   radiation emitter
R   control or switching device
S   transistor, low power, switching
T   control or switching device
U   transistor, high power, switching
X   diode, rectifier
Y   diode, rectifier
Z   diode, voltage reference

Further letters after the numbers usually indicate package variations. Device packages are fairly standard and are designated by established codes.

INTEGRATED CIRCUIT NUMBERS

New integrated circuits have a manufacturer's number that usually consists of two or three letters followed by a serial number. The letters are specific to the manufacturers and will usually also specify the type of circuit: linear, digital, bipolar or FET. Since it is an advantage to the user to have several sources of supply, a manufacturer will encourage the use of a particular circuit by allowing other firms to make the circuit to the same specifications. Therefore, the same circuit may appear under the numbers assigned by several manufacturers. In this case the serial number is usually preserved with just different letters. The common operational amplifiers such as the 741 and 356 thus occur as: AD741, μA741, LM741, etc., and as LF356, μAF356, etc.

If two or four units are placed in one package (dual or quad units), the numbering is related: μA747, MC4741. A letter suffix may indicate a special version, either in one quality (such as μA741S for a fast or high-frequency version) or in the package type (metal can or plastic), or the temperature range over which the specifications are guaranteed (Military $-55°C$ to $+125°C$, Industrial $-25°C$ to $+85°C$, or Commercial $0°C$ to $+70°C$). The suffix notations are not standard. The temperature specifications are important since the cost can increase considerably for high-specification devices, which are rarely needed for laboratory work.

In digital circuits a similar numbering system is used with the same or similar numbers to indicate a logic family and common serial numbers, often for the same gate between families. Thus the CMOS logic family occurs in several series such as CD4xxx or MC14xxx and the TTL family as N74xxx, DM74xxx or SN74xxx with subfamilies 74Sxxx, 74LSxxx, and 74ALSxxx to indicate high speed, low power high speed, and advanced low power high speed.

STANDARD DEVICES

Some particular device designs are very popular and are used as the standard or first choice component in a circuit where a generic component such as an operational amplifier or comparator is required. This is often because they are easy to use with few specific problems such as special bias circuits or a susceptibility to instability. A less usual device with a special property is only sought and selected if that special property is actually required. If only a few standard devices are used wherever possible, then stock levels can be kept low and replacement of failed devices is easy. The list of standard devices given here is only a suggestion but may provide a start for a new laboratory. There is no substitute for a collection of manufacturers' data books.

Resistors

Metal film resistors are recommended for most purposes. Although they are not the cheapest type of resistor, they are reliable and have good stability and low noise. Such high-quality devices are essential in parts of the circuit with low signal levels and it is usually better to stock only one type.

Capacitors

The type of capacitor used depends primarily on the range in which the required value falls, since each type is only made over a limited range:

1–10 000 pF: Mica dielectric capacitors have low loss and low inductance.
100 pf–0.1 μF: Ceramic dielectric capacitors have low inductance, but have fairly high loss and are temperature-dependent.
0.001–10 μF: Various plastic film dielectric capacitors have generally low loss and leakage, but the inductance may be fairly large. The specifications need to be consulted for properties such as temperature stability and charge retention after attempts at discharge.
0.1–1000 μF: Electrolytic capacitors only have a size small enough for general use. However, they must have one terminal always at a positive potential with respect to the other although small a.c. signals may be applied across them. They have high inductance. They have high a.c. loss and d.c. leakage and are not very reliable. However, they are used for power supply filtering, decoupling, and signal coupling purposes. Tantalum electrolytic capacitors have a better performance and may be used in more critical applications.

Diodes

The 1N4148 is a general-purpose signal diode with:

Minimum continuous reverse voltage	75 V
Maximum forward current	200 mA
Maximum reverse leakage current at 20 V	25 nA
Maximum capacitance	4 pF

Power diodes are often bought and used in a bridge arrangement. Usually power diodes easily satisfy the properties that are required of them in laboratory use.

Bipolar transistors

There are many general-purpose bipolar transistors that can be used satis-factorily for laboratory purposes. The BC109 (figure A1.3) is intended for low-noise audiofrequency applications, but has high gain, high frequency, and moderate power abilities:

Maximum V_{CE}	20 V
Maximum I_C	200 mA
Maximum P	300 mW
Minimum f_t	300 MHz
Typical h_{fe}, h_{FE}	~900

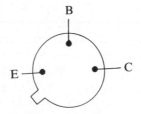

Fig. A1.3   Bottom view of the pins of the BC109.

Junction field-effect transistors

The 2N3819 (figure A1.4) is an n-channel JFET designed to be a general-purpose amplifier as well as an analog switch:

Maximum V_{DS}	25 V
Maximum reverse V_{GS}	−25 V
Maximum I_D	10 mA
Maximum P	200 mW
Minimum g_m	2 mS
Typical r_{on}	200 Ω

Fig. A1.4   Bottom view of the pins of the 2N3819.

Operational amplifiers

741	general-purpose, bipolar input, compensated (figure A1.5)
356	general-purpose, JFET input, compensated, easier to use than the 741 because of lower input current (figure A1.5)
357	uncompensated version of 356
318	high-speed, uncompensated, 15 MHz, 70 V/μs
LM343	high-voltage, 0, $\pm$34 V power supplies
OP-07	high-performance in several parameters
OP-27	low-noise
ICL7600	commutating auto-zero, low offset voltage, noisy
ICL7650	chopper-stabilized, low offset voltage, noisy
LH0002	unity gain, output current booster

Typical Values	*741*	*356*
Unity-gain frequency	1.5 MHz	5.0 MHz
Slew rate	0.5 V/μs	10 V/μs
Input bias current	80 nA	30 pA
Input offset current	20 nA	3 pA
Input offset voltage	1 mV	1 mV
Input impedance	$2 \times 10^6\,\Omega$	$10^{12}\,\Omega$
Common-mode rejection	30 000	100 000
Low-frequency voltage gain	200 000	200 000
Maximum output current	20 mA	20 mA
Supply voltage $V^+ - V^-$	10–36 V	10–36 V

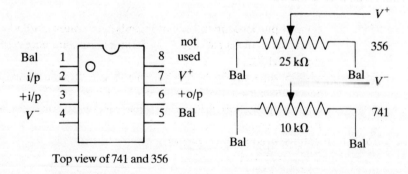

Top view of 741 and 356

Fig. A1.5 Pin notation and offset balance circuits of the 356 and 741 operational amplifiers.

Linear integrated circuits

LM363	instrumentation amplifier
AD524	instrumentation amplifier
CA3080	transconductance amplifier
MC1494	multiplier
AD433	power-law generator
AD536	true r.m.s., or a.c.–d.c. converter
LH0070	voltage reference, 10.000 V
ZN423	voltage reference, 1.26 V
LM334Z	programmable current source, 1 μA–10 mA
311	comparator, prone to oscillation (figure A1.6)
339	comparator

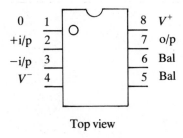

Top view

Fig. A1.6 Pin notation of the 311 comparator.

Timers and oscillators

555	general-purpose timer, oscillator, pulse generator, and other functions as the constituent comparators, etc., are accessible (figure A1.7).
7555	CMOS version of 555, much easier to use than 555 since it needs less current and loads supply less (figure A1.7)
8038	function generator, square, triangle, sine-wave oscillator to 100 kHz, voltage-controlled
LM331	voltage–frequency converter
4024	TTL 25 MHz
4047	CMOS 1 MHz
74LS624	TTL 20 MHz
74S124	TTL 85 MHz

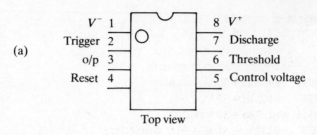

$$4{\cdot}5\,\text{V}<(V^+ - V^-)<18\,\text{V}$$

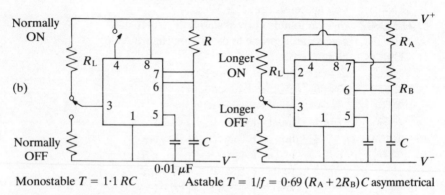

Monostable $T = 1{\cdot}1\,RC$ Astable $T = 1/f = 0{\cdot}69\,(R_A + 2R_B)\,C$ asymmetrical

Fig. A1.7 Pin notation for 555 and 7555 timers (a) and example circuits for monostable and astable multivibrators (b).

Signal-processing integrated circuits

    LF398   sample and hold
    GAP-01   analog processing circuit, switched amplifiers plus com-
                  parator for PSD, rectifier, etc.
    DAC0800   multiplying eight-bit digital–analog converter

Voltage regulators

Three-terminal regulator integrated circuits. Fixed voltage of xx volts:

    78xx or 340T-xx series: positive xx volts
    79xx or 320T-xx series: negative xx volts

for example

μA78MO5HC	+5 V, 0.5 A
μA7805UC	+5 V, 1.0 A
LM340T-5	+5 V, 1.0 A
μA7815UC	+15 V, 1.0 A
LM340T-15	+15 V, 1.0 A

μA7915UC -15 V, 1.0 A
LM320T-15 -15 V, 1.0 A

Variable voltage

LM317H $+1.2$ to $+37$ V, 0.5 A
LM317T $+1.2$ to $+37$ V, 1.5 A
LM337H -1.2 to -37 V, 0.5 A
LM337T -1.2 to -37 V, 1.5 A

Logic gates

CMOS	TTL	
4001	74-02	quad two-input NOR
4011	74-00	quad two-input NAND
4070	74-86	quad two-input XOR
4069	74-04	hex inverter
40106	74-14	hex inverting Schmitt trigger
4049	–	hex inverter and CMOS–TTL interface
4585	74-85	four-bit magnitude comparator
4028	74-42	BCD-decimal (1 of 10) decoder
4511	74-48	BCD-7 segment decoder
4013	74-74	dual D-type flip-flop
4043	–	quad R–S flip-flop
4027	74-109	dual J–K flip-flop
4018	–	divide-by-N counter (2 through 10)
4029	–	divide-by-10 or 16 counter (up/down)
4014	74-91	eight-stage shift register
565	74-297	phase-locked loop
4046	74-297	phase-locked loop
4052	–	dual four-input analog multiplexer
4066	–	quad analog or digital switch
DG304	–	dual analog switch SPST
DG305	–	dual analog switch SPDT
DG306	–	dual analog switch DPST
DG307	–	dual analog switch SPDT

TTL subfamilies have gate power and switching speeds as follows:

74xx	10 mW	35 MHz	original TTL high power
74LSxx	2 mW	45 MHz	low power, fast
74ALSxx	1 mW	50 MHz	improved LS
74Sxx	20 mW	75 MHz	fast
74Fxx	4 mW	115 MHz	very fast, low power

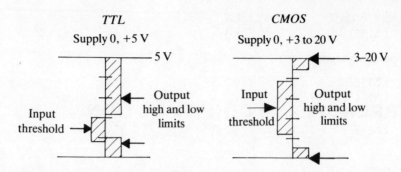

Fig. A1.8 The specified logic levels for TTL and CMOS logic circuits. The acceptable ranges of values are shown shaded and typical values are indicated with arrows. All unused inputs must be connected to logic 0 or 1. Unused TTL inputs float to logic 1.

There are also CMOS subfamilies that have different speeds. As well as the 4xxx series, there are the 74Cxxx and 74HCxxx series, which are CMOS devices that simulate the equivalent TTL devices.

The B-suffix version has protection and high output power and is usually used. CMOS is prone to damage by static electricity so that care must be taken in handling it. Significant power is dissipated only while the gates are switching. It can be run at 0, +5 V to be compatible with TTL, but is then rather slow.

APPENDIX 2   CONSTRUCTION TECHNIQUES

INTRODUCTION

The way a circuit is actually constructed can affect its performance, its reliability, and the ease by which it can be repaired and modified by the designer or someone who has to use the circuit later.

SOLDERING

The most common fault in a circuit is a poorly soldered joint. At worst the joint makes no electrical contact so that all or part of the circuit does not work. In a sensitive part of the circuit a joint with a large resistance can have a severe effect. Often in this case the resistance fluctuates with time so that a random noise voltage signal is produced in the circuit if a current flows through the joint. The intensity spectrum of such a signal often has a $1/f$ dependence. Poor-quality joints are not always easy to detect, so that a good strategy is to ensure that all joints are good initially. The importance of a good soldering technique cannot be overstressed.

The items to be soldered should be clean and bright. Most components now have gold, silver or solder coatings which do not tarnish but components with poor surfaces should be 'tinned' by melting a thin layer of liquid solder over the surface and ensuring that the layer is smooth and continuous by wiping it when hot with a damp cloth or sponge or chemically cleaning it with a flux. For soldering, the iron should have a controlled temperature or have a physical size and power input such that the job will be heated up to a temperature sufficient to melt the solder in one or two seconds. Solder guns are normally too powerful. The tip of the iron should be clean, bright, and shiny, with a thin, continuous layer of molten solder on it.

The components to be soldered should be held firmly together. For a permanent join, or one that may be subject to vibration or other forces, a good mechanical joint should be made. If, however, the joint may need to be unsoldered and will only be used in a laboratory environment, then the solder may be used for the mechanical as well as the electrical joint. However, it should be emphasized that extreme care must be taken that the components do not move while the solder is hardening since then the solder may crystallize and create a very bad-quality joint. The tip of the iron is then held onto the joint and the solder is melted onto the components, rather than the iron. Sufficient solder is needed on the iron to make good thermal contact. The iron is removed and the joint held still until the solder has hardened. Only sufficient solder just to cover the joint should be used.

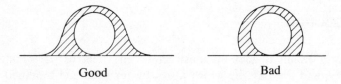

Good   Bad

Fig. A2.1   Schematic diagrams of good and bad soldered joints.

A good joint will have smooth, shiny solder, which appears to flow smoothly onto the components with a small angle of contact as if it 'wets' the component. A bad joint may have a matt, crazed solder surface and appears to ball up on the surface in a 'dry joint'. These are shown in figure A2.1.

A circuit may be constructed in many different ways. Because most active devices have a wide bandwidth, care must be taken in the layout to reduce stray capacitances and pick-up so that the high-frequency performance is not affected and there is insufficient positive feedback to cause oscillation at high frequency. In general, therefore, the circuit should be as compact as possible. However, it is wise to leave sufficient space for later modifications, which are quite common in experimental circuits. There are many proprietary circuit boards that enable the design to be compact. For preliminary circuit evaluation, there are boards with arrays of small sockets so that integrated circuits, transistors, and passive components may be interconnected by just pushing the wire terminations into appropriate sockets. For rapid prototype construction, there are varieties of wire-wrap boards. The terminals here are metal posts with sharp corners which cut through the thin plastic insulation of the interconnecting wires and the pressure is sufficient to make a small cold weld between the terminal and the wire. For reliable construction or mass production, full, soldered, printed circuit techniques are most suitable.

CIRCUIT LAYOUT

The layout of the circuit is important. Fortunately the best and the most logical circuit arrangements both have the signal progressing through the circuit from one side to the other much as the circuit diagram is usually drawn. In this way low-level and high-level signals are usually well separated. In large circuits the signal path may have to be folded or there may be several distinct subcircuits which have to be placed aside from the main signal path. Then care must be taken that there is no possibility of pick-up between these parts of the circuit. This is the most troublesome at high frequencies and with low-level signals. Pick-up has been described in chapter 4. In some circuits it may be necessary to place subcircuits within separate screened enclosures or to place dividing screens between sensitive sections. In these cases care should be taken that no earth loops are created. Even if the board layout is good, the input and output terminals of the whole circuit may be placed adjacent on the front panel and then the output lead has to be taken from the back of the circuit board to the front panel and the input lead kept short. In this case, the cable should be screened. In large circuits, signals that are common to several boards may be distributed by multiple parallel wires and multi-way connectors. Care should be taken that the signals on adjacent wires will not interact, since the mutual inductance and capacitance may be considerable for long parallel wires.

Although earth loops and capacitive coupling most often cause problems, there can also be magnetic coupling if there are inductors and transformers in the circuit. If there is a likelihood of coupling between the magnetic flux, the coils should be magnetically screened, located far apart, and their optimum relative orientation determined. Similarly there can be thermal feedback and degradation of the circuit performance if any high power dissipation devices are located near thermally sensitive parts of the circuit.

A good construction technique is to use a *groundplane*. Here the circuit earth is made a continuous plane adjacent to the circuit board. This is most easily accomplished with double-sided printed circuit board in which one side is reserved for the ground. All unused conductors on a printed circuit board can also be earthed. In this way the earth lead has low resistance and inductance so that earth-loop effects are reduced, there is also good screening between circuits so that mutual capacitance is reduced, and there is large capacitance to earth to improve power line decoupling. For high frequencies, the groundplane technique approaches a strip-line construction.

Mutual interaction between circuits can take place along the power supply lines if they are not perfect constant-voltage equipotentials. These lines should therefore have low resistance and, for high-frequency or pulse circuits, low inductance. Thick, straight conductors should be used. The lines should also be decoupled at many places to decrease the effective high-frequency output impedance of the power supply. Capacitors of low inductance (say 0.01 μF ceramic disk) should be connected between any positive or negative supply lines and earth on each circuit board, perhaps for each circuit subsection, and sometimes next to a particular integrated circuit. Extra components used in this way are rarely wasted since faults that may be difficult to detect are prevented. On each circuit board a larger decoupling capacitor (say 1–10 μF) may also be added for better low-frequency regulation.

To simplify the construction, testing, and fault finding, a logical wire color coding scheme should be used. Not only should this separate the positive, negative, and earth power leads, but also signal, feedback, input, and output leads. The details are perhaps best left to the individual experimenter and circuit.

HIGH-FREQUENCY CIRCUITS

For circuits in which there is a possibility of some high-frequency signal components, more care must be taken in screening the sections of the circuit. To prevent mutual interference, well screened boxes must be placed round each circuit sub-unit. The high-frequency signals may be led between the boxes along suitably screened cables. Power supply current and other low-frequency signals must be transmitted on conductors that will not pass high frequencies. Suitable low-pass filters may be combined into the leadthrough, where the conductor passes through the screening box wall with a series inductor and capacitors to the box from each side as shown in figure A2.2.

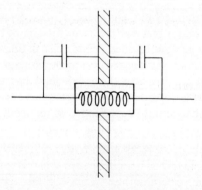

Fig. A2.2   High-frequency signals can be prevented from passing through a screen on a wire by placing a low-pass filter in the lead.

Such circuits produce an impedance mismatch, and hence some reflective loss, as well as low-pass filtering. For less stringent filtering, ferrite beads can be used. These are small beads made of a lossy ferrite material with high permeability. When threaded on a wire, such a bead increases the inductance and high-frequency loss so that high-frequency signals are inhibited from passing along the wire.

Many circuits contain high-frequency signals, often in the form of fast-risetime pulses containing high Fourier components. Pick-up of such signals can be easy. Considerable attention should be given to the control of unwanted high-frequency signals entering a circuit and also leaving a circuit since prevention and cure are both necessary simultaneously. Other high-frequency signal sources are from switched-mode power supplies, sparks, and radio transmitters. The problem is called radiofrequency interference (r.f.i.) or electromagnetic interference (e.m.i.). Good manufacturing practice now requires that all circuits and instruments should be screened to reduce high-frequency emissions to an acceptable level. This is done by enclosing the whole circuits in a screen thicker than the skin depth of the signal in the screen. All holes in the screen should be made smaller across than the wavelength of the radiation and joints should conduct well or be in the form of waveguide chokes. All high-frequency signal cables must be well screened and all power cables must include a high cut-off filter.

CIRCUIT DIAGRAMS

A circuit is not complete without a full diagram and documentation. Copies should be kept on file, given to the user, and perhaps put inside the circuit cabinet itself. Care should be taken to draw the circuit diagram so that it can be easily understood by another person at a later date. Conventional and logical layout should be used so that expected features such as a differential amplifier can be easily recognized. The signal flow should be the conventional left to right and the power supply lines should be suitably spaced vertically to correspond to the relative voltage levels. The circuit earth should be indicated by a single bold horizontal line. The use of earth symbols at isolated places in the circuit and at various vertical levels on the page should be discouraged since the full current flow in the circuit is lost and earth-loop problems may not be recognized.

Diagrams with two or three levels of complexity and detail may be needed for large circuits with perhaps an overall signal block diagram to identify the different operations performed and their sequence. This may also indicate the subcircuits or circuit board layout. The full circuit diagram may be too complex to include the pin number identification on the integrated circuits so it can be kept as a symbolic diagram with triangles for amplifiers, etc. A separate detailed layout diagram can be kept for the details of the wiring with all the power supply connections, screening considerations, and other finer points. An annotated photograph of the circuit can also be useful.

FAULT LOCATION

Considerable skill is needed to discover the fault in a circuit that is not operating correctly. Experience and practice are valuable and refine the technique of fault location, which is a combination of knowledge of what is likely to go wrong and a logical program of testing progressively through the circuit. Considerable economy of effort can be made when experience has been gained of which tests and changes are easy to make and which are more difficult. Thus voltages can be measured more easily than currents or resistances, components can easily be shorted out, resistances easily reduced, and capacitances increased with parallel components.

If a circuit does not appear to be operating at all, a logical procedure would be to check the power supply, mains voltage and fuses, d.c. supplies and fuses. At this point it is worth considering whether there is really good evidence that there is a fault since frequently apparent faults do not really exist. Check that any variable controls or switches are set correctly. Check that your trusted test equipment, voltmeters, oscilloscopes, etc., and especially their leads are working correctly. Faulty leads are a frequent problem. If the fault persists, each circuit must be investigated in the most logical way with a test on each subcircuit in some suitable order.

The most frequent problems are bad soldered joints (both making poor contact and shorting between adjacent conductors, especially in printed circuit boards), bad leads, bad connector contacts, and defective components: in order, electrolytic capacitors, integrated circuits, discrete active components, and discrete passive components.

Information on what has failed may be obtained by seeing, smelling or feeling an overheated component. Circuit elements or subcircuits may oscillate (parasitic oscillation). This low-level oscillation may prevent proper operation of this or another part of the circuit. Such oscillations may be discovered by observing the output of the circuit for a change when the oscillation level is altered. Since the oscillation is normally marginal and the feedback is through a small stray capacitance, the level will change significantly when a finger, with its extra loss and capacitance to earth, is moved near the oscillating circuit element. However, beware of high voltages when moving your finger around!

Interference problems may be investigated by physically moving the circuit, inserting extra filters on the mains supply, screening with aluminum foil or breaking any suspected earth loops.

APPENDIX 3 FOURIER SERIES AND TRANSFORMS

INTRODUCTION

The most common representation of a signal is as a time-varying quantity such as a voltage $V(t)$. This perspective is reinforced by the easy observation of this signal using an oscilloscope. However, the same information can be presented by a spectrum $G(\omega)$, and the display and direct measurement of the frequency description of a signal is possible with a spectrum analyzer. Although equivalent information is presented in the display of the signal as a function of time ('in the time domain') and as a function of frequency ('in the frequency domain'), the visualization or analysis of the information may be much easier in one presentation than the other. It is almost only by chance that oscilloscopes were developed before spectrum analyzers and that we are accustomed to think mainly in the time domain. As an example, if a signal with a given waveform in the time domain is passed through a filter, its waveform is changed. It is not easy to characterize the effect of the filter on different waveforms since the change seems to depend a lot on the detailed shape of each input waveform. The analysis is easier if it is made in the frequency domain since the spectrum of the input signal is modified directly by multiplication by the transfer characteristics of the filter at each frequency to give the output spectrum and waveform.

A familiarity with the representations of a signal in both the time and frequency domains will enable a choice to be made of the best way of analyzing a problem.

Fourier analysis relates the information expressed in the time and frequency domains. For repetitive signals, Fourier series are used, while for non-repetitive signals, the mathematical technique is the Fourier transform. The same principles and mathematical techniques also hold between any pair of variables with reciprocal dimensions, here time and $(\text{time})^{-1}$. Another common Fourier pair is the variation with distance and the spatial frequency.

FOURIER SERIES

If $f(t)$ is a signal that repeats in time T, or has a repetition frequency $1/T$ or angular repetition frequency $\omega_0 = 2\pi/T$, then it can be represented as a sum of sine and cosine waves at this frequency and harmonics or multiples of this frequency. There are several equivalent ways of expressing this:

$$f(t) = \sum_{n=0}^{\infty} (a_n \cos n\omega_0 t + b_n \sin n\omega_0 t) \tag{A3.1}$$

$$= \sum_{n=0}^{\infty} c_n \cos(n\omega_0 + \phi_n) \tag{A3.2}$$

$$= \sum_{n=0}^{\infty} d_n \sin(n\omega_0 t + \theta_n) \tag{A3.3}$$

$$= \sum_{n=-\infty}^{\infty} g_n \exp(+jn\omega_0 t) \tag{A3.4}$$

In each representation there is a pair of coefficients for each term (n value). These can be evaluated using the integrals

$$a_0 = \frac{1}{T} \int_{t}^{t+T} f(t)\, dt \tag{A3.5}$$

$$a_n = c_n \cos\phi_n = d_n \sin\theta_n$$

$$= g_n + g_{-n} = \frac{2}{T} \int_{t}^{t+T} f(t)\cos n\omega_0 t\, dt \qquad \text{for } n \geq 1 \tag{A3.6}$$

$$b_n = -c_n \sin\phi_n = d_n \cos\theta_n$$

$$= j(g_n - g_{-n}) = \frac{2}{T} \int_{t}^{t+T} f(t)\sin n\omega_0 t\, dt \qquad \text{for } n \geq 1 \tag{A3.7}$$

$$g_n = \frac{1}{T} \int_{t}^{t+T} f(t)\exp(-jn\omega_0 t)\, dt \qquad \text{for all } n \tag{A3.8}$$

From these we have the relations (for $n \geq 1$):

$$g_n = \tfrac{1}{2}(a_n - jb_n)$$

$$g_{-n} = \tfrac{1}{2}(a_n + jb_n)$$

$$c_n^2 = d_n^2 = a_n^2 + b_n^2 = 4g_n g_{-n}$$

$$\tan\phi_n = -b_n/a_n \qquad \tan\theta_n = a_n/b_n$$

It can be seen that the apparent use of negative frequencies ($n < 0$) in (A3.4) is just a mathematical manipulation which expresses the sine and cosine components in a different way.

For a given waveform the actual series can be simplified if a suitable choice of the time origin is taken. Then the integrals can be made simple and the series will have fewer non-zero coefficients. For example, if $t = 0$ is chosen so that the waveform is symmetrical about this point $V(t) = V(-t)$, then all the sine terms will vanish. Similarly if $V(t) = -V(-t)$, then all the cosine terms are zero. The coefficient a_0 is the mean time average or d.c. value of the waveform. The Fourier series of some common waveforms are shown in figure A3.1. Note that between figures A3.1(a) and (b) the time origin has been changed so that one waveform is symmetrical and the other asymmetrical. This results in series and spectra that are less similar than might be expected from the similarity of the time traces.

FOURIER TRANSFORMS

For a non-repetitive signal the mathematical process for changing between the signal $V(t)$ in the time domain and its spectrum $G(\omega)$, or Fourier transform, in the frequency domain is the Fourier integral. A similar integral exists for the reverse transform:

$$V(t) = \frac{1}{2\pi} \int_{-\infty}^{\infty} G(\omega)\exp(j\omega t)\,d\omega \qquad (A3.9)$$

$$G(\omega) = \int_{-\infty}^{\infty} V(t)\exp(-j\omega t)\,dt \qquad (A3.10)$$

Examples of common waveforms and their transforms are given in figure A3.2.

An understanding of the effect of the transform operation is valuable in relating a waveform to its spectrum. In figure A3.2, negative and positive

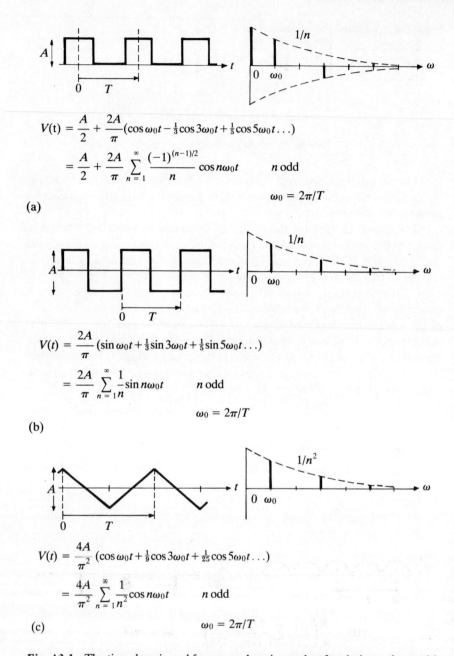

$$V(t) = \frac{A}{2} + \frac{2A}{\pi}(\cos \omega_0 t - \tfrac{1}{3}\cos 3\omega_0 t + \tfrac{1}{5}\cos 5\omega_0 t \ldots)$$

$$= \frac{A}{2} + \frac{2A}{\pi}\sum_{n=1}^{\infty}\frac{(-1)^{(n-1)/2}}{n}\cos n\omega_0 t \qquad n \text{ odd}$$

$$\omega_0 = 2\pi/T$$

(a)

$$V(t) = \frac{2A}{\pi}(\sin \omega_0 t + \tfrac{1}{3}\sin 3\omega_0 t + \tfrac{1}{5}\sin 5\omega_0 t \ldots)$$

$$= \frac{2A}{\pi}\sum_{n=1}^{\infty}\frac{1}{n}\sin n\omega_0 t \qquad n \text{ odd}$$

$$\omega_0 = 2\pi/T$$

(b)

$$V(t) = \frac{4A}{\pi^2}(\cos \omega_0 t + \tfrac{1}{9}\cos 3\omega_0 t + \tfrac{1}{25}\cos 5\omega_0 t \ldots)$$

$$= \frac{4A}{\pi^2}\sum_{n=1}^{\infty}\frac{1}{n^2}\cos n\omega_0 t \qquad n \text{ odd}$$

$$\omega_0 = 2\pi/T$$

(c)

Fig. A3.1 The time domain and frequency domain graphs of typical waveforms: (a) a positive-only square wave; (b) a symmetrical square wave; (c) a triangular wave; (d) a saw-tooth wave; (e) a repetitive delta function; (f) a half-wave rectified sine wave; (g) a full-wave rectified sine wave.

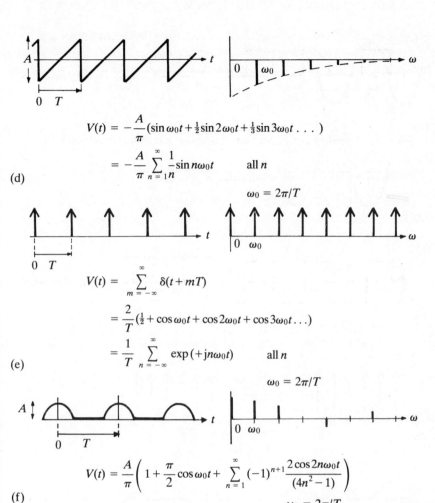

$$V(t) = -\frac{A}{\pi}(\sin \omega_0 t + \tfrac{1}{2}\sin 2\omega_0 t + \tfrac{1}{3}\sin 3\omega_0 t \dots)$$

(d)
$$= -\frac{A}{\pi}\sum_{n=1}^{\infty}\frac{1}{n}\sin n\omega_0 t \qquad \text{all } n$$

$$\omega_0 = 2\pi/T$$

$$V(t) = \sum_{m=-\infty}^{\infty}\delta(t+mT)$$

$$= \frac{2}{T}(\tfrac{1}{2} + \cos \omega_0 t + \cos 2\omega_0 t + \cos 3\omega_0 t \dots)$$

(e)
$$= \frac{1}{T}\sum_{n=-\infty}^{\infty}\exp(+jn\omega_0 t) \qquad \text{all } n$$

$$\omega_0 = 2\pi/T$$

$$V(t) = \frac{A}{\pi}\left(1 + \frac{\pi}{2}\cos \omega_0 t + \sum_{n=1}^{\infty}(-1)^{n+1}\frac{2\cos 2n\omega_0 t}{(4n^2 - 1)}\right)$$

(f)
$$\omega_0 = 2\pi/T$$

$$V(t) = \frac{A}{\pi}\left(2 - \sum_{n=1}^{\infty}\frac{4\cos 2n\omega_0 t}{(4n^2 - 1)}\right) \qquad \omega_0 = 2\pi/T$$

(g)

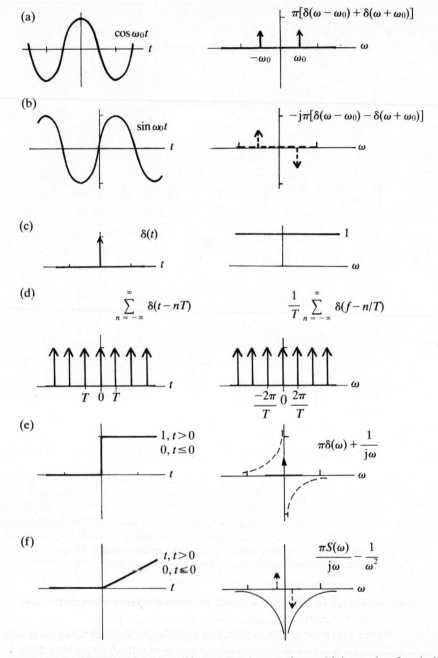

Fig. A3.2 The time domain, $V(t)$, and Fourier transform, $G(\omega)$, graphs of typical waveforms: (a) a cosine wave; (b) a sine wave; (c) a single delta function; (d) a repetitive delta function; (e) a step function; (f) a ramp function; (g) a Gaussian pulse; (h) a square pulse; (i) a triangular pulse.

(g)

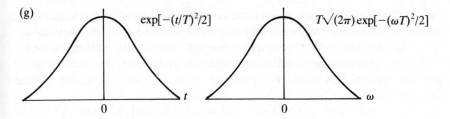

$$\exp[-(t/T)^2/2]$$

$$T\sqrt{(2\pi)}\exp[-(\omega T)^2/2]$$

(h)

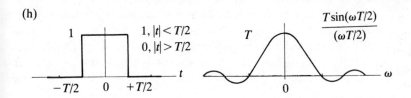

$$1, |t| < T/2$$
$$0, |t| > T/2$$

$$\frac{T\sin(\omega T/2)}{(\omega T/2)}$$

(i)

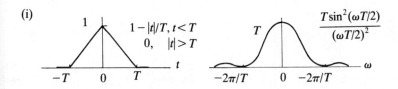

$$1 - |t|/T, t < T$$
$$0, \quad |t| > T$$

$$\frac{T\sin^2(\omega T/2)}{(\omega T/2)^2}$$

frequencies are shown. The cosine and sine wave signals of figures A3.2(a) and (b) are repetitive and have simple delta function transforms corresponding to single spectral components. The Gaussian curve shown in figure A3.2(g) is the function that transforms into the same shape. Since the variables t and ω are reciprocally related, the widths of the time pulse and the peak in the spectrum are inversely related; a short pulse has a wide spectrum, etc. This is also apparent in figures A3.2(h) and (i). As the pulse becomes sharper through the sequence of figures A3.2(g), (i), (h), the spectrum develops more oscillations. Since the transform integral and its inverse involve similar operations, the sketches shown for $V(t)$ and $G(\omega)$ could be interchanged with suitable scaling. Thus a time-domain waveform with a shape like the curve on the right-hand side of figure A3.2(h) has a spectrum that has a very sharp cut-off like the graph on the left-hand side.

The delta function impulse of figure A3.2(c) has a constant-amplitude spectrum at all frequencies. In practice a pulse would have a non-zero width so that the spectrum would have a finite extent. The repetitive delta function of figure A3.2(d) has a repetitive delta function spectrum as seen in figure

A3.1(e). Two common asymmetrical waveforms are shown in figures A3.2(e) and (f), together with their transforms.

Transform pairs have properties that enable the simple transform pairs to be used to generate the transforms of more complex waveforms. If two time signals are added, then their spectra add:

$$AV_1(t) + BV_2(t) = AG_1(\omega) + BG_2(\omega) \tag{A3.11}$$

If the signal is enlarged in time, it contracts in frequency:

$$V(kT) = \frac{1}{|k|} G(\omega/k) \tag{A3.12}$$

A modulation of a sine wave at ω_0 produces a shift of the spectrum of the modulation waveform $V(t)$ from $\omega = 0$ to $\omega = \pm\omega_0$:

$$V(t)\exp(\pm j\omega_0 t) = G(\omega \pm \omega_0) \tag{A3.13}$$

If a time signal is differentiated, then the spectrum is multiplied by $(j\omega)$:

$$\frac{d^n}{dt^n} V(t) = (j\omega)^n G(\omega) \tag{A3.14}$$

If two signals are multiplied, then the spectra of the signals are convolved:

$$V_1(t) \times V_2(t) = \int_{-\infty}^{\infty} G_1(\omega_1) G_2(\omega - \omega_1)\, d\omega_1 \equiv \int_{-\infty}^{\infty} G_1(\omega - \omega_1) G_2(\omega_1)\, d\omega_1$$

This operation is perhaps more often used in the inverse. If the spectrum $G(\omega)$ of a signal $V_1(t)$ is modified by passing through a filter with response $H(\omega)$, then the output signal $V_2(t)$ will have a spectrum $G(\omega) H(\omega)$ so that V_2 can be found from the Fourier transform integral of this spectrum.

CONVOLUTION

The signal can be evaluated in another way by the operation of convolution, which is described by

$$V_2(t) = \int_{-\infty}^{\infty} V_1(\tau) h(t - \tau)\, d\tau \equiv \int_{-\infty}^{\infty} h(\tau) V_1(t - \tau)\, d\tau$$

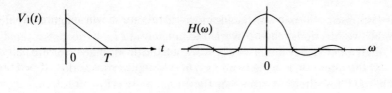

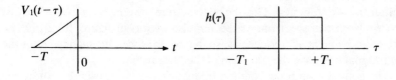

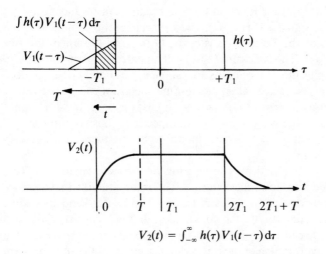

$$V_2(t) = \int_{-\infty}^{\infty} h(\tau) V_1(t-\tau) \, d\tau$$

Fig. A3.3 The construction of the convolution $V_2(t)$ of the function $V_1(t)$.

where $V_1(t)$, $G(\omega)$ and $h(t)$, $H(\omega)$ are transform pairs. The operation of convolution expressed in the above integral involves the integration of the product of two functions as one is moved relative to the other. This is shown in figure A3.3.

Consider a triangular pulse $V_1(t)$ applied to a filter with a transfer function $H(\omega)$. The output signal $V_2(t)$ will be the convolution of V_1 with the Fourier transform, $h(t)$, of $H(\omega)$ which is taken to be a square response. For each value of t the integral is calculated of $h(\tau)$ multiplied with $V_1(t-\tau)$, the time function reversed and displaced. The result is zero until the sharp rise of $V_1(t-\tau)$ overlaps with $h(\tau)$ at $t = -T$. Then the response is a slope that decreases as the smaller part of V_1 becomes multiplied with $h(\tau)$. There is a flat response as the narrow triangle moves to become totally enclosed by $h(\tau)$. As the two functions cease to overlap completely at $2T_1$, V_2 decreases rapidly, but then more slowly until $t = 2T_1 + T$ when the product goes to zero.

If the filter is very wide-band then $h(\tau)$ is very narrow and $V_2(t) = V_1(t)$. Similarly if the filter is narrow then the output pulse is low and stretched out.

A particular case of a filter response is when the input signal is an impulse or delta function. The output time response is then the Fourier transform of the filter transfer function. This can be seen from the convolution analysis just given or from the spectrum of the impulse shown in figure A3.2(c). The spectrum is equal at all frequencies, so that when passed through the filter the output signal will have the spectrum of the filter response.

The convolution process in the frequency domain is useful to study the product of two time functions, which occurs in amplitude modulation. As an example, if a slow time function $V_1(t)$ modulates a faster function $V_2(t)$, then the combined signal is $V_1(t) V_2(t)$. The spectrum of this combined signal is the convolution of the Fourier transforms, $G_1(\omega)$ and $G_2(\omega)$, of the functions $V_1(t)$ and $V_2(t)$. The spectrum $G_2(\omega)$ will be narrower than that of $G_1(\omega)$. In many examples the convolutions are simple to evaluate. For example, if both signals are cosine waves at ω_1 and ω_2, the spectrum consists of two pairs of delta functions at $\pm(\omega_2 \pm \omega_1)$ as seen in chapter 6. If the slow signal $V_1(t)$ modulates a cosine wave at ω_2 then the spectrum consists of the spectrum of $V_1(t)$ centered at $\pm\omega_2$. This corresponds to the frequency shift described by equation (A3.13).

If $V_2(t)$ is the repetitive sampling function shown in figure A3.2(d), it can be modulated by a slow function $V_1(t)$. This is the situation that occurs when a signal is sampled as a time series as described in chapter 9 and appendix 5. The sampled spectrum will be the convolution and will consist of the spectrum $G_1(\omega)$ of $V_1(t)$ centered on each of the harmonics of the spectrum $G_2(\omega)$ of $V_2(\omega)$. The overlapping of these individual sections of the spectrum when the width of $G_1(\omega)$ is larger than the spacing produces aliasing effects.

FURTHER READING

R. Bracewell, *The Fourier Transform and its Applications*, McGraw-Hill (1965).

D. C. Champeney, *Fourier Transforms and their Physical Applications*, Academic Press (1973).

APPENDIX 4   CORRELATION

INTRODUCTION

The correlation process is valuable for signal processing and enables much information to be recovered when it is mixed with other signals. The basic correlation integrals have been given in chapter 9.

The *autocorrelation function* of a signal $V_A(t)$ is

$$C_{AA}(t) = \frac{1}{t_1} \int_0^{t_1} V_A(t) V_A(t-\tau) d\tau \qquad (A4.1)$$

and the *cross-correlation function* of two signals $V_A(t)$ and $V_B(t)$ is

$$C_{AB}(\tau) = \frac{1}{t_1} \int_0^{t_1} V_A(t) V_B(t-\tau) d\tau \qquad (A4.2)$$

Here t_1 is a time that is long compared with any significant signal period. For some signals one may have to calculate the limit of the integral as $t_1 \rightarrow \infty$.

AUTOCORRELATION

The construction of the autocorrelation integral can be seen in figure A4.1. The function is multiplied by itself displaced by an amount τ and the integral of this product is evaluated. This produces a value of the autocorrelation for this value of τ to give the function $C_{AA}(\tau)$. The operation has similarities with the convolution integral described in appendix 3, but there one function in the

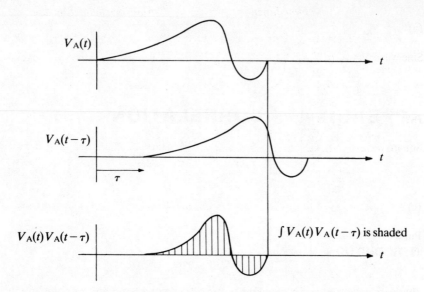

Fig. A4.1 The evaluation of the autocorrelation function is shown for the waveform $V_A(t)$. The shaded area is the correlation integral.

product is reversed in time. A circuit for performing the operation electronically is shown in figure A4.2.

Some examples of the autocorrelation function of some common waveforms are shown in figure A4.3.

Some properties of the autocorrelation function are easily seen. The symmetry of the equation is such that the function is even in τ so that the graph for $\tau < 0$ need not be drawn. The function will have a maximum at $\tau = 0$ (there may be others of the same size or smaller) with a value $\overline{V_A^2(t)}$, the mean-square value or intensity, since at each time the signal is multiplied by itself. The autocorrelation function reveals any periodicity within the signal $V_A(t)$ since the mean-square value of any periodic component will be evaluated every time the delay τ is an integral multiple of the period T. Thus the autocorrelation function reveals the intensity of any spectral component and gives the same information as the power spectrum of the signal.

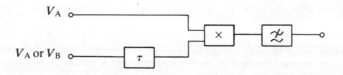

Fig. A4.2 The block diagram of a circuit to evaluate the auto- or cross-correlation functions.

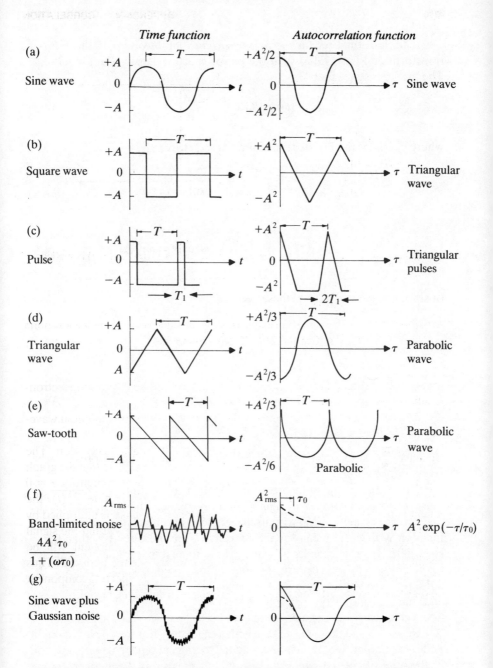

Fig. A4.3 The time domain and autocorrelation functions of some common wave-forms: (a) a sine wave; (b) a square wave; (c) a repetitive pulse; (d) a triangular wave; (e) a saw-tooth wave; (f) band-limited noise; (g) sine wave plus Gaussian noise.

This is formalized in the *Wiener–Khintchine theorem*. If the Fourier transform of $V(t)$ is $G(\omega)$ then the power spectral density $P(\omega) = |G(\omega)|^2$. The theorem states that

$$P(\omega) = |G(\omega)|^2 = c_{AA}(\omega) \tag{A4.3}$$

where $c_{AA}(\omega)$ is the Fourier transform of $C_{AA}(\tau)$ given by

$$c_{AA}(\omega) = \int_{-\infty}^{\infty} C_{AA}(\tau) \exp(-j\omega\tau)\,d\tau \tag{A4.4}$$

$$C_{AA}(\tau) = \frac{1}{2\pi} \int_{-\infty}^{\infty} c_{AA}(\omega) \exp(+j\omega\tau)\,d\omega \tag{A4.5}$$

or since $C_{AA}(\tau) = C_{AA}(-\tau)$ these become

$$c_{AA}(\omega) = 2 \int_{0}^{\infty} C_{AA}(\tau) \cos \omega\tau\,d\tau \tag{A4.6}$$

$$C_{AA}(\tau) = \frac{1}{\pi} \int_{0}^{\infty} c_{AA}(\omega) \cos \omega\tau\,d\omega \tag{A4.7}$$

Because the autocorrelation function involves intensities, it loses relative phase information.

The value of the autocorrelation function for improving the signal-to-noise ratio is illustrated in figure A4.3. A random noise signal has, by definition, no relationship with itself displaced in time. The autocorrelation function is thus the mean-square intensity of the noise for $\tau = 0$ and zero elsewhere. In practice noise will always have some upper frequency limit due to the physical process causing the noise or the circuit in which it exists. If the noise is filtered by a simple RC low-pass filter, then the noise is band-limited and has an intensity spectrum $4A^2\tau_0\,d\omega/[1 + (\omega\tau_0)^2]$ where $1/\tau_0$ is the filter characteristic angular frequency. The autocorrelation function is $A^2 \exp(-\tau/\tau_0)$ and thus goes to zero with a characteristic time displacement of τ_0. It is not repetitive. If the noise is added to a signal repetitive with a period T, the intensity of the signal can be found by measuring the autocorrelation function at T or nT, $C_{AA}(T)$ or $C_{AA}(nT)$. The repetitive signal correlates but not the noise. This is the basic principle behind many signal recovery techniques for repetitive signals and will be enlarged after consideration of the cross-correlation function.

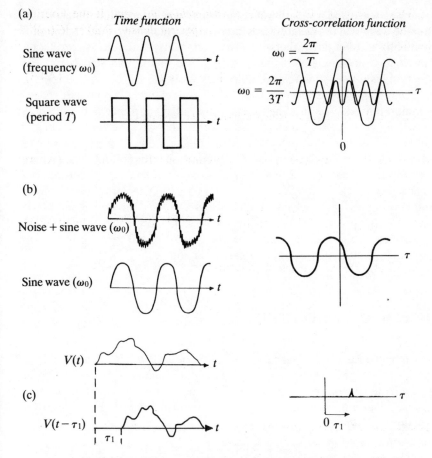

Fig. A4.4 The time domain and cross-correlation functions of pairs of some common functions: (a) sine wave at a frequency ω_0 and a square wave of period T; (b) noise plus a sine wave at a frequency ω_0 and a sine wave at a frequency ω_0; (c) an arbitrary waveform $V(t)$ and the same waveform delayed, $V(t-\tau_1)$.

CROSS-CORRELATION

The cross-correlation function is calculated using the integral of equation (A4.2). The procedure is similar to that described for the autocorrelation function earlier and shown in figure A4.1 but one of the two product functions is V_B. The electronic circuit is also shown in figure A4.2. Two examples of the cross-correlation function are shown in figure A4.4.

The cross-correlation function has the property of revealing any common periodicity between the two signals being correlated. Thus if the two signals are a sine wave and a square wave, the cross-correlation will be sinusoidal if the sine wave is at the square-wave fundamental frequency, or odd harmonics of it, but will be zero otherwise. The periodicity of the cross-correlation function is independent of the relative phase of the two signals but the function is shifted by the relative time delay.

If the signals, which need not be periodic, have a component that is common but is shifted in time in one signal, relative to that in the other as shown in figure A4.4(c), then the cross-correlation will have a maximum at a time equal to this time delay. Then the function equals the mean-square intensity of the common component. The function is thus useful for searching for common signals with a time delay. Examples of this use are for random signals propagating through a medium or a system. Detectors at two separate points produce signals which, when correlated, reveal the propagation time between the points. This is the basis of fluid flow gages which detect turbulence in the flow and in measurements of sound velocity with low-amplitude, continuous, random signals as the source.

OPTIMAL AND MATCHED FILTERS

If a signal consists of the desired signal plus noise, then it is often possible to enhance the signal-to-noise ratio by passing the total signal through a filter that will pass the desired signal more than it passes the noise. There exists an *optimal filter* for maximizing the signal-to-noise ratio. It has a transfer function

$$H(\omega) = P_s(\omega)/[P_s(\omega) + P_n(\omega)] \tag{A4.8}$$

where $P_s(\omega)$ and $P_n(\omega)$ are the power spectra of the signal and the noise. That such a transfer function exists of course does not imply that such a filter can in fact be made, but often a reasonable approximation is possible.

Sometimes the problem is different. All that is required is a large response when a signal of a known shape $V(t)$ is received together with noise. This occurs for example with radar signals. Then all the signal energy has to be bunched to appear at the output at the same time, t_0, to give a large signal-to-noise ratio. In this case a *matched filter* is needed and this has the impulse response

$$h(t) = V(t_0 - t)$$

or the transfer function

$$H(\omega) = V^*(\omega) \exp(-j\omega t_0) \tag{A4.9}$$

Cross-correlation detection also produces an output with high signal-to-noise ratio for a selected input signal. If one input signal to a cross-correlator is the desired signal plus noise and the other is a noiseless reference signal of the waveform that it is desired to detect, as shown in figure A4.4(b), then the cross-correlation function will reveal the common periodicity for each Fourier component and not include the noise. The signal-to-noise ratio is enhanced. Any waveform can be used and, since all the Fourier components of the reference have a suitable amplitude and phase, the correlation signal will have a maximum at a time delay τ when the signal and reference are in phase. This is the principle behind the phase-sensitive detector (chapter 6). In that example the input signal is a sine or square wave of constant amplitude. The relative phase is shifted to change τ until the signals are in phase and the correlator output is a maximum.

CEPSTRUM ANALYSIS

Cepstrum ('spectrum' rewritten) analysis is signal analysis using the cepstrum function $C_P(\tau)$, which is the Fourier transform of $\log P(\omega)$, where $P(\omega)$ is the power spectrum of the signal $V(t)$. If the Fourier transform of $V(t)$ is $G(\omega)$, then $P(\omega) = |G(\omega)|^2$. From equation (A4.3) we have $P(\omega) = |G(\omega)|^2 = c_{xx}(\omega)$, so that the cepstrum function is the Fourier transform of $\log P(\omega)$ whereas the autocorrelation function is the Fourier transform of $P(\omega)$.

The advantage of cepstrum analysis is that the addition of the logs of functions represents the product of the functions themselves. Consider as an example a filter with response $H(\omega)$ so that $G_2(\omega) = G_1(\omega) H(\omega)$ where $G_1(\omega)$ is the spectrum of the input function $V_1(t)$ and $G_2(\omega)$ is the spectrum of the output function $V_2(t)$. The time function $V_2(t)$ is the convolution of $V_1(t)$ and $h(t)$, where $h(t)$ is the Fourier transform of $H(\omega)$. Now $\log G_2(\omega) = \log G_1(\omega) + \log H(\omega)$ or, squaring, $P_2(\omega) = P_1(\omega)|H(\omega)|^2$ and

$$\log P_2(\omega) = \log P_1(\omega) + 2\log H(\omega)$$

Since Fourier transforms of functions add if the functions themselves add, the Fourier transform of this last equation leads to

$$C_{P_2}(\tau) = C_{P_1}(\tau) + 2C_{P_H}(\tau)$$

Thus deconvolution in the time domain can be achieved by subtraction of the cepstrum functions if either P_2 or H is known. This log function has practical advantages since the dynamic range is less than for a linear function. It is of particular value in the identification of periodicities in the spectrum of a signal such as those caused by reflections or echoes.

FURTHER READING

D. C. Champeney, *Fourier Transforms and their Physical Applications*, Academic Press (1973).

E. B. Magrab and D. S. Blomquist, *The Measurement of Time-Varying Phenomena*, Wiley (1971).

R. B. Randall and J. Hee, 'Cepstrum analysis', *Wireless World*, February (1982).

APPENDIX 5   TIME-SERIES ANALYSIS

INTRODUCTION

With the readily accessible power of the digital computer, signals can be processed digitally. Once the signal has been converted into a set of numbers, many forms of mathematical processing are possible. The basic technique is to acquire the signal with an analog–digital converter (ADC; chapter 8). This inevitably leads to loss of information because of the limited quantization resolution, accuracy, and speed of response. Care must therefore be taken that these are sufficient in a given system for the purpose required. Usually the ADC is operated at a fixed speed f_s so that the analog signal is sampled at regular periods $1/f_s$ and a set of voltage values are produced corresponding to the signal at times n/f_s for $0 < n < N$.

This set of data, a time series, can be used to calculate many quantities: the time series may be stored, smoothed, differentiated, filtered or successive repetitions averaged, etc. The spectrum of the time series may be calculated by Fourier transformation and this spectrum stored, smoothed, differentiated, filtered or successive repetitions averaged, etc. Other functions such as correlation functions may also be computed. With dedicated computers these operations and others may be available at a single command. The limitations of the basic process must be understood if the most benefit is to be obtained.

SAMPLING

The *sampling theorem* states that:

To reproduce a signal with a Fourier component at a frequency f, the sampling rate f_s must be at least $2f$ ($f_s \geq 2f$).

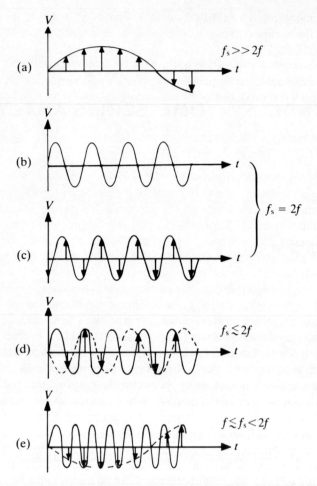

Fig. A5.1 Sampling of a sine wave at a frequency f. In (a) the sampling frequency f_s is much higher than $2f$ and the samples will reproduce the original waveform faithfully. If $f_s = 2f$ the reconstructed signal will be ambiguous and depend on the relative phases of the sample and input signals as shown in (b) and (c). If the sampling rate is slow so that $f_s < 2f$ then the signal can be reconstructed at a low frequency, shown in broken lines in (d) and (e).

The factor of 2 can be said to arise because both the amplitude and phase information are needed.

The signal and sampling periods are shown in figure A5.1. If the sampling rate is very fast as in figure A5.1(a) the signal is well reproduced. If the sampling rate $f_s = 2f$ as in figures A5.1(b) and (c) then the resulting time series will be ambiguous since it will depend on the relative phase of the signal and the sampling pulses. Also the signal would naturally be reconstructed from the time series as a z.f. (d.c.) signal. In figures A5.1(d) and (e) it can be seen that the sampled signal would sensibly be reconstructed at a lower frequency if $f_s < 2f$.

This incorrect reproduction of the signal for sampling rates that are too low has considerable consequences. Not only is the signal not reproduced correctly but it is reproduced as if it were another signal. This process is called *aliasing*.

A signal at frequency f, sampled at a rate f_s, will be reproduced as a signal at $f - f_s$ if $f_s < 2f$.

The logical reproduction process is to fit as low a frequency (or smoothest) curve through the sampled points as possible. From figures A5.1(d) and (e) it can be seen that a false result will be produced. To prevent this effect, an anti-alias filter is needed before the sampling operation so that no significant signal frequency components remain at frequencies above $f_s/2$. Since filters have a finite transition region between pass and stop, the low-pass anti-alias filter has to have a characteristic frequency near $f_s/4$ or $f_s/8$ so that the attenuation at f_s is sufficient to reduce any signal to below the ADC detection limit.

The sampling theorem and the aliasing problem can be understood in relation to the spectra of the sampling pulses shown in figure A3.2(d). Since it is a repetitive signal, the spectrum contains components at all harmonics. Since each sampling signal is a delta function that contains all frequencies equally (see figure A3.2(c)), all the harmonics have equal size. The pulses of the sampled signal are not delta functions with infinite height but are modulated by the signal. In the frequency domain each spectral delta function is changed to the individual spectrum of the modulating signal. Thus for a sampled sine wave at f shown in figure A5.2 the Fourier components develop sidebands at $nf_s \pm f$. If $f_s = 2f$ the sidebands from adjacent harmonics coincide and overlap if $f_s < 2f$. Since there is no way of identifying to which harmonic a sideband really belongs, there is ambiguity if $f_s < 2f$, hence the sampling theorem result. If the sideband is automatically related to the

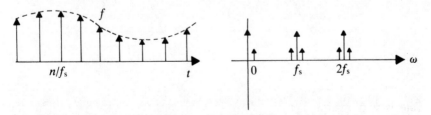

Fig. A5.2   A sine wave at a frequency f is sampled at a frequency f_s. The spectrum consists of the spectrum of the sample pulses at f_s and all harmonics and sidebands at $\pm f$ relative to each harmonic.

nearest harmonic, then it will be reproduced as a signal at $|f - nf_s|$ where n is the harmonic number that will give a minimum frequency of reproduction. This is the aliasing theorem result. The sampling process is the multiplication of the sampling delta functions with the signal to be sampled. Since the delta functions contain signals at all Fourier components, this is an example of the modulation process introduced in chapter 6.

The problems of sampling and aliasing arise from the finite sampling rate. Other problems arise at low frequencies because of the finite period over which the samples are taken and hence the finite number of samples. For many purposes, especially when the spectrum is involved, the computation on the time series is on a finite number, say N, consecutive samples taken over a time period N/f_s. This finite time interval limits the lowest frequency that can be reproduced to f_s/N. The calculation does not involve any data for times outside this time interval and hence the result cannot reflect the behavior of the signal at those times.

FAST FOURIER TRANSFORM

The usual computational procedure, or algorithm, used to compute the Fourier transform is the fast Fourier transform (FFT). This procedure only involves $N \log_2 N$ calculations whereas there are N^2 if a full Fourier transform

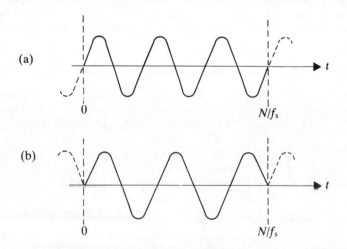

Fig. A5.3   In the calculation of the FFT it is assumed that the N sample pulses, taken over a time N/f_s, represent a sample of a signal that repeats every N/f_s seconds. For the sine-wave signal shown in (a) this is true but if the sine-wave sample shown in (b) is assumed to repeat, the calculated spectrum will not be the desired single frequency.

calculation is done. For N sampled points it produces $N/2$ discrete frequency spectral terms. A discrete spectrum is derived from a discrete time series. As part of the simplification in the calculation it is assumed that the time signal over the period N/f_s repeats indefinitely. This may lead to errors if this is not in fact true. The differences between the shape of the assumed repetitive waveforms shown in figures A5.3(a) and (b) are very apparent and the extra cusps in figure A5.3(b) are not realistic and will introduce extra high-frequency components. Thus an erroneous spectrum will be produced by the assumption.

This problem is called truncation or windowing. To reduce it, the amplitude of the time samples is artificially reduced smoothly to zero at each end of the sample block by multiplying the actual block of data by a function that is equal to unity over most of the time but decreases to zero at each end. This is not necessary for transient signals which themselves reach zero at each end if they are totally contained within the time period. If no artificial window function is used then a 'uniform window' is assumed. A commonly used window is the 'Hanning function'. For high accuracy of amplitude measurements a 'flat-top window' is used which simulates a flat pass-band filter.

DIGITAL FILTERS

Signal fitering can be readily performed in the frequency domain by modification of the spectrum. Consider, for example, a signal with a large unwanted interfering component at 100 Hz. The spectrum can be calculated by a Fourier transform, the amplitude at 100 Hz reduced to zero, or perhaps to an average of the adjacent frequency amplitudes, and then the signal reformed into the time domain by another Fourier transform. From this example it is apparent that more complex filter functions may be achieved by the appropriate weighting of the amplitude and phase of each component of the frequency-domain signal. Since the spectrum data have to be derived from the original time-series data, it should be unnecessary to go through all the stages of transform. All that is necessary is that each individual output time signal element be constructed from a suitable combination of the corresponding input signal element and contributions from other signal elements at other times.

If we designate the particular time sample by n then the time series at the filter output, $V_2(n)$, can be derived from the input time series $V_1(n)$ by

$$V_2(n) = a_0 V_1(n) + a_1 V_1(n-1) + a_2 V_1(n-2) + \ldots \qquad (A5.1)$$

This is a *non-recursive filter, finite impulse response* (FIR) *filter* or *transversal filter* and represents a weighted sum of all previous inputs. These inputs have been delayed in time by integral amounts. Because of the delay nature of these filters, and the time taken for the computation, the output signal is not a real-time function of the input.

The non-recursive formula is not efficient since it requires, in general, an infinite number of terms. Often the computation can be simplified by using a previous output signal. Each previous output signal contains considerable suitable information since it has been derived from previous input samples. *Recursive filters* or *infinite impulse response* (IIR) *filters* use a weighted sum of both input and output data. Thus

$$V_2(n) = [a_0 V_1(n) + a_1 V_1(n-1) + a_2 V_1(n-2) + \ldots]$$

$$- [b_1 V_2(n-1) + b_2 V_2(n-2) + \ldots] \qquad (A5.2)$$

A schematic circuit is shown in figure A5.4 for either the digital or analog computation.

A simple example of a digital filter is a smoothing operation (low-pass filtering) for producing a running average of a data stream. Then one might have, for a three-point average

$$V_2(n) = \frac{1}{2c_2 + c_1} [c_2 V_1(n-1) + c_1 V_1(n) + c_2 V_1(n+1) \qquad (A5.3)$$

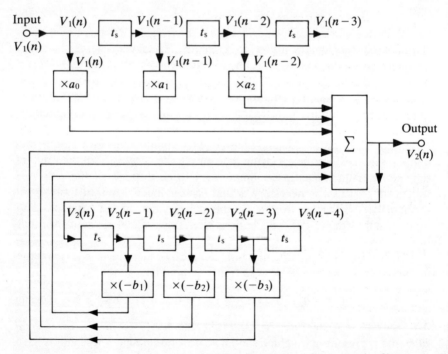

Fig. A5.4. Schematic circuit, or computational procedure, for a recursive filter.

or for a five-point average

$$V_2(n) = \frac{1}{2c_3 + 2c_2 + c_1}[c_3 V_1(n-2) + c_2 V_1(n-1) + c_1 V_1(n)$$

$$+ c_2 V_1(n+1) + c_3 V_1(n+2)] \qquad (A5.4)$$

and in general $c_1 > c_2 > c_3$.

The analysis of such a system illustrates an important calculation for sampled systems. If the input signal is sampled at discrete, regular, intervals we have

$$V_1(t) = x(0)\delta(t) + x(1)\delta(t - t_s) + x(2)\delta(t - 2t_s) + \ldots \qquad (A5.5)$$

which can be Fourier-transformed using equation (A3.10)

$$G(\omega) = \int_{-\infty}^{\infty} V(t)\exp(-j\omega t)\,dt$$

into

$$G(\omega) = x(0) + x(1)e^{-j\omega t_s} + x(2)e^{-2j\omega t_s} + x(3)e^{-3j\omega t_s} + \ldots \qquad (A5.6)$$

The discrete samples in the time domain become discrete samples in the frequency domain. The factor $e^{-j\omega t_s}$ represents a phase-shift proportional to frequency and hence a constant time delay t_s. The factor $z = e^{j\omega t_s}$ represents a time advance of t_s and is called the shift operator. The spectrum $G(\omega)$ can therefore be expressed in terms of this variable as

$$G(z) = x(0) + x(1)z^{-1} + x(2)z^{-2} + x(3)z^{-3} + \ldots \qquad (A5.7)$$

which has coefficients $x(n)$ which equal $V_1(n)$. This convenient representation is the z-transform.

We take as an example a low-pass filter with response

$$V_2(n) = V_1(n-1) + aV_1(n-2) + a^2 V_1(n-3) + a^3 V_1(n-4) + \ldots \qquad (A5.8)$$

which, for $a < 1$, represents an exponentially decaying response. This equation indicates the implementation of the non-recursive filter method. If the equation is inspected it can be rewritten as

$$V_2(n) = V_1(n-1) + aV_2(n-1) \qquad (A5.9)$$

which is recursive and obviously easier to implement. The transfer function can be found from equation (A5.8), using the relationship between (A5.5) and (A5.7) as

$$H(z) = z^{-1} + az^{-2} + a^2 z^{-3} + a^3 z^{-4} + \ldots$$

$$= 1/(z - a) \tag{A5.10}$$

Alternately we have from (A5.9)

$$V_1(n) = V_2(n - 1) - aV_2(n) = zV_2(n) - aV_2(n)$$

and since

$$H(z) \equiv V_2(z)/V_1(z)$$

we have

$$H(z) = 1/(z - a)$$

If we consider the input signal as a single pulse then the output decays by a factor a each sampling period t_s so that $a = \exp(-t_s/\tau)$ and τ is the characteristic decay time of the filter.

FURTHER READING

E. J. Angelo, 'A tutorial introduction to digital filtering', *Bell Syst. Tech. J.* **60** (1981) 1499–546.
C. Chatfield, *Analysis of Time Series*, Chapman and Hall (1984).
P. A. Lynn, *The Analysis and Processing of Signals*, Macmillan (1973).
E. B. Magrab and D. S. Blomquist, *The Measurement of Time-Varying Phenomena*, Wiley (1971).
T. J. Terrell, *Introduction to Digital Filters*, Macmillan (1980).

APPENDIX 6   ACTIVE FILTERS

INTRODUCTION

There are many applications for which a high-quality filter is needed. Examples are to prevent aliasing in sampled systems (anti-alias filter, chapter 9 and appendix 5), to remove the sampling pulses when a sampled signal is returned to a continuous signal, and to filter out noise but leave the signal unchanged in order to enhance the signal-to-noise ratio (chapter 4).

For uses without very stringent requirements, the passive RC filter is usually adequate. Inductors are rarely used since they are bulky and are not very ideal. However, the resistance and capacitance values can become very large for filters with low characteristic frequencies and also, if more than one stage has to be cascaded, there will be mutual loading between the stages so that the total response will not be simply the product of the individual transfer functions of each stage. The design therefore becomes difficult. The latter problem can be solved by inserting buffer amplifiers between the stages, but if amplifiers are to be used it is better to build active filters, in which the negative feedback is used to its full advantage. In active filters the value of some of the components can be reduced by an amount equal to the loop gain as in the simple integrator and differentiator (chapter 2). In the circuits described here, however, advantage is not taken of this since bandwidth and stability are given priority.

The basic forms of filter are the low-pass, high-pass, band-pass, band-reject, and all-pass. The last has a constant-amplitude transfer function with frequency but produces a frequency-dependent phase-shift. For each of these forms of filter there are many possible circuits with different characteristics. For reference, the second-order equations for these basic filters in terms of their characteristic frequency ω_0 and the damping factor d $(= 1/Q$, the reciprocal of the quality factor) are given by $V_{out}/V_{in} = H(j\omega/\omega_0)$:

low-pass
$$H(j\omega/\omega_0) = 1/[1 + d(j\omega/\omega_0) + (j\omega/\omega_0)^2]$$
high-pass
$$H(j\omega/\omega_0) = (j\omega/\omega_0)^2/[1 + d(j\omega/\omega_0) + (j\omega/\omega_0)^2]$$
band-pass
$$H(j\omega/\omega_0) = d(j\omega/\omega_0)/[1 + d(j\omega/\omega_0) + (j\omega/\omega_0)^2]$$
band-reject
$$H(j\omega/\omega_0) = [1 + (j\omega/\omega_0)^2]/[1 + d(j\omega/\omega_0) + (j\omega/\omega_0)^2]$$
all-pass
$$H(j\omega/\omega_0) = [1 - d(j\omega/\omega_0) + (j\omega/\omega_0)^2]/[1 + d(j\omega/\omega_0) + (j\omega/\omega_0)^2]$$

CHOICE OF FILTER TYPE

Each RC filter stage produces one pole and one order or power of (ω/ω_0) in the characteristic equation, so that sharp filters need high-order and multi-stage circuits. Even for a simple type of filter with a fixed order there are many possible variations. These are best described using the low-pass filter as an example although the high-pass filter follows in an analogous way.

The characteristic frequency of each RC combination in the complete cascaded filter circuit can be chosen so that the net effect is to optimize one of several qualities of the total filter. These qualities are principally the flatness of the magnitude of the amplitude transfer function below the characteristic frequency ω_0 of the total filter, the rapidity of the attenuation with frequency above ω_0, and the linearity of the phase–frequency relationship. Although these choices can be made the amplitude response for all filters will drop at $1/\omega_n$, or at $6n$ dB/octave, for a filter of order n (n-pole filter) for $\omega \gg \omega_0$. The general form for $H(j\omega/\omega_0)$ is (using the low-pass filter as an example) of a polynomial in the denominator. The coefficients of the polynomials are determined by the required properties of the response. These polynomials are given in other texts (see further reading).

The *Butterworth filter* has a very flat frequency below ω_0 but has a poor response to transients since its phase–frequency relationship is far from linear. This filter is used for anti-alias purposes and to transmit signal amplitudes faithfully.

The *Chebychev filters* are a family of filters with ripples in the magnitude of the transfer function below ω_0 but a sharp drop with frequency just above ω_0. The members of this family differ in the compromise between the magnitude of the ripple and the sharpness of the roll-off. This filter is used where great selectivity is needed, for example where one frequency must be accepted and another rejected.

The *Bessel, Thompson* or *maximally flat delay* (MFD) *filter* has a linear

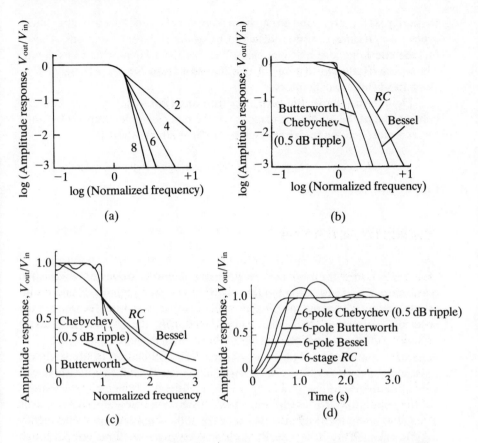

Fig. A6.1 The response of different types of low-pass filter: (a) the relative amplitude response of Butterworth low-pass filters of two, four, six and eight poles on logarithmic scales; (b) a comparison of the relative amplitude response of various six-pole low-pass filters on logarithmic scales; (c) as (b) but on linear scales; (d) the step response of various six-pole low-pass filters with 3 dB points at 1 Hz.

phase variation with frequency for $\omega < \omega_0$ and hence has a constant time delay in this range. Since each Fourier component is shifted by the same time, the signal is transmitted without a change in shape but a time delay is introduced. It does not produce a sharp cut-off. The Bessel polynomials define the exact transfer function and can be found in the texts given in the further reading. This filter is used for transient waveforms, time delays, and to produce a running average of a signal.

The *elliptic* or *Cauer filter* gives a steeper transition than the Chebychev by introducing ripples in the stop band as well as in the pass band. Because of these ripples the stop-band attenuation is not very large. There are other filter types that produce compromises appropriate for different situations. These include the Legendre and Gaussian filters and the Paynter or transitional Thompson–Butterworth filter, which has properties between those of the Bessel and Butterworth filters.

Figure A6.1 shows the variations with order for a Butterworth filter, a comparison of the amplitude response of the main six-pole filters on log and linear scales, and the transient response of these filters.

FILTER REALIZATION

The method of actually constructing a filter of a particular type will depend on practical considerations. These might include the magnitude of the components but less obvious are the accuracy needed for the component values in order to produce the required filter characteristics, the circuit stability for oscillation, the effect of the limitations of the operational amplifiers such as input and output impedance, bandwidth, slew rate, and maximum output voltage. The existence of high input impedance (JFET) operational amplifiers in dual and quad packages enables very compact filters to be made. In general, to obtain a good filter response the individual components used will have to have their values measured since, although resistors can be obtained with close tolerance, capacitors have poor tolerance, and either the resistors or the capacitors (or both) may have to have non-'preferred' values. Typically, component accuracy better than 10% is needed, and 5% or 2% may be needed for Chebychev and high-order filters. Good temperature stability may also be needed for the passive components.

An experimenter usually needs a filter only to satisfy some simple need, so that a full analysis is not required here but can be obtained from the further reading if necessary. Three approaches are outlined and for simplicity only even-order filters are described since each amplifier can accommodate either order one or two and hence there is usually little reason to have an odd-order filter.

The basic circuit is the *Sallen–Key filter*, which has low gain and is stable with a large bandwidth. There are two main design methods, the unity-gain Sallen–Key filter and the equal-component-value Sallen–Key filter, or the voltage-controlled voltage source (VCVS) filter. The basic low-pass and high-pass circuit elements for two-pole filters are shown in figure A6.2. Four-, six-, and eight-pole filters are obtained by cascading two-pole units with the correct component values. It should be noted that to obtain the required response all the stages must be designed together since the phases interact. For the unity-gain design the circuit values are given in table A6.1. In general the capacitors will have to be made up from a combination of individual

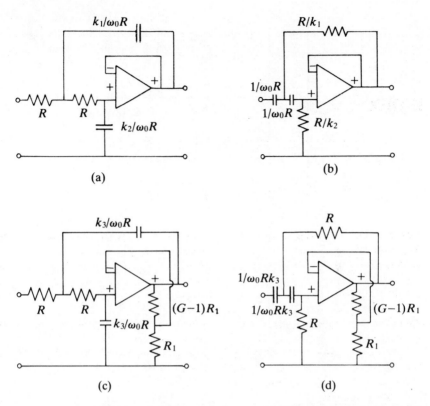

Fig. A6.2 The unity-gain Sallen–Key filters: (a) two-pole low-pass and (b) two pole high-pass. For these circuits refer to Table A6.1. The equal-component-value Sallen–Key filters: (c) two-pole low-pass and (d) two-pole high-pass. For these circuits refer to Table A6.2. The values shown are in ohms, farads and ω_0 is the 3 dB angular frequency of the filter.

components. Usually R will be chosen as large as possible so that the capacitors will be small. The procedure is to choose n and the filter type and then ω_0. Table A6.1 gives k_1 and k_2 for each two-pole element and R is chosen for convenience. The values of R in the different two-pole sections need not be the same. The high-pass filter is designed in a similar way but the capacitance values are the same and the resistance values unequal. The gain of this type of Sallen–Key filter is unity on the pass side of the characteristic frequency.

The equal-component-value design has two advantages. The resistors and capacitors each have equal values in each two-pole stage so that less selection is necessary. Also each stage has gain so that as the bandwidth is reduced through the filter the full bandwidth r.m.s. signal is kept nearly

Table A6.1 Unity-gain Sallen–Key low-pass and high-pass filters. Refer to figures A6.2(a) and (b).

Poles	Butterworth k_1	k_2	Transitional k_1	k_2	Bessel k_1	k_2	Chebychev 0.1 dB k_1	k_2	Chebychev 0.5 dB k_1	k_2	Chebychev 2 dB k_1	k_2
2	1.414	0.707	1.287	0.777	0.907	0.680	1.638	0.696	1.949	0.653	2.672	0.525
4	1.082	0.924	1.090	0.960	0.735	0.675	1.901	1.241	2.582	1.298	4.021	1.163
	2.613	0.383	2.206	0.472	1.012	0.390	4.592	0.241	6.233	0.180	9.707	0.115
6	1.035	0.966	1.060	1.001	0.635	0.610	2.553	1.776	3.592	1.921	5.750	1.769
	1.414	0.707	1.338	0.761	0.723	0.484	3.487	0.492	4.907	0.374	7.853	0.243
	3.863	0.259	2.721	0.340	1.073	0.256	9.531	0.111	13.40	0.079	21.46	0.049
8	1.019	0.981	1.051	1.017	0.567	0.554	3.270	2.323	4.665	2.547	7.539	2.367
	1.202	0.832	1.191	0.876	0.609	0.486	3.857	0.689	5.502	0.530	8.896	0.347
	1.800	0.556	1.613	0.615	0.726	0.359	5.773	0.240	8.237	0.171	13.31	0.107
	5.125	0.195	3.373	0.268	1.116	0.186	16.44	0.063	23.45	0.044	37.91	0.027

Table A6.2 Equal-component-value Sallen–Key low-pass and high-pass filters. Refer to figures A6.2(c) and (d).

Poles	Butterworth k_3	G	Transitional k_3	G	Bessel k_3	G	Chebychev 0.1 dB k_3	G	Chebychev 0.5 dB k_3	G	Chebychev 2 dB k_3	G
2	1.000	1.586	1.000	1.446	0.785	1.268	1.067	1.697	1.129	1.842	1.184	2.114
4	1.000	1.152	1.023	1.123	0.704	1.084	1.536	1.384	1.831	1.582	2.162	1.924
	1.000	2.235	0.977	2.035	0.628	1.759	1.052	2.542	1.060	2.660	1.057	2.782
6	1.000	1.068	1.030	1.056	0.622	1.040	2.129	1.332	2.627	1.537	3.189	1.891
	1.000	1.586	1.009	1.492	0.591	1.364	1.309	2.249	1.355	2.448	1.380	2.648
	1.000	2.483	0.962	2.293	0.524	2.023	1.029	2.784	1.029	2.846	1.026	2.904
8	1.000	1.038	1.034	1.032	0.561	1.024	2.756	1.314	3.447	1.522	4.224	1.879
	1.000	1.337	1.021	1.284	0.544	1.213	1.630	2.155	1.708	2.379	1.756	2.605
	1.000	1.889	0.996	1.765	0.510	1.593	1.177	2.592	1.188	2.711	1.192	2.821
	1.000	2.610	0.951	2.436	0.455	2.184	1.017	2.876	1.017	2.913	1.014	2.946

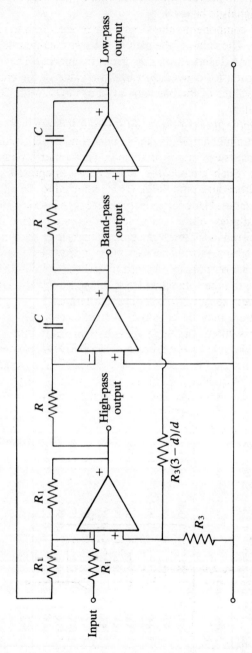

Fig. A6.3 The state-variable filter.

constant. This helps to prevent the introduction of significant amplifier noise and allows large signals to be used.

For the equal-component-value design the procedure is to choose n, ω_0, and the filter type. The value of the gain G for each two-pole section is then taken from table A6.2 and R_1 chosen for convenience. The value of the resistance R is chosen for convenience and the value of the capacitances is chosen using the values of the constant k_3 from table A6.2. The high-pass filter design is similar.

The *state-variable filter* is a very useful circuit. It consists of two cascaded integrators and a summer amplifier. The basic second-order circuit is shown in figure A6.3. It consists essentially of an analog computer for damped simple harmonic motion. Such circuits are available as integrated circuits with complete design procedures and the reader is referred to the manufacturers' literature (AF100 series, National Semiconductor; UAF series, Burr–Brown). The capacitors and a few of the resistors are integrated within the circuit so that only a few external resistors are needed. This circuit acts simultaneously as a low-pass, high-pass or band-pass filter using the output terminals indicated. It has two outputs in quadrature and the gain and characteristic frequency are easy to tune with either the Q or the bandwidth kept constant. The circuit is not very sensitive to component tolerance.

Band-pass filters may be constructed from a cascaded connection of low- and high-pass filters but high Q values are not then possible. As well as the state-variable circuit already described, the Sallen–Key circuit shown in figure A6.4 can be used. Here the characteristic frequency ω_0 and the gain G at this frequency are chosen together with the Q provided that $2Q^2 > G$. If C is selected for convenience then $R_1 = Q/G\omega_0 C$, $R_3 = 2Q/\omega_0 C$ and $R_1 R_2/(R_1 + R_2) = 1/2Q\omega_0 C$.

Band-reject or *notch filters* based on the Twin-Tee circuit have been described in chapter 4.

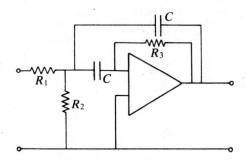

Fig. A6.4   Active band-pass filter.

All-pass filters produce a variable phase-shift but constant amplitude with frequency. They are used as constant-amplitude phase-shifters in circuits such as the reference channel of a phase-sensitive detector (PSD). The passive all-pass filter is described in chapter 1 (figure 1.14) and an active circuit is shown in appendix 7.

Other analog methods of producing filters are the switched-capacitor filters and *N*-path filters. In general these are not very suitable for high-precision applications since they work by analog sampling techniques. Therefore, an anti-aliasing pre-filter will be needed and a final filter to smooth the sampling pulses. Since these are analog filters there must be a strong need for the rest of the filter to be of a sampling type. Their main advantage is that the characteristic frequency of the filter is controlled by a clock signal and can hence be easily tuned electronically. There are integrated circuit versions (MF10, National Semiconductor; R5600 series, Reticon) and the manufacturers provide a detailed description of the design procedure.

The *N*-path filter is described in chapter 9 and digital filters in appendix 5.

FURTHER READING

F. Al-Nasser, 'Tables shorten design time for active filters', *Electronics*, October 23 (1972) 113–8.

K. G. Beauchamp and C. K. Yuen, *Data Acquisition for Signal Analysis*, Allen and Unwin (1980).

C. Chen, *Active Filter Design*, Hayden (1982).

M. S. Ghausi and K. R. Laker, *Modern Filter Design: Active RC and Switched Capacitor*, Prentice-Hall (1981).

J. G. Graeme, G. E. Tobey, and L. P. Huelsman (eds), *Operational Amplifiers: Design and Applications*, McGraw-Hill (1971).

P. Horowitz and W. Hill, *The Art of Electronics*, Cambridge University Press (1980).

D. Lancaster, *Active Filter Cookbook*, H. W. Sams (1982).

R. R. Shepard, 'Active filters: Part 12', *Electronics*, August 18 (1969) 82–91.

I. E. Shepherd, *Operational Amplifiers*, Longman (1981).

A. B. Williams, *Active Filter Design*, Artech House (1975).

APPENDIX 7   OPERATIONAL AMPLIFIER CIRCUIT CATALOG

In this appendix are a collection of operational amplifier circuits that are commonly used. Each can be analyzed using the approximate methods described in chapter 2 and the resulting transfer function is given. The full analysis can also be made if the loop gain cannot be taken as infinite. A more complete description of some of the circuits is given in chapter 2. In using these circuits, care should be taken that the frequency response is adequate, that the loop gain is large and negative at all the signal frequencies, and that the circuit is stable. The choice of the type of operational amplifier will depend on the requirements of the particular circuit on offset current, output impedance, slew rate, etc.

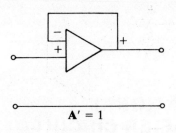

$$\mathbf{A}' = 1$$

Buffer

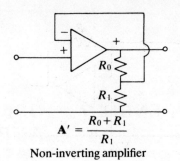

$$\mathbf{A}' = \frac{R_0 + R_1}{R_1}$$

Non-inverting amplifier

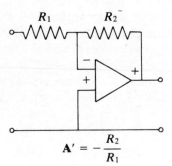

$$\mathbf{A}' = -\frac{R_2}{R_1}$$

Inverting amplifier (resistance)

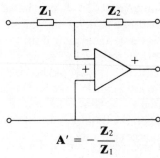

$$\mathbf{A}' = -\frac{\mathbf{Z}_2}{\mathbf{Z}_1}$$

Inverting amplifier (linear impedance)

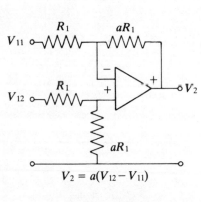

$$V_2 = a(V_{12} - V_{11})$$

Differential amplifier

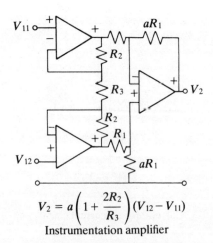

$$V_2 = a\left(1 + \frac{2R_2}{R_3}\right)(V_{12} - V_{11})$$

Instrumentation amplifier

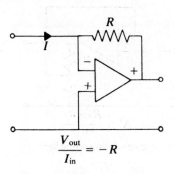

$$\frac{V_{out}}{I_{in}} = -R$$

Current–voltage converter

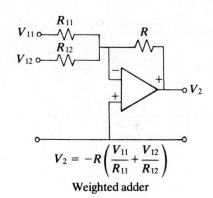

$$V_2 = -R\left(\frac{V_{11}}{R_{11}} + \frac{V_{12}}{R_{12}}\right)$$

Weighted adder

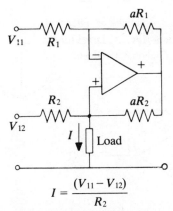

$$I = \frac{V_{in}}{R}$$

Current driver (current clamp)
(floating load)

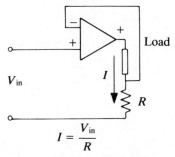

$$I = \frac{V_{in}}{R}$$

Current driver (current clamp)
(floating load)

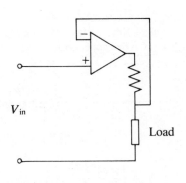

$$I = \frac{(V_{11} - V_{12})}{R_2}$$

Current driver (current clamp)
(earthed load)

Voltage clamp

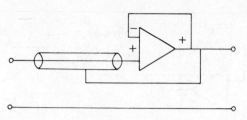

Active guard

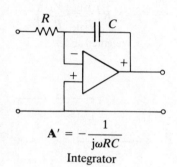

$$\mathbf{A}' = -\frac{1}{j\omega RC}$$

Integrator

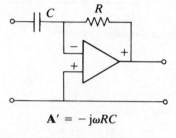

$$\mathbf{A}' = -j\omega RC$$

Differentiator

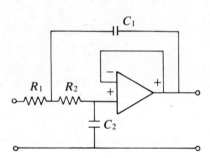

Low-pass filter

Sallen–Key, use tables for R_1, R_2, C_1, C_2. See appendix 6.

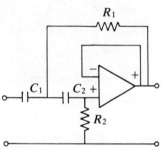

High-pass filter

Sallen–Key, use tables for R_1, R_2, C_1, C_2. See appendix 6.

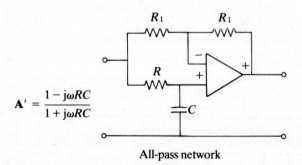

$$\mathbf{A}' = \frac{1 - j\omega RC}{1 + j\omega RC}$$

All-pass network

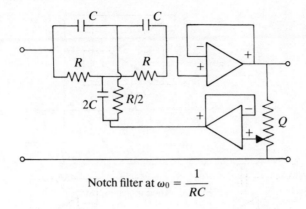

Notch filter at $\omega_0 = \dfrac{1}{RC}$

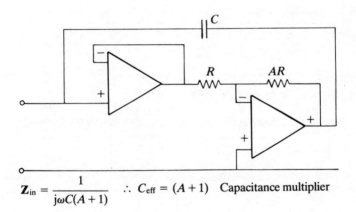

$\mathbf{Z}_{in} = \dfrac{1}{j\omega C(A+1)}$ $\quad \therefore C_{eff} = (A+1)$ Capacitance multiplier

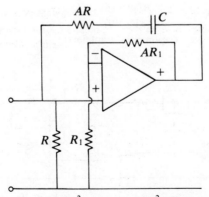

$\mathbf{Z}_{in} = R + j\omega ACR^2 \therefore |L_{eff} = ACR^2$ with $Q_L = \omega ACR$

Inductance simulation

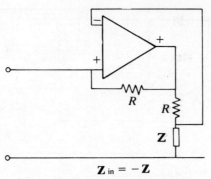

$$\mathbf{Z}_{in} = -\mathbf{Z}$$

Negative impedance generator

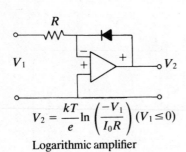

$$V_2 = \frac{kT}{e} \ln\left(\frac{-V_1}{I_0 R}\right) \; (V_1 \leq 0)$$

Logarithmic amplifier

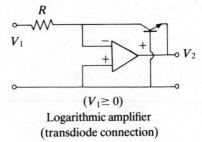

$$(V_1 \geq 0)$$

Logarithmic amplifier
(transdiode connection)

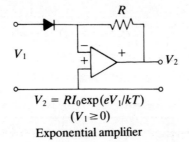

$$V_2 = RI_0 \exp(eV_1/kT)$$
$$(V_1 \geq 0)$$

Exponential amplifier

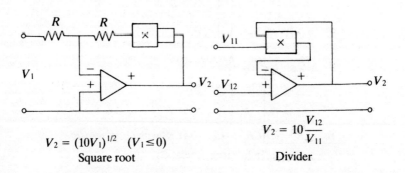

$$V_2 = (10V_1)^{1/2} \quad (V_1 \leq 0)$$

Square root

$$V_2 = 10 \frac{V_{12}}{V_{11}}$$

Divider

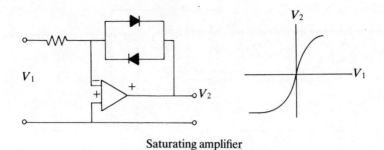

Saturating amplifier

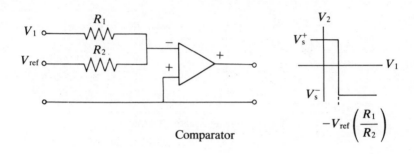

Comparator

$$-V_{ref}\left(\frac{R_1}{R_2}\right)$$

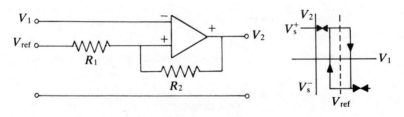

Schmitt trigger, comparator with hysteresis, bistable multivibrator

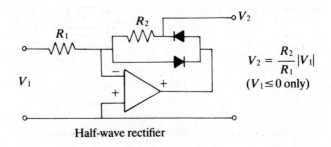

$$V_2 = \frac{R_2}{R_1}|V_1|$$
$$(V_1 \le 0 \text{ only})$$

Half-wave rectifier

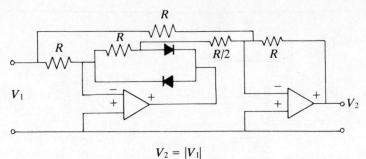

$$V_2 = |V_1|$$

Full-wave rectifier

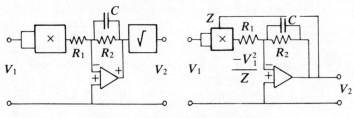

True root-mean-square (TRMS)

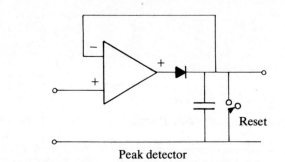

Peak detector

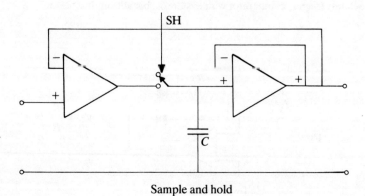

Sample and hold

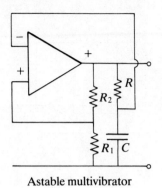

Astable multivibrator

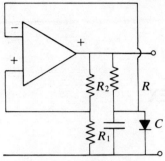

Monostable multivibrator

INDEX